TSR™

Fiend Folio™

TOME OF CREATURES MALEVOLENT AND BENIGN

AN ALPHABETICAL LISTING
OF MONSTERS FOR USE WITH
ADVANCED DUNGEONS & DRAGONS™
ADVENTURES, INCLUDING ATTACKS,
DAMAGE, SPECIAL ABILITIES,
AND DESCRIPTIONS; RANDOM
ENCOUNTER TABLES BY LEVEL;
AND MORE.

Edited by Don Turnbull,
Managing Director of TSR UK, Ltd.

Illustrations by:
Chris Baker,
Jeff Dee,
Emmanuel,
Albie Fiore,
Alan Hunter,
Russ Nicholson,
Erol Otus,
Jim Roslof,
David C. Sutherland III,
Bill Willingham,
Polly Wilson,
Tony Yates.

Cover by Emmanuel

TSR Hobbies, Inc.
POB 756
LAKE GENEVA, WI 53147

ISBN 0-935696-21-0

Printed in the U.S.A.

FOREWORD

The **FIEND FOLIO**™ Tome of Creatures Malevolent and Benign is the first major British contribution to the **ADVANCED DUN-GEONS & DRAGONS**™ game system.

If at any time there were doubts whether **AD&D**™ games would be popular in Britain, they were rapidly discarded. So many are its adherents that it is hard to believe the game has only been available over here for less than five years. Though in sheer population terms the game could never command the numerical support in Britain as it does in the U.S.A., the enthusiasm with which British gamers have greeted this American inspiration is not so arbitrarily constrained. Here, as in its country of origin, the **AD&D** system has been a truly remarkable success and it is appropriate that, sooner or later, major contributions to it should stem from an initiative which is substantially British.

Hence the **FIEND FOLIO** Tome. In effect, it is an all-new companion volume to that excellent compendium the **AD&D Monster Manual**. Such will be evident to those who now have copies of both, not only because of the nature of its contents but also because the tome unashamedly emulates its elder brother in its high quality of presentation. The **FIEND FOLIO** Tome is my first official **AD&D** work; from the outset I was determined that it should be on a qualitative par with the other **AD&D** works - not only the **Monster Manual** but also the other handbooks. **AD&D** enthusiasts deserve something more than mediocrity and the many contributors to this volume deserve a high-quality presentation of their creations. The **FIEND FOLIO** Tome would be desperately inadequate were its presentation not of the same superior quality as those earlier TSR publications which put them head and shoulders above their competitors.

Those familiar with the **Monster Manual** will therefore recognize the **FIEND FOLIO** format since the general layout and the method of presenting the monster contents are the same. The purpose of the **FIEND FOLIO** Tome, too, is complementary to that of the **Monster Manual** -to extend the range of monsters available for use in **AD&D** games and to collect all the newcomers into one volume for easy reference. A few of the monsters in the book relate in one way or another to creatures which appear in the **Monster Manual**, so small relevant sections of the **Monster Manual** are here reprinted, by kind permission, and there are also some cross-references to the **Monster Manual**. Though it is probably true that most owners of this tome will alredy have a copy of the **Monster Manual**, the number of cross-references has been kept to a minimum. It is helpful, but not essential, to own both works.

There is one major difference between the two volumes - the source of their contents. The **Monster Manual** is very largely the sole work of one person - Gary Gygax - who not only created and developed most of the **Monster Manual** monsters himself but also developed those he did not personally create. The new monsters in the **FIEND FOLIO** Tome, however, are the creations of many people. Some time ago, the editor of a UK magazine asked readers to submit their monster creations to a regular feature which became known as the Fiend Factory. The response was quite enormous and many worthwhile contributions reached the editorial offices. As editor of the feature, I never lacked new and interesting monsters to fill the Factory pages each issue - indeed (for a magazine has inevitable limitations on space) it very soon became evident that many worthwhile creations would not be published until long, long after their submission, if at all. At the same time, the readers were praising the feature and demanding more! So there was a goodly supply of, and a strident demand for, additional **AD&D** monsters - and these two factors gave birth to the **FIEND FOLIO** Tome of Creatures Malevolent and Benign.

This volume therefore contains an overwhelming majority of monsters which were originally submitted for the Fiend Factory feature. A small fraction of them have already appeared in the Factory (though not in as developed a form as they appear here) while a larger number have come straight from creation via development to this book without pausing at the Factory en route. Additionally the **FIEND FOLIO** Tome includes new monsters from TSR in Lake Geneva, USA.

Which brings me to my first debt of gratitude - to the contributors. There are many names - too many to list here, but they are all listed in the index to the rear of this volume next to the name of their creation. To all these people, my warm and most sincere thanks. Quite literally, the **FIEND FOLIO** Tome would not have been possible without you.

It is worth noting that contributions to the **FIEND FOLIO** Tome have come from many parts of the world - the U.K., the U.S.A., Australia, Canada and Europe. The **AD&D** games are spreading!)

My own task has been quite a simple one - to select monsters for inclusion, to develop them as necessary and write the statistics and texts, to assemble the entries in coherent form and to produce the various tables. Perhaps selection was not so easy a task after all, for there were over 1,000 contributions to consider; I have been able to be quite ruthless in selection to ensure that the monsters which finally did appear were of the highest quality and originality. To have sacrificed quantity for quality in this way is, I believe, what discerning **AD&D** enthusiasts would want me to have done. On the development side my efforts have been variable. Some "originals" were almost fully developed when they reached me and not a great deal of work was required to add the final touches to them. At the opposite end of the developmental spectrum, other contributions arrived incomplete and embryonic, with the tip of a good idea just showing above the surface, as it were; these needed development to "flesh them out" into complete and coherent form. A few names have been changed and a few characteristics altered (most for good and sufficient reasons, some out of sheer instinct) but substantially the task has been to build on creations rather than to re-work them entirely. So, in the final analysis, and excluding those which appeared in the TSR Modules, I must bear final responsibility for the presentation of all the **FIEND FOLIO** monsters.

Here I must make more acknowledgements and express more thanks. Throughout the project I have received very helpful advice and guidance from Lawrence Schick and from Gary Gygax, who gave me a great deal of editorial rope in my first **AD&D** project but made sure I did not hang myself. Since I began work on the **FIEND FOLIO** Tome in the U.K. at the same time as the **Dungeon Masters Guide** was being finalized in America, it was important for the one to be compatible with the other and for the Tome to be as up-to-date as possible, and I am particularly grateful to Gary for letting me in on the secrets of the **Dungeons Masters Guide** before it was published. To Gary must also go a very special acknowledgement and very warm thanks, for without his creativity there would be no **AD&D** games and no **FIEND FOLIO** Tome. And I owe particular thanks to Albie Fiore, who in addition to being a major contributor to the **FIEND FOLIO** project has done an enormous amount of work during its preparation - acting as my second pair of eyes, bringing to my attention possible deficiencies and inconsistencies, suggesting improvements and coordinating all the printing. Albie's help has been invaluable.

The quality of the art work in the Tome is, I believe, particularly good and I am sure the readers will appreciate the endeavours of the artists, who have my praise, thanks and envy!

I will make only one apology in respect of the **FIEND FOLIO** Tome and it is this. There are many, many places in the text where it is necessary to refer to a person (for instance to the victim of a monster's attacks) who is not identified as to gender. In such places it is tempting, though I believe unnecessarily pedantic, to lapse into the cumbersome and ugly style of "he or she", "him or her" and other such awkwardnesses. (The English language has not yet bent to accomodate these alleged requirements of modern society and if the products are to be words like "himr" and "hisr" I devoutly hope it never will). Early in the proceedings, I decided to eschew such clumsiness, and if there is a reader who is offended by this, it is to him that I apologise. Or, of course, to her. Let me confirm that, unless there are specific contextual indications to the contrary, all references in this book to males apply equally, *mutatis mutandis*, to females.

Finally, to my most important expression of thanks. If anyone has suffered during the preparation of this book, that person is the lady who shares my life. Nevertheless, June has displayed enormous tolerance, despite the late-night clattering of the typewriter the liberal bestrewing of **FIEND FOLIO** Tome drafts on all available horizontal surfaces in our home and my apparently infinite preoccupation with the project. I owe her my very special gratitude and offer her the consolation that it is now all over....until the next time.

Don Turnbull

Cambridge, England.
August, 1979

ALPHABETICAL TABLE OF CONTENTS

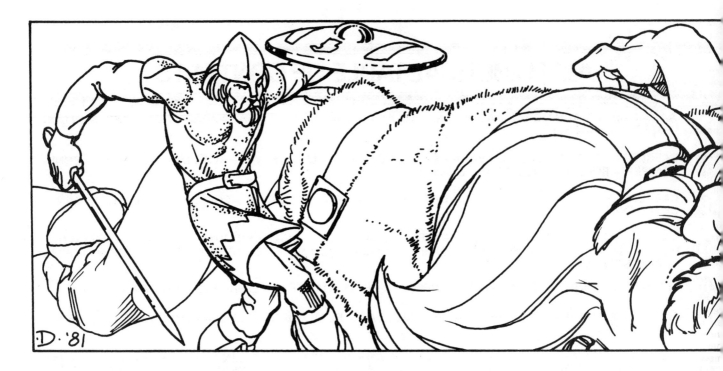

EXPLANATORY NOTES

As in other collections of the same nature, the term *"monster"* has two different meanings in the **FIEND FOLIO**™ Tome. Its first — and more important — meaning is to designate any creature encountered, hostile or otherwise, human, humanoid or beast. Thus the term is used generically to signify the subject of an encounter; until the party of adventurers are certain what they have met, it is a "monster". The secondary use of the term is the more traditional one — to signify a wicked or horrible creature of some sort.

The two meanings of the term are not necessarily mutually exclusive but nor are they necessarily identical in encounter terms. Thus, if a party encounters a monster which turns out to be an evil wizard, the latter is probably a monster in the second sense of the word, too; however, if the encounter is with a pacific creature with no malign intent, the second sense is inappropriate. **ADVANCED DUNGEONS & DRAGONS**™ players will almost certainly be familiar with these two uses of the word already; those who are newcomers may find them a little confusing at first, but experience will soon determine which of the two uses of the word is appropriate in the particular context.

Note that, despite this terminology, a human (and nearhuman) encountered as a monster always uses the combat matrix for humans when attacking. In other words dwarves, elves, gnomes, half-elves, halflings, half-orcs and humans always use the human attack matrix whether they are "monsters" or "player-characters".

Each **FIEND FOLIO** monster is given a full description in the text which follows; additionally, each has been assigned a value for each of a number of parameters which collectively describe its behaviour, combat mode and so forth in general terms. The parameters are explained here.

FREQUENCY refers to the likelihood of a particular creature being encountered in a region or area where it might be an inhabitant, denoting the rarity or otherwise of the monster in such areas. *Very rare* indicates a 4% chance of occurrence; *rare* indicates an 11% chance; *uncommon* indicates a 20% chance and *common* indicates a 65% chance. These probabilities are reflected, with necessary minor approximations such as are well within the limits of statistical variation, in the *Monster Level Tables*. There are some variations within each category — for example, some creatures which are *"very rare"* will in fact be rarer than others under the same general description.

NUMBER APPEARING indicates a good average spread. Generally, if a creature is encountered in or near its lair, it can be expected to appear in such numbers, while further away from its lair it will be encountered in smaller numbers. Again, there are exceptions to this

—intelligent, organized monsters forming a war party for a specif[ic] raiding or punitive mission may be encountered in considerab[le] numbers some distance from their lair, while encounters with the sam[e] creatures near their lair may, fortuitously, be with small numbers [of] "scouts" or "perimeter guards". The number-range indicated shou[ld] therefore be used only as a guideline and should be altered to suit t[he] circumstances particular to any adventure as the need arises.

More specifically, the number-range indicated is not necessarily r[e]commended for underground (dungeon) encounters. Since many a[d]ventures take place in dungeons, however, an additional section aft[er] the *Encounter Listings* gives guidance on the numbers of ea[ch] monster-type likely to be encountered in such locations.

ARMOUR CLASS describes the general type of protection worn [by] humans, near-human or humanoid monsters, protection inherent t[o a] monster due to its physical structure and/or magical nature and t[he] degree of difficulty of hitting a monster due to its speed, reflexes a[nd] so forth. All these factors are combined into a single *armour cla[ss]* value. Referees need not adjust this value to take account of hi[gh] dexterity. Where necessary, alterations to the AC value are included [in] the monster's individual description if these need to be made in part[ic]ular circumstances.

MOVE shows the relative speed of the monster on a constant bas[is.] Higher speeds may be possible for very short periods. The creature[s] *movement rate* can be scaled to whatever time period is desired [by] adjusting the ground scale accordingly. In certain cases, more th[an] one number is given under this heading; this indicates that the mons[ter] can travel in two or more different media or modes:—

X"	=	monster's movement rate in its normal medium
/X"	=	monster's flying in addition to a normal mode of travel
//X"	=	monster's swimming speed, in addition to a normal mode
(X")	=	monster's burrowing speed, in addition to a normal mode
*X"	=	monster's speed in a web, in addition to a normal mode

If a single number is given, that does not automatically mean that [the] monster only moves along the ground (though it does in most case[s]) —the main text must be consulted to make the meaning clear. Thus [a] monster whose only means of locomotion is flying will have a sing[le] number — and this is, in this case, a flying speed.

HIT DICE indicated how to calculate the number of hit points [a] monster can withstand before dying. Unless stated otherwise, hit d[ice]

8-sided points per die). The indicated number of dice are rolled and the resulting numbers added together to arrive at the monster's total hit points.

Some monsters have hit points which are less than the full 1-8 range of an 8-sided die (d8), and these are indicated by a range of hit points. Thus, if a creature has 1-4 hit points, a 4-sided die is rolled to determine its hit points.

Other monsters have hit points additional to the number derived from their hit dice; this is indicated by a plus sign followed by the number of additional hit points. This, if a monster has "HIT DICE: 5+3", five 8-sided dice are rolled, the number are added together and 3 is added to the result; this monster will have a range of 5-40 hit points plus 3 hit points, or 8-43 hit points.

IN LAIR indicates the chance of encountering the monster in question where it domiciles and stores its treasure (if any). Note that some monsters are never found in their lairs; this is either because the lair is inaccessible (or unknown) or because the monster simply does not have a fixed lair and is a true wandering monster.

Note that certain monsters have their lairs on planes other than the Prime Material Plane; clearly, these monsters will never be encountered in their lair if the encounter takes place on the Prime Material Plane, or any other plane which is not the monster's plane of residence. However, some monsters whose normal lairs are on planes other than the Prime Material may have established lairs there of a temporary nature, in the pursuit of a particular purpose or mission.

TREASURE TYPE refers to the table at the rear of this book. The table shows the treasure-types and numbers of the individual components of the treasure, together with the probability that the treasure will contain that component. Thus, treasure type J indicates there will always be 3-24 copper pieces per individual encountered, but never any silver, electrum, gold, platinum, gems, jewellery, maps or magical items. In contrast, treasure type P indicates that only silver and/or electrum pieces may be present, the former at a probability of 30% and the latter at a probability of 25% (so there is a chance that there will be no treasure at all). Thus, if individual treasure is indicated, each individual monster of that type will, or may, carry the treasure shown. Otherwise, treasure is only found in a monster's lair (which, in normal circumstances, will also contain the monster on guard). However, even if an encounter takes place in the lair of a monster with a particular treasure type, this does not automatically mean that the adventurers will gain the treasure if they defeat the monster. If dice rolls indicate that a particular treasure component is not in the monster's lair, it is simply not there; it is thus quite possible to gain no treasure from defeating a monster in its lair, despite the fact that a treasure type is indicated.

Treasure types are based on the appearance of a mean number of monsters of that particular type, as indicated by the "number appearing". In instances where fewer, or more, monsters of that type are encountered, the treasure should be reduced, or increased, in value.

Larger treasures of a given type are denoted by a multiplier in parenses ((x2) for instance) — not to be confused with treasure type X.

NUMBER OF ATTACKS shows the number of basic attacks, excluding special attacks, the monster is able to make during a given melee round. This number may be modified by spells such as haste and slow. It does not include unusual or special attack forms. Multiple attacks usually indicate the use of serveral modes of attack during the same melee round — for example a monster which rakes with its two claws and inflicts a bite in the same melee round would be given 3 attacks.

DAMAGE PER ATTACK simply indicates the amount (number of hit points) of damage a given attack will inflict on a victim when it hits, expressed as a range of hit points of damage. Refer to the main text for a more detailed explanation of the monster's modes of attack and the damage which each might inflict. If a monster uses a weapon in its attack, the damage will not be shown since it will vary according to the type of weapon used.

SPECIAL ATTACKS detail such special attack modes as dragon breath, magic-use and so forth. Refer to the main text for a detailed explanation of these, including the method and frequency of the at-

tack, the damage it inflicts and any special effects which might result from it.

SPECIAL DEFENSES are almost self-explanatory and are detailed in the main text in the same manner as are special attacks. They will include the use of defensive magic, camouflage abilities and so forth.

MAGIC RESISTANCE indicates the percentage chance of a spell absolutely failing if it is cast at, or on, the monster in question. The basis of the figure is a spell cast by a magic-user of the 11th experience level; the figure must be adjusted upwards by 5% for each experience level below 11th, or downwards by 5% for each experience level above 11th, of the spell-caster. Thus, a monster with 95% magic resistance cannot be affected by a spell cast by a magic-user of the 10th experience level or lower, while a 12th level magic-user has a 10% chance of affecting it.

Note that, even if a spell does "overcome the magic resistance" of a monster, the monster is still entitled to normal saving throws.

INTELLIGENCE indicates the basic equivalent of the human intelligence quotient (at least in concept even if IQ itself appears now to be much disgraced). Certain monsters are instinctively cunning or particularly devious in their encounter behaviour, and if this is so it will be indicated in the text. The intelligence ratings correspond roughly to the following character intelligence scores:

0	Non-intelligent, or intelligence not ratable
1	Animal intelligence
2-4	Semi-intelligent
5-7	Low intelligence
8-10	Average (human) intelligence
11-12	Very intelligent
13-14	Highly intelligent
15-16	Exceptionally intelligent
17-18	Genius-level intelligence
19-20	Supra-genius
21+	Godlike intelligence

ALIGNMENT indicates the characteristic bent of the monster towards law or chaos, good or evil, or towards neutral behaviour, perhaps modified by good or evil intent. A monster's alignment will have a significant effect on the way it behaves when it is encountered, the way in which it reacts to certain situations, and so forth.

SIZE is abbreviated as: S = smaller than a typical human; M = approximately man-sized (5' - 7' tall and approximately the build of a man); and L = larger than man-sized in one way or another and generally a greater mass than a man. Amongst other things, the size of a monster will govern the amount of damage inflicted on it by a successful hit from a particular weapon.

PSIONIC ABILITY and ATTACK/DEFENCE MODES indicate the general psionic capabilities, if any, of the monster. Some monsters have suspected, rather than confirmed, psionic powers and where this is the case the text will so indicate.

LEVEL and EXPERIENCE POINT VALUE are determined by the method indicated in ADVANCED DUNGEONS & DRAGONS Dungeon Masters Guide. If a monster has varying hit dice and/or "experience levels", values for each are shown.

The figures and facts given under these headings indicate the general parameters of the monster in question. In each case, there follows a description of the monster in detail — its behaviour, normal habitat, attack/defence styles, special characteristics and so on. A sketch of a typical creature of the type is included where necessary.

In the main text relating to monsters which are capable of flying appears mention of the monster's Aerial Manoeuvrability Class. This is a general grading, from A at one extreme to E at the other, which indicates the monster's general capability to manoeuvre when in the air. A monster with manoeuvrability class A is quick and highly manoeuvrable in the air —difficult to hit and capable of rapid and fundamental changes of direction. At the other extreme, a monster of class E is slow-flying and ponderous —relatively an easy target and incapable of sharp turns, requiring a good deal of space to accomplish more than a very minor change in direction of flight.

AARAKOCRA — ACHAIERAI — ADHERER — ALEAX — ALGOID — AL- MI'RAJ — APPARITION —
ASSASSIN BUG — ASTRAL SEARCHER

AARAKOCRA (*Bird-Man*)

FREQUENCY: *Very rare*
NO. APPEARING: *1—10*
ARMOUR CLASS: *7*
MOVE: *6''/36''*
HIT DICE: *1+2*
% IN LAIR: *5%*
TREASURE TYPE: *D*
NO. OF ATTACKS: *2*
DAMAGE/ATTACK: *1—3/1—3*
    or by weapon type
SPECIAL ATTACKS: *Nil*
SPECIAL DEFENCES: *Nil*
MAGIC RESISTANCE: *Standard*
INTELLIGENCE: *Average*
ALIGNMENT: *Neutral good*
SIZE: *M(20' wing span)*
PSIONIC ABILITY: *Nil*
    Attack/Defence Modes: *Nil*
LEVEL/X.P. VALUE: *II/28 + 2 per hit point*

The aarakocra are a race of intelligent avian humanoids. Their society consists of small tribes of about 11—30; each tribe has a hunting territory of about 10,000 square miles. The bird-men live on high peaks in the mountains, where they can soar all day on the winds and the thermals.

Aarakocra have little to do with humankind beyond the occasional poaching of a farm animal (they appear incapable of distinguishing between domestic and wild animals, for this act is not one motivated by malice). They have even less to do with demi-humans and actively dislike humanoids. Infrequently, an aarakocra may agree to give information to, or act as a scout for, humans in exchange for shiny coins or gems. As they are extremely reluctant to leave their familiar mountains such an act will only very rarely take place outside the bird-man's own territory.

Aarakocra stand about 5' high but they have a wing span of 20'. Their wings/arms are built somewhat like those of a pterodactyl, with a hand half-way along each leading edge. The wing-section beyond the hand has as its leading edge an extremely lengthened and strengthened outer finger which locks in place during flight. The wing-hands cannot grasp while in flight, but when the bird-man is on the ground and the wings are folded back, the hands are nearly as useful as normal human hands. Each hand consists of three normal-sized fingers and an opposable thumb.

The bird-man's mighty wing muscles are anchored in a bony keel which projects forward from the chest a full foot beyond the normal extent of a human chest. The legs are powerful, with 'backward-bending' knees and dangerous-looking talons on the feet. The feet are actually more dangerous than they appear: the talons can unlock and fold back, uncovering a pair of fully-functional hands, each with three tough, powerful fingers and a thumb.

It is these nether 'hands' that the bird-man employs in aerial combat, either using the talons alone or clutching heavy fletched javelins, used for stabbing or for throwing. Each feathered warrior usually carries half a dozen of these javelins, which do 2-8 hit points of damage each, strapped to its chest in individual sheaths. Aarakocra are remarkably adept at flinging these javelins while in the air, incurring none of the 'to hit' penalties used in aerial missile fire.

Their most devastating form of attack is to dive upon a victim with a javelin in each nether hand, building up great speed. The bird-man pulls out of the dive just as it reaches its target and snaps the javelins forward into its prey with great force and accuracy, meanwhile emitting a blood-curdling shriek. Such attacks are at +4 hit

probability and do double damage if successful, but the aarakocra needs at least 200' of dive to perform them properly.

Aarakocra share with eagles the ability to plummet a great distance vertically downwards and pull out at the last moment. For the purposes of aerial combat, they are manoeuvrability class C. Rather than fling it away, a bird-man will save its last javelin for stabbing purposes in battle.

The aarakocra are oviparous and the females tend the eggs during their 8-month incubation period. It is these temporarily nest-bound females which fabricate all the javelins, tools and other small items the tribe uses (the males do no work other than hunting). The females also weave the brilliant feathered banners and pennants which fly above the tribal nest and mark out their territory (each tribe has a unique, highly individual design). The sight of an aarakocra weaving is said to be impressive, as they do so while resting on their backs and using all four hands at the same time. Individually, their hands are not as dextrous as those of a human, but the extra pair more than compensates for this.

Aarakocra speak their own language and that of the giant eagles, with which they are on mutually respectful terms. 10% of aarakocra also speak the common tongue. They get on very well with all forms of air elemental, and any five aarakocra can summon an air elemental by chanting and flying through an intricate aerial dance (this takes three melee rounds). The air elemental will comply with the bird-men's requests as a favour, but will not fight to the death on their behalf, returning to its own plane (if it can) before such an eventuality could occur. The bird-men are known to have tribal shamans.

Colour of plumage among the aarakocra varies from tribe to tribe, but the males are always crested and gaudier than the females. This is especially true during the once-yearly mating season when the plumage of the males shows up in particularly striking fashion. Their beaks are about 5'' long, grey-black and in shape somewhat between that of a parrot and an eagle. The beak can deliver a nasty bite (1-3 hit points of damage) but is rarely used for fighting unless the bird-man is trapped on the ground. Their faces are in no way similar to human faces, though their eyes are set frontally on the head to provide binocular vision, and in fact their sight is so keen that they can distinguish detail at considerable distances. Though they are powerful, they are also light — an adult weight is typically in the range 50-80 pounds — and are unwilling to become involved in ground melee or fights which could result in grappling, since their hollow bones are quite fragile and could break if, for instance, a bird-man is thrown heavily to the ground. The aarokocra are extremely susceptible to claustrophobia. Such is their fear of being closed in that they will not even enter buildings, and only a mad or insanely-desperate bird-man would venture below ground.

Aarakocra can carry up to 1,500 g.p. weight (150 pounds) each.

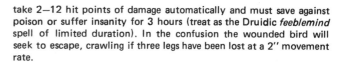

ACHAIERAI

FREQUENCY: *Very rare*
NO. APPEARING: *1-8*
ARMOUR CLASS:
    Body 8; Legs −1
MOVE: *18"*
HIT DICE: *Body 40 hits points;*
    legs 15 hit points each
% IN LAIR: *5%*
TREASURE TYPE: *F*
NO. OF ATTACKS: *3*
DAMAGE/ATTACK:
    1−8/1−8/1−10
SPECIAL ATTACKS: *Nil*
SPECIAL DEFENCES:
    Toxic Smoke
MAGIC RESISTANCE: *35%*
INTELLIGENCE: *Average*
ALIGNMENT: *Chaotic evil*
SIZE: *L (15' tall)*
PSIONIC ABILITY: *Nil*
    Attack/Defence Modes: *Nil*
LEVEL/X.P. VALUE: *VII/1,300 + 14 per hit points = 2,700*

Though the foul motives which caused these loathsome birds to be first summoned from the infernal regions are now lost from memory, remnants of the original achaierai flock still stalk the earth, haunting shadowy places and underground passages. In form they consist of a huge spherical head-body, with a powerful beak and feathery crest, atop four long legs ending in strong claws. Man-sized opponents cannot usually attack the soft body but can only reach the hard, metallic legs. Likewise it will not usually be able to reach a victim with its beak and will therefore fight with two claws, doing 1−8 hit points of damage each.

A beak attack, when this is possible, will have the hit probability of a 9-dice monster, while the claws attack with the hit probability of a 4-dice monster in all cases. If a beak attack is delivered, it will inflict 1−10 hit points of damage on the victim.

The achaierai often travel in groups and, though a group need never check morale, each individual bird will try to flee if it loses a leg (a total of 15 hit points of damage or more on a particular leg will break it from the body). Though flightless (the rudimentary wings are scarcely visible and will not support flight), a bird often eludes pursuers with its long strides. Its movement rate is unaffected by the loss of a single leg, but the loss of two legs halves movement rate. An injured leg will regenerate fully in about two days but the birds do not possess other regenerative powers and a leg which has been completely lost will not be re-grown.

If a bird loses three legs, or is otherwise seriously wounded, it will release a cloud of black toxic smoke which in shape and size approximates to a sphere of 10' radius. All within the cloud (except achaierai)

take 2−12 hit points of damage automatically and must save against poison or suffer insanity for 3 hours (treat as the Druidic *feeblemind* spell of limited duration). In the confusion the wounded bird will seek to escape, crawling if three legs have been lost at a 2" movement rate.

Description: The legs are a metallic blue-grey, the body-head a dull scarlet with deep red blotches. The eyes are steel-blue and the wings blue-green. A wide range of crest colours have been observed, the most common being a bright flame-red.

ADHERER

FREQUENCY: *Rare*
NO. APPEARING: *1-4*
ARMOUR CLASS: *3*
MOVE: *9"*
HIT DICE: *4*
% IN LAIR: *20%*
TREASURE TYPE: *Nil*
NO. OF ATTACKS: *1*
DAMAGE/ATTACK: *1-3*
SPECIAL ATTACKS: *Adhesion*
    — see below
SPECIAL DEFENCES: *See below*
MAGIC RESISTANCE: *See below*
INTELLIGENCE: *Semi-*
ALIGNMENT: *Lawful evil*
SIZE: *M*
PSIONIC ABILITY: *Nil*
    Attack/Defence Modes: *Nil*
LEVEL/X.P. VALUE:
    III/150 + 4 per hit point

This curious creature bears a close resemblance to a mummy — man-sized and with loose folds of dirty white skin which appear on first sight to be a mummy's bandages. Coincidentally, the creature is just as vulnerable to fire as is a mummy due to a resinous solvent in its body fluids. (See ADVANCED DUNGEONS & DRAGONS MONSTER MANUAL — *Mummy*). It is immune to all first-level magic-user spells except *magic missile* which causes it 3−18 hit points of damage per missile.

The creature's skin constantly exudes a sour-smelling glue-like substance with very powerful adhesive properties; any material except stone will adhere to it and only fire, boiling water or the creature's own voluntary secretions will break the adhesion. Thus any weapon which hits the beast will adhere to it (and only deliver half damage). Similarly the creature will stick to any character it hits with its two-handed flailing fist attack (which also inflicts 1−3 hit points of damage on the victim); its favourite tactic is to bind up an opponent in this fashion and use him as an involuntary shield.

The adhesive properties of the secretion wear off in 5−10 turns after the beast is killed.

Usually the adherer will catch its prey by waiting in ambush, camouflaging itself by rolling in dirt, sticks, and leaves and then artfully arranging larger pieces of debris to conceal its form. Any prey (regardless of size) passing near its 'hideout' will trigger its attack response and the adherer will pounce on the closest target, attempting to hit and to cling with bulldog-like tenacity until the prey expires. However, if it is spotted and attacked before any potential prey has come into pouncing range (with missile fire, or sometimes even loud noises), it will become confused and beat a hasty retreat.

Boiling water (or boiling liquid of other types) will cause the adherer 1−3 hit points of damage if a sizeable quantity is thrown over the beast (the contents of a large bucket would just suffice if thrown from close enough to minimise 'spread') and this will inhibit its adhesive properties for the subsequent melee round.

The adherer's taste for prey is wide-ranging and it will usually attack, given a suitable opportunity. The only exception to this is the spider — the adherer will never attack a spider of whatever variety and sometimes it has been known to co-operate with them in trapping prey.

Despite its appearance, the adherer is not an undead creature.

EMMANUEL

ALEAX

FREQUENCY: *Very rare*
NO. APPEARING: *1*
ARMOUR CLASS: *See below*
MOVE: *12″*
HIT DICE: *See below*
% IN LAIR: *Nil*
TREASURE TYPE: *Nil*
NO. OF ATTACKS: *See below*
DAMAGE/ATTACK: *See below*
SPECIAL ATTACKS: *Nil*
SPECIAL DEFENCES:
   Regeneration —see below
MAGIC RESISTANCE: *100%*
INTELLIGENCE: *Genius*
ALIGNMENT: *See below*
SIZE: *M*
PSIONIC ABILITY: *Nil*
   Attack/Defence Modes: *Nil*
LEVEL/X.P. VALUE: *See below*

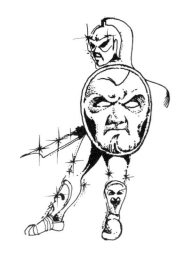

An aleax is a physical manifestation of the vengeance of certain gods. There is but one aleax for each such god, sent to punish and redeem those who stray from alignment, fail to sacrifice enough treasure or otherwise anger their god. An aleax will never be met by chance.

An aleax appears in human form and will closely resemble his intended victim. To that victim, the aleax will appear bathed in shimmering light which varies in colour according to the god's alignment — golden for lawful good, deep purple for lawful evil, everchanging rose-and-blue hues for chaotic good, and so forth. On appearance, the aleax will attack his intended victim — he cannot be detected in any way by others, nor will physical or magical attacks touch the aleax except those from his victim. To an observer, the victim appears to be in conflict with a totally invisible, totally invulnerable being.

To the victim, the aleax will be in all respects (except as indicated elsewhere) his own exact duplicate. It will have the same characteristics, hit points, armour, weapons and so on. There are but two differences in combat:

a) the aleax *regenerates* after being first wounded; the round after the wound is taken, it *regenerates* 1 hit point, the next round 2 hit points, then 4 hit points, then 8 hit points and so on until it is killed (reduced to zero hit points or below) or all hits are restored. If it is then hit again, the progression starts again at 1 hit point;

b) any hit scored against an aleax on an unmodified roll of 19 does double damage, and any hit on an unmodified 20 does quadruple damage.. (Note that damage inflicted by the aleax on its victim is normal, whatever the 'to hit' roll).

A victim killed by an aleax loses all treasure (even if cached — gods are near-omniscient!) and half his experience points. The character is then automatically *raised* and may then begin life again at the appropriate experience level. All the victim's magical items lose their magical properties, scrolls become blank, potions become inert and so on. No resurrection is necessary and the character will not receive a further visitation from an aleax providing he remains true to his god thereafter.

If an intended victim kills an aleax, that person is taken to Heaven (or Olympus, Hell, Valhalla as appropriate) to serve his god personally for a year and a day. On return, the character will regain all former possessions (which in this case retain their properties and powers, though they are not available for use by another character during the owner's absence) and the deity will almost certainly (95% chance) add an extra reward (e.g. a powerful magical item, promotion to the next highest experience level etc. — at the referee's discretion).

As it appears, an aleax will, in the victim's alignment language, utter a few brief words to indicate that the victim is to be punished by his god. Otherwise an aleax will never converse, no matter under what duress.

ALGOID

FREQUENCY: *Very rare*
NO. APPEARING: *1-6*
ARMOUR CLASS: *5*
MOVE: *6″*
HIT DICE: *5*
% IN LAIR: *20%*
TREASURE TYPE: *D(x½)*
NO. OF ATTACKS: *2*
DAMAGE/ATTACK: *1—10/1—10*
SPECIAL ATTACKS: *Nil*
SPECIAL DEFENCES: *Immune*
   to edged weapons of less
   than +2 bonus
MAGIC RESISTANCE:
   Immune to fireballs and
   lightning; otherwise
   standard
INTELLIGENCE: *Semi-*
ALIGNMENT: *Chaotic neutral*
SIZE: *M*
PSIONIC ABILITY: *101-120*
   (and see below)
   Attack/Defence Modes: *A*
LEVEL/X.P. VALUE:
   V/280 + 5 per hit point

This creature appears as a green humanoid with coarse, rough features. Its appearance is misleading, however — it is in fact a colony of algae which, assembled in this form, has developed some mobility and a rudimentary intelligence. Its form is only of a temporary nature.

It is immune to psionic attacks but can deliver one *mind blast* per day. It attacks otherwise with its powerful fists each of which can inflict 1—10 hit points of damage.

Edged weapons will pass through an algoid without doing any damage, unless they have a magical bonus of +2 or better in which case they inflict half normal damage. Blunt weapons — magical or otherwise — will do full damage.

The algoid has control over certain types of trees, similar to the control exerted over trees by the treant (see ADVANCED DUNGEONS & DRAGONS, MONSTER MANUAL — *Treant*). The types of tree over which the algoid has control are those which will be found near its normal habitat (swamp, lakeside pasture — at all events close to water of some kind whether stagnant or otherwise); thus it will be able to control two willows, water-oaks, cypresses or other similar varieties of tree. Trees thus controlled move at 3″ rate and strike with two attacks per round for 1—10 hit points of damage each.

Despite their immunity to certain forms of magical attack (*fireball, lightning*) algoids are particularly vulnerable to *part water* and *lower water* spells, each of which inflict 1—6 hit points of damage per experience level of the spell-caster.

AL-MI'RAJ

FREQUENCY: *Very rare*
NO. APPEARING: *2—20*
ARMOUR CLASS: *6*
MOVE: *18″*
HIT DICE: *1*
% IN LAIR: *5%*
TREASURE TYPE: *Nil*
NO. OF ATTACKS: *1*
DAMAGE/ATTACK: *1—4*
SPECIAL ATTACKS: *Nil*
SPECIAL DEFENCES: *Nil*
MAGIC RESISTANCE: *See below*
INTELLIGENCE: *Animal*
ALIGNMENT: *Neutral*
SIZE: *S (3' tall)*
PSIONIC ABILITY: *Nil*
   Attack/Defence Modes: *Nil*
LEVEL/X.P. VALUE:
   1/10 + 1 per hit point

The al-mi'raj generally roams pastures and woodlands but is sometimes discovered in dungeons. Its lair is usually a small cave just below ground.

The creature resembles a large yellow hare with a long (1½'-2') black horn protruding forwards from the centre of its forehead, resembling that of a unicorn. In melee it will stab with its horn, its nimbleness giving the horn damage potential of a dagger (1—4 hit points of damage).

Its intellect is severely limited and its behaviour unpredictable — for instance it may well attack for no good reason. If it is captured alive when young, the beast shows a surprising aptitude for training and its fearlessness makes it a useful companion.

The al-mi'raj has a particularly acute sense of smell and sharp eyesight.

APPARITION

FREQUENCY: *Very rare*
NO. APPEARING: *1—4*
ARMOUR CLASS: *0*
MOVE: *24"*
HIT DICE: *8*
% IN LAIR: *20%*
TREASURE TYPE: *E*
NO. OF ATTACKS: *1*
DAMAGE/ATTACK: *See below*
SPECIAL ATTACKS: *Nil*
SPECIAL DEFENCES: *Can only be hit by magical or silver weapons*
MAGIC RESISTANCE: *Standard*
INTELLIGENCE: *Average*
ALIGNMENT: *Chaotic evil*
SIZE: *M*
PSIONIC ABILITY: *Nil*
    Attack/Defence Modes: *Nil*
LEVEL/X.P. VALUE:
    VI/1,000 + 10 per hit point

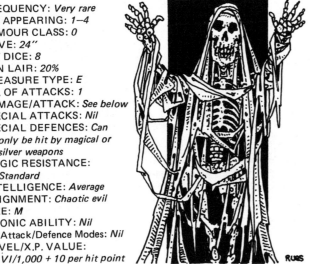

This ghastly undead creature exists mainly on the *Ethereal Plane*, though when making its 'attack' it can be hit, as if armour class 0, by magical or silver weapons. An apparition is turned as a spectre. It will be reluctant to approach mirrors or anything made of silver.

The apparition has an emotive *E.S.P.* ability which enables it to sense potential victims up to 100' away. It surprises a party or an individual on a roll of 1—5 (d6) due to its uncanny appearance from wall, floor or ceiling, using the surprise thus gained to close the distance between it and its victim. When in sight it appears as an insubstantial skeletal being in a thin white robe.

In actuality the apparition is unable physically to attack. However its chosen victim will feel bony claw-like fingers at the throat — this effect is felt even through armour.

Even though the victim may be aware that the apparition cannot physically do them harm, the suggestion is immensely strong. The victim must roll 3d6; a total under the victim's intelligence means that the suggestion is ineffective and the victim is immune (though only to that individual apparition). However a total equal to or greater than the victim's intelligence means that they are stricken with horror and must again roll 3d6. This score is matched against their constitution. If the total is less than the constitution the victim flees in terror for 1—4 melee rounds (and may be attacked again in so doing). However if the total is equal to or greater than the constitution the victim suffers a massive heart seizure and dies instantly.

A slain victim may be *raised* but if the body is left, or no attempt is made within one hour to *raise* it, it will rise as an apparition in 2-8 hours.

The apparition may be attacked 'normally' on the *Ethereal Plane* by characters able to move and fight on that plane, but remains on the

Prime Material Plane for only one melee round per victim attacked and it is only during this period that it can be attacked by non-ethereal means.

To make its 'attack' the apparition need not score a hit in the usual sense so no 'to hit' roll is required.

ASSASSIN BUG

FREQUENCY: *Rare*
NO. APPEARING: *2*
ARMOUR CLASS: *5*
MOVE: *6"/18"*
HIT DICE: *1+1*
% IN LAIR: *50%*
TREASURE TYPE: *Nil*
NO. OF ATTACKS: *1*
DAMAGE/ATTACK: *1—4*
SPECIAL ATTACKS:
    Paralysation
SPECIAL DEFENCES: *Nil*
MAGIC RESISTANCE: *Standard*
INTELLIGENCE: *Animal*
ALIGNMENT: *Neutral*
SIZE: *S (up to 2' long)*
PSIONIC ABILITY: *Nil*
    Attack/Defence Modes: *Nil*
LEVEL/X.P. VALUE:
    II/65 + 2 per hit point

Resembling giant bluebottle flies with four limbs — miniature arms and legs — the assassin bugs are rarely seen except during their mating season (one day in every two months) when a male and a female may be encountered flying in search of a host for their offspring. The natural host is human, but assassin bugs have been known to lay their eggs in demi-humans and (rarely) humanoids.

The male will always attack first, biting a victim for 1—4 hit points of damage while the female flies nearby, as close to the intended victim as possible consistent with not risking being attacked. If the male's attack succeeds, its saliva will paralyse the affected area of the victim's body unless the victim makes his saving roll at +2. The male will continue to attack until destroyed. For purposes of aerial combat, they are manoeuvrability class C.

As soon as one of the male's attacks has achieved the desired paralysation, the female (which detects the scent of the male saliva) will 'attack' the affected area. If successful, the female implants her egg into the victim's body. The female will die as soon as the egg has been implanted.

The egg will hatch, producing 7-12 larvae, 13-24 hours after it has been implanted. During this period only a very powerful spell such as a *limited wish* or *heal* will remove or kill the egg. When the larvae hatch, each one will cause 1 hit point of damage to the host each hour as it devours the host's internal organs. After 2 weeks the larvae will leave the host, burrowing out through the area in which the egg was originally implanted and causing an additional 5—8 hit points of damage per larva as they do so. As soon as they are outside the body, they will metamorphose into fully-grown assassin bugs.

While the larvae are in the host's body, they can be killed by a number of spells cast on the host:

Cure serious wounds — will kill one larva per experience level of the caster above the 6th level;
Cure critical wounds — will kill all larvae;
Heal — will kill all larvae and restore all but 5—8 of the victim's hit points.
A *limited wish* or similar spell can also be effective during this period.

Assassin bug eggs are regarded as great delicacies by trolls, troglodytes and bugbears. The eggs themselves are 4-5" long and oval, coloured a deep blue.

Description: Assassin bugs are generally the colour of bluebottle flies though the female tends to be a lighter shade than the male. The four limbs are the colour of human flesh. The wings are nearly transparent but have a faint silver hue.

ASTRAL SEARCHER

FREQUENCY: *Very rare*
NO. APPEARING: *4–24*
ARMOUR CLASS: *10*
MOVE: *12"*
HIT DICE: *2*
% IN LAIR: *Nil*
TREASURE TYPE: *Nil*
NO. OF ATTACKS: *1*
DAMAGE/ATTACK: *1–6*
SPECIAL ATTACKS: *All*
    victims AC5
SPECIAL DEFENCES: *Nil*
MAGIC RESISTANCE: *50%*
INTELLIGENCE: *Non-*
ALIGNMENT: *Any*
SIZE: *M*
PSIONIC ABILITY: *Nil*
    Attack/Defence Modes: *Nil*
LEVEL/X.P. VALUE:
    III/73 + 2 per hit point

Astral searchers — mindless shells of nebulous humanoid shape — are created by concentrated and/or traumatic human thought. Violent death, spells cast while on the *Astral Plane* and astral combat often result in the creation of astral searchers (an event quite unknown to their creator or source). Driven by their past connection with material beings, astral searchers seek material bodies with complete singleness of purpose. Wandering the *Astral Plane*, they search for weak points in the fabric connecting the *Astral* to the *Prime Material Plane;* they cluster at such points, waiting for the stress lines to become collinear so that they can pass from the *Astral* to the *Material* through the singularities thus created. Such weak points exist naturally; they may

also be created during astral travel (4% chance) in which case they exist only temporarily.

When they have been able to cross to the *Prime Material Plane*, astral searchers emerge there and attack the nearest living humanoids in the hope of possessing their bodies. Astral searchers attack the psyche (so all victims are treated as AC5 against their attack, regardless of physical or magical protection) though their victims will believe the attack to be physical and will sustain damage accordingly. All damage inflicted by astral searchers is illusory and will fade in 3-12 rounds following the termination of the astral searchers' attack.

If an astral searcher reduces its victim to zero hit points or below, the mind and personality of the victim are destroyed and the astral searcher possesses the body. It acquires the victim's physical abilities and hit points (as all damage from the astral searcher's attack now disappears) but not the former owner's personality, and alignment should be re-determined at random. The possessed body becomes a new non-player character in the body of a player character and what this non-player-character may do is entirely in the hands of the referee, who must have regard to the body's alignment in determining its action.

Astral searchers can be *exorcised* from a body, but the original psyche will have been completely destroyed and the player character cannot be *raised* or brought back. If an astral searcher is driven out of a body, the empty corpus will then be an open invitation to possession by a demon or other similar creature (at the discretion of the referee).

Astral searchers may be attacked physically; destruction of the materialised searcher body will result in the destruction and dissipation of the astral searcher itself. Since they exist simultaneously on two planes, astral searchers are 50% resistant to magic.

Astral searchers are not in any respect undead.

BABBLER — BAT, GIANT — BERBALANG — BLINDHEIM — BLOOD HAWK — BLOODWORM, GIANT — BONESNAPPER — BOOKA — BULLYWUG — BUNYIP

BABBLER

FREQUENCY: *Very rare*
NO. APPEARING: *1–4*
ARMOUR CLASS: *6*
MOVE: *6" or 12" (see below)*
HIT DICE: *5*
% IN LAIR: *15%*
TREASURE TYPE: *B*
NO. OF ATTACKS: *3*
DAMAGE/ATTACK:
    1–6/1–6/1–8
SPECIAL ATTACKS: *See below*
SPECIAL DEFENCES: *Nil*
MAGIC RESISTANCE: *Standard*
INTELLIGENCE: *Average but*
    high cunning
ALIGNMENT: *Chaotic evil*
SIZE: *L (8' tall)*
PSIONIC ABILITY: *Nil*
    Attack/Defence Modes: *Nil*
LEVEL/X.P. VALUE:
    III/130 + 5 per hit point

Weird mutations of lizard men, babblers are large ponderous marsh-dwellers, known as marsh-gibberers to native tribes dwelling near their swamp habitat. Their predominant colour is a dirty yellow, though their undersides are grey. Mottled grey patches create weird designs on their muscular bodies. In form, the babbler resembles a small jorgosaurus with a flexible, tough tail employed to keep the creature stable in erect movement.

Normal movement is a surprisingly fast (12" rate) slither on its stomach, but in melee the babbler must stand erect, in which posture its movement rate is reduced to 6", in order to use its two foreclaws

(1–6 hit points of damage each) and its bite (1–8 hit points of damage). It has a particularly large mouth, filled with rows of sharp teeth.

When moving on its belly the babbler is difficult to detect (25% chance) but animals will smell it some distance away. If it is undetected in approach it can strike from behind as a 4th level thief, doing double damage and gaining a bonus of +4 on the 'to hit' roll.

The babbler is particularly fond of human flesh and will attack humans unless outnumbered by more than two to one. Raiding parties of marsh-dwelling lizard men have been observed to be led by one, two or even three babblers in an evil quest for human flesh.

The babbler communicates with its kind in a quasi-lingual babbling tongue which defies efforts at analysis and learning by humans. It can understand the common tongue in a rudimentary fashion.

BAT, *Giant*

FREQUENCY: *Uncommon*
NO. APPEARING: *3–18*
ARMOUR CLASS: *8*
MOVE: *3"/18"*
HIT DICE: *1-4 hit points or 1*
% IN LAIR: *50%*
TREASURE TYPE: *Nil*
NO. OF ATTACKS: *1*
DAMAGE/ATTACK:
    1–2 or 1–4
SPECIAL ATTACKS: *Nil*
SPECIAL DEFENCES: *See
    below*
MAGIC RESISTANCE:
    Standard
INTELLIGENCE: *Non-*
ALIGNMENT: *Neutral*
SIZE: *S*
PSIONIC ABILITY: *Nil*
    Attack/Defence Modes: *Nil*
LEVEL/X.P. VALUE:
    *I/5 + 1 per hit point or
    I/10 +1 per hit point*

These creatures — giant versions of the carnivorous variety of the ordinary bat, with bodies 3' long and a wingspan of 5'–6' — dwell in dark caverns, usually underground. In flight they emit a high-pitched whistling sound, a navigational device which compensates for their poor eyesight.

Giant bats are highly manoeuvrable in flight — anyone with a dexterity of less than 13 who fires a missile at a flying giant bat does so at −3 hit probability. For purposes of aerial combat, they are manoeuvrability class C.

The creature must land — usually on its victim — to attack with its bite (1–2 or 1–4 points of damage). 1% of victims bitten by giant bats contract rabies.

Only 10% of giant bats are of the 1 hit die variety.

BERBALANG

FREQUENCY: *Very rare*
NO. APPEARING: *1*
ARMOUR CLASS: *6*
MOVE: *6"/24"*
HIT DICE: *1+1*
% IN LAIR: *See below*
TREASURE TYPE: *D*
NO. OF ATTACKS: *3*
DAMAGE/ATTACK:
    1–4/1–4/1–6
SPECIAL ATTACKS: *Nil*
SPECIAL DEFENCES: *Nil*
MAGIC RESISTANCE:
    Standard
INTELLIGENCE: *Very*
ALIGNMENT: *Chaotic evil*
SIZE: *M*
PSIONIC ABILITY: *Nil*
    Attack/Defence Modes: *Nil*
LEVEL/X.P. VALUE:
    III/65 + 2 per hit point

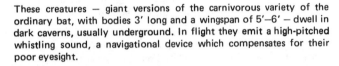

The berbalang is a solitary biped with leathery skin and bat-like wings. Its eyes are white and watery and its powers of infravision are twice as effective as elves' (120' range).

The creature spends the greater part of each month in an apparently dormant state, hibernating preferably in a well-hidden cave. Though seemingly comatose, the berbalang is actually roaming the *Astral Plane* where it spends its time hunting and killing creatures weaker than itself and engaging in bizarre and complex courtship and mating rituals with other berbalangs. If its body is discovered and interfered

with during the creature's astral roaming, the berbalang will attempt to return to the body and animate it; however this can take a long time (1-100 rounds) depending on the berbalang's actual distance away across the planes. If the body is destroyed, the astral berbalang dies as well. For this reason the creature takes a great deal of care in hiding itself and is very ingenious in this regard.

For three days each month at the time of the full moon, the berbalang returns to its material body, only to alter its form of trance and send forth a physical projection of itself upon the *Prime Material Plane*. The projection flies in search of food — a freshly-killed human corpse. The projection is physical in the sense that it can receive and inflict damage — in this respect it is a duplicate of the original. The berbalang can use all of the senses of the projection and will command (and essentially 'is') the projection in its quest for food. The projection can range up to 3 miles from the material berbalang body. The projection fights, if it needs to do so, in the same way as the berbalang — with its two claws (1–4 hit points of damage each) and a bite for 1–6 hit points of damage.

If the projection is hit and suffers damage it immediately takes flight, returning at flying speed (24" rate) to the body which will be unable to project again for a number of days equal to the number of hit points lost. If the projection is 'killed' it disappears, and there is a 75% chance that the original will also die from system shock.

If the berbalang survives an attack, it will eventually seek revenge upon its attacker, though this may be delayed while the body recovers. If a wounded projection is followed back to the berbalang lair, the followers may be taken aback when they confront the unwounded physical creature.

If the protection is forced back to the body before the berbalang was able to feed, or if the projection was destroyed before feeding, a new projection will go forth again as soon as possible (after the compulsory period of recovery) regardless of the phase of the moon.

To keep from depleting its food supply or arousing too great a local alarm, a berbalang will move its physical body to a new area every three or four months. They always travel by night and avoid confrontations when they are actually physically present. Since berbalangs live on the edge of civilisation, where lack of organisation allows them free rein, a berbalang is very rarely encountered in its physical form unless adventurers happen upon its lair or follow its projection back to its body.

If a projection kills a human it will immediately pick up the body and fly, at full rate, back to the host which will immediately emerge from its trance. While in flight, the projection will be feeding on the body — a fully-grown human can thus be devoured in one turn, leaving only the bones, garments and equipment.

For the purposes of aerial combat, the berbalang and its projection are both manoeuvrability class B.

How the berbalang derives sustenance when only its projection feeds and how it reproduces when all mating activity takes place on the *Astral Plane*, are mysteries so far unexplained.

BLINDHEIM

FREQUENCY: *Very rare*
NO. APPEARING: *1—4*
ARMOUR CLASS: *See below*
MOVE: *9"*
HIT DICE: *4+2*
% IN LAIR: *5%*
TREASURE TYPE: *B*
NO. OF ATTACKS: *1*
DAMAGE/ATTACK: *1—8*
SPECIAL ATTACKS:
   Blinding stare
SPECIAL DEFENCES: *Nil*
MAGIC RESISTANCE:
   Standard
INTELLIGENCE: *Animal*
ALIGNMENT: *Chaotic evil*
SIZE: *S (4' tall)*
PSIONIC ABILITY: *Nil*
   Attack/Defence Modes: *Nil*
LEVEL/X.P. VALUE:
   III/130 + 5 per hit point

RUSS

This subterranean creature is a yellow frog-like humanoid with huge eyes that shine like searchlights. While in repose, the beast keeps its eyes 'turned off' by means of an extra eyelid; however it can 'attack' instantaneously by opening its eyes, and its acute sense of hearing will usually indicate to it the direction of its 'target'. Those who come within its beams at a range of 30' or less must save (as against wands) or be blinded for 11—20 turns. Anyone with infravision in that range must save at —3.

Those not blinded will still be unable to look directly at the beast so its effective armour class is 1. However if for any reason an attacker is immune to bright light, the blindheim's true armour class is 3.

When at close quarters, the blindheim attacks with a vicious bite which inflicts 1—8 hit points of damage.

The creature is coloured in varying shades of yellow, the darker shades on its back contrasting with lighter shades on its underbelly. If the eyes of a dead blindheim are opened, they are seen to be a dull gold in colour.

BLOOD HAWK

FREQUENCY: *Uncommon*
NO. APPEARING: *4—15(d12+3)*
ARMOUR CLASS: *7*
MOVE: *24"*
HIT DICE: *1+1*
% IN LAIR: *25%*
TREASURE TYPE: *Qx2*
NO. OF ATTACKS: *3*
DAMAGE/ATTACK:
   1—4/1—4/1—6
SPECIAL ATTACKS: *Nil*
SPECIAL DEFENCES: *Nil*
MAGIC RESISTANCE: *Standard*
INTELLIGENCE: *Semi-*
ALIGNMENT: *Neutral*
SIZE: *S*
PSIONIC ABILITY: *Nil*
   Attack/Defence Modes: *Nil*
LEVEL/X.P. VALUE:
   I/20 + 2 per hit point

Blood hawks resemble normal hawks in size alone, as their beaks are razor sharp and their talons unusually strong. Their wings are similar to those of an eagle, giving them considerable speed in flight. For purposes of aerial combat, they are manoeuvrability class B.

They attack with their beaks (1—6 hit points of damage) and two sets of talons (1—4 hit points of damage each set), swooping swiftly and silently onto their victims. Blood hawks are fond of human flesh and will continue to attack humans even when the melee is going against them.

They will pick at the dead bodies of their prey, not only for food but also for gems with which they line their nests as an allurement to blood hawk females. All other types of treasure will be ignored.

In colour the blood hawk is a uniform medium grey.

BLOODWORM, *Giant*

FREQUENCY: *Rare*
NO. APPEARING: *1—4*
ARMOUR CLASS: *4*
MOVE: *6"*
HIT DICE: *6*
% IN LAIR: *50%*
TREASURE TYPE: *Q*
NO. OF ATTACKS: *1*
DAMAGE/ATTACK: *1—8*
   + blood drain
SPECIAL ATTACKS: *Nil*
SPECIAL DEFENCES: *Nil*
MAGIC RESISTANCE:
   Standard
INTELLIGENCE: *Non-*
ALIGNMENT: *Neutral*
SIZE: *L (20' long)*
PSIONIC ABILITY: *Nil*
   Attack/Defence Modes: *Nil*
LEVEL/X.P. VALUE:
   IV/225 + 6 per hit point

Giant bloodworms are usually found in the shallow pools of underground caverns. They cannot swim, but propel themselves along the bottom of such pools or on nearby firm ground. Their underbelly is a dark slimy brown while their upper surface is mottled green. Lying half in, half out of a pool, a giant bloodworm is easily mistaken in dim light for a moss-covered boulder.

A giant bloodworm will only attack if hungry (they will eat once a week) or if trodden on. When the giant bloodworm does attack, it will attempt to fasten its large suckered mouth onto a victim. If successful, it will drain blood from its victim each subsequent round. Though the initial attack requires a successful 'to hit' roll and causes no damage, subsequent blood drains are automatic, requiring no 'to hit' roll, and deliver 1—8 hit points of damage until the bloodworm dies or releases its grasp.

Giant bloodworms are particularly vulnerable to fire — they take double damage from all fire attacks and save at —2 against magical fire. A successful fire attack is the only way, short of killing the beast, to force it to relax its grip on a victim, though if the bloodworm is not killed, it will attempt to re-attach itself to a victim immediately.

BONESNAPPER

FREQUENCY: *Rare*
NO. APPEARING: *1—3*
ARMOUR CLASS: *4*
MOVE: *6"*
HIT DICE: *4*
% IN LAIR: *20%*
TREASURE TYPE: *C*
NO. OF ATTACKS: *2*
DAMAGE/ATTACK: *1—8/1—4*
SPECIAL ATTACKS: *Nil*
SPECIAL DEFENCES: *Nil*
MAGIC RESISTANCE: *Standard*
INTELLIGENCE: *Non-*
ALIGNMENT: *Neutral*
SIZE: *M (5' high)*
PSIONIC ABILITY: *Nil*
   Attack/Defence Modes: *Nil*
LEVEL/X.P. VALUE:
   III/60 + 4 per hit point

The bonesnapper is a small descendant of a long-extinct class of carnivorous dinosaur, as stupid as it is aggressive. The large jaw contains many sharp teeth which it uses to inflict 1—8 hit points of damage in melee; at the same time, the tail sweeps round to deliver 1–4 hit points of damage on the same victim. Its aggressive nature leads it always to fight to the death.

Though non-intelligent, the bonesnapper has inherited a primeval instinct for the collection of human bones, particularly jawbones, which it uses to decorate its subterranean lair. The number of such bones discovered in a lair will give a good indication of the occupant's status among its kind.

Description: The bonesnapper is a grey-green colour mottled with dark grey spots and patches. It has tiny scarlet eyes and yellow-white teeth.

BOOKA

FREQUENCY: *Uncommon*
NO. APPEARING: *1–4*
ARMOUR CLASS: *7*
MOVE: *12''/18''*
HIT DICE: *1–4 hit points*
% IN LAIR: *75%*
TREASURE TYPE: *J*
NO. OF ATTACKS: *Nil*
DAMAGE/ATTACK: *Nil*
SPECIAL ATTACKS: *See below*
SPECIAL DEFENCES: *See below*
MAGIC RESISTANCE: *10%*
INTELLIGENCE: *Very*
ALIGNMENT: *Neutral*
　　　　　(chaotic good)
SIZE: *S*
PSIONIC ABILITY: *Nil*
　　Attack/Defence Modes: *Nil*
LEVEL/X.P. VALUE:
　　I/9 + 1 per hit point

The booka are sprite-like creatures given to dwelling in attics, in eaves and on sunny rooftops. They hate cold, and in such climes will always be inside, near chimneys. On bright, sunny mornings they will sweep the stairs or porch of the place they dwell in, always doing so when there is nobody around to observe them. If disturbed when involved in such tasks, they will become angry and immediately remove to a new home.

Booka are very fast-moving and can also fly. They can become invisible at will, even when running or flying. They hate evil creatures and will play tricks on them if given the opportunity — hiding valued objects, tangling things like rope, hair, clothing etc., and generally causing trouble.

If a booka is captured or harmed in any way, it is certain that others of its ilk aware of this act will bring dozens of other booka to cause mischief and trouble until the offender frees the captive or makes amends for the harm by giving a valuable gift (such as a sack of gold,

jewellery or even something magical) to the booka, placing the item offered on a roof-top and leaving it for a day. Failure to placate angry booka will eventually result in some sort of fatal accident, for the creatures will place snares and traps for the offender.

A booka is only about 1' tall. Both males and females tend to have large features and thin bodies. They can be described, at best, as 'homely'. For purposes of aerial combat, they are manoeuvrability class A, though they will avoid combat of this or any other sort by means of their invisibility, if at all possible.

BULLYWUG

FREQUENCY: *Rare*
NO. APPEARING: *10–80*
ARMOUR CLASS: *6 (or better)*
MOVE: *3''//15''*
HIT DICE: *1*
% IN LAIR: *20%*
TREASURE TYPE: *J, K, M, Q(x5)*
　　& C(magic only) in lair
NO. OF ATTACKS: *3 or 1*
DAMAGE/ATTACK:
　　1–2/1–2/2–5 or by weapon
SPECIAL ATTACKS: *Hop*
SPECIAL DEFENCES: *Camouflage*
MAGIC RESISTANCE: *Standard*
INTELLIGENCE: *Low to average*
ALIGNMENT: *Chaotic evil*
SIZE: *S to M*
PSIONIC ABILITY: *Nil*
　　Attack/Defence Modes: *Nil*
LEVEL/X.P. VALUE:
　　Regular = I/18 + 1 per hit point
　　Leader = II/36 + 2 per hit point
　　Shaman or Great Chief =
　　　　III/80 + 3 per hit point

The bullywugs are a batrachian race of bipedal monsters which inhabit wet places — rainy forests, marshes, damp caves or virtually any other place which is shady or dark and has water nearby, for bullywugs need to dampen their skins from time to time.

Some types of these creatures are more intelligent than others. The intelligent groups tend to dwell in caves or deserted human habitations, and they will usually have armour, shields and various forms of weapons (use the example of human bandits for arms and armour). The less advanced bullywugs hate their more intelligent fellows and war upon them.

Unless encumbered by armour and shield, a bullywug is able to swim rapidly. Even with such encumbrance, a bullywug can swim at 9'' speed. Likewise, with or without adornment, a bullywug can hop forward 3'' or upwards 1½''. In doing so, the creature adds +1 to its 'to hit' die roll or rolls. If it is using an impaling weapon, the bullywug delivers double damage as a result of a successful hopping attack.

The hopping attack with a weapon is their normal means of melee. However bullywugs without access to weapons, or those which have been disarmed, will still hop to the attack in which case they use two claws (1—2 hit points of damage each) and a bite (2—5 hit points of damage).

Bullywugs have a chameleon-like power; their skin colouration can be grey, green or brown in light or dark shades. Thus, if motionless and in an area which allows use of camouflage power, a bullywug is 75% unlikely to be noticed (this applies to infravision as well, as the colour alteration also alters body heat). When attacking unnoticed from camouflage conditions, the bullywug has a 3 in 6 chance of surprising its victim (5 in 6 if hopping to the attack).

The major weakness of these creatures is that unless they are employing long weapons, their attacks always take place after those of their opponents, due to slow speed of movement or exposure while hopping. Note that a weapon can be set against a hop just as against a charge (which, in effect, a hop is).

Bullywugs form organised bands and are always led by a large individual with a full 8 hit points. If 30 or more of these creatures are encountered, there will be at least 5 large individuals and a leader of 10—13 hit points (effectively a 2-dice monster) doing +1 damage on all attacks. Those using armour etc. will also have a 10% chance per ten creatures in the group of having a tribal shaman of 11—14 hit points. Groups of 60 or more will have a great chief of 16—19 hit points which does +2 damage on all attacks.

These creatures will readily serve chaotic evil masters, human or otherwise. It is rumoured that bullywug-human crossbreeds are viable and that certain degenerate humans dwell in mixed communities with these monsters, serving unnamed things from caverns deep beneath the earth.

The bullywugs have their own, rather primitive language and the more intelligent ones can converse haltingly in the common tongue, though their vocabulary is rather limited. They are held in disdain by sahuagin, who will occasionally raid a bullywug lair for sport and out of sheer malice, eating any captive alive. Lizard men will rarely associate with bullywugs, though there is no open hostility towards them.

BUNYIP

FREQUENCY: *Rare*
NO. APPEARING: *1*
ARMOUR CLASS: *10*
MOVE: *12"*
HIT DICE: *5*
% IN LAIR: *30%*
TREASURE TYPE: *Nil*
NO. OF ATTACKS: *1*
DAMAGE/ATTACK: *1—6*
SPECIAL ATTACKS: *Nil*
SPECIAL DEFENCES: *Nil*
MAGIC RESISTANCE: *Standard*
INTELLIGENCE: *Animal*
ALIGNMENT: *Neutral*
    (chaotic good)
SIZE: *M (6' long)*
PSIONIC ABILITY: *Nil*
    Attack/Defence Modes: *Nil*
LEVEL/X.P. VALUE:
    III/90 + 5 per hit point

The bunyip is an aquatic beast resembling a seal covered in thick black fur, with a black mane and unusually powerful jaws. It dwells in lakes, marshes and sluggish rivers.

It is a mischievous beast of playful intent, but is large and strong enough to tip over a small boat. It can also sense the approach of human beings and may (50% chance) rise momentarily above the surface to roar at a nearby party of adventurers; all members of the party who are below the 4th experience level must save at —2 against wands or flee in panic.

If a small creature such as a dwarf is struggling in the water, the bunyip will usually (80% chance) bite in an attempt to sever and swallow a limb, but it will not attack anything larger than a dwarf except in self-defence or unless the victim is already bleeding. A successful bite by the bunyip's powerful jaws inflicts 1—6 hit points of damage. If it attacks on a 'to hit' roll of 20, a limb of the victim is severed (determine at random or according to the circumstances of the attack).

 CARBUNCLE — CARYATID COLUMN — CATERWAUL — CIFAL — CLUBNEK — COFFER CORPSE — CRABMAN — CRYPT THING

CARBUNCLE

FREQUENCY: *Rare*
NO. APPEARING: *1*
ARMOUR CLASS: *2*
MOVE: *3"*
HIT DICE: *1*
% IN LAIR: *10%*
TREASURE TYPE: *Nil*
    (but see below)
NO. OF ATTACKS: *Nil*
DAMAGE/ATTACK: *Nil*
SPECIAL ATTACKS: *Nil*
SPECIAL DEFENCES: *See below*
MAGIC RESISTANCE: *Standard*
INTELLIGENCE: *Low — average*
ALIGNMENT: *Neutral with*
    chaotic tendencies
SIZE: *S (3' long)*
PSIONIC ABILITY: *Nil*
    Attack/Defence Modes: *Nil*
LEVEL/X.P. VALUE:
    I/14 + 1 per hit point

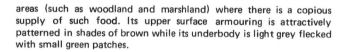

This small creature is similar to an armadillo with an 'armoured' upper surface of small interlocking 'plates' of tough leathery skin. It feeds exclusively on leaves and small insects and is rarely found outside

areas (such as woodland and marshland) where there is a copious supply of such food. Its upper surface armouring is attractively patterned in shades of brown while its underbody is light grey flecked with small green patches.

Set in its head, immediately above its eyes, is a large ruby. This is actually part of the animal and if the beast dies the ruby will shatter into worthless dust. The creature may, however, be coaxed into giving up its ruby by a wizard (or anyone of equal status) who uses a charm monster or charm animal ability. The gem is usually (70%) 500 gp value though rare specimens (25%) have 1,000 gp gems and there is a 5% chance that a carbuncle will have a 5,000 gp gem. If successfully removed a carbuncle's gem will regrow at the rate of 100 gp per month. The value of the gem may change each time it regrows.

The creature has *empathy* and *telepathy*, communicating via the latter, and also slight powers of prophecy concerning the immediate future. Its power of *empathy* enables it to understand the character of each person it encounters and know what that person knows, though its intelligence does not permit it to formulate more than very basic concepts.

If attacked, it puts up no resistance and is easily captured. It can will itself to die, however — it has no fear or conception of death and will give up its life if placed under duress. It will usually approach a party of adventurers and communicate the value of its gem to them, seeking to accompany the party. When this objective has been achieved, however, and it has gained the confidence of the party, its malicious nature will lead it to try to cause disruption within the group, using selective *telepathy* and prophecies, true and false, to breed hostility, suspicion and even fighting between party members. Alternatively — but rarely — it may communicate secretly with nearby monsters to enrage them into attacking the party. Its motives in spreading such dissidence are not entirely clear, but it is the belief of certain sages that the carbuncle's inability to comprehend death makes it fascinated by combat and particularly by death, to the extent that it will do its utmost to promote such events.

Having achieved its objective, the carbuncle will watch the events in morbid fascination then, choosing an opportune moment, it will quietly slip away.

CARYATID COLUMN

FREQUENCY: *Very rare*
NO. APPEARING: *1–12*
ARMOUR CLASS: *5*
MOVE: *6"*
HIT DICE: *22 hit points*
% IN LAIR: *Nil*
TREASURE TYPE: *Nil*
NO. OF ATTACKS: *1*
DAMAGE/ATTACK: *2–8*
SPECIAL ATTACKS: *Nil*
SPECIAL DEFENCES: *See below*
MAGIC RESISTANCE: *All saving throws at +4*
INTELLIGENCE: *Non-*
ALIGNMENT: *Neutral*
SIZE: *M (7' tall)*
PSIONIC ABILITY: *Nil*
    Attack/Defence Modes: *Nil*
LEVEL/X.P. VALUE: *V/280*

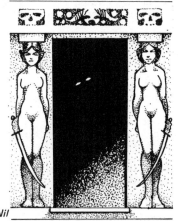

Caryatid columns are much like stone golems (see **ADVANCED DUNGEONS & DRAGONS MONSTER MANUAL** — *Golem, Stone*) in that they are created by means of a magical *tome* or by a magic-user of 16th level or higher, who must use the same spells as for the creation of a stone golem; however the cost is slightly higher and the time taken doubles because of the intricacy of the creation.

The result is a slim, decorative stone pillar about 7' high. A casual glance will reveal nothing more than this decorative piece of stone-work which will perhaps stand with an identical partner either side of the entrance into a chamber, chapel or throne-room. Closer inspection will reveal that the column is not, as would be expected, radially symmetrical about its longitudinal axis and has the very slender shape of a human female. Once such detail has been discerned, it will be clear to the observer that one of the 'hands' of the female, held close to her side, carries a slim sword which blends into the rest of the stone so smoothly that it is near-invisible.

A caryatid column will always have a specific defensive function (and will never be met as a wandering monster). This might be to guard a treasure-chest, to prevent intrusion into a particular area or another similar task. This task will have been set by the creator who, if near at hand when the column animates, will be able to control it with simple verbal commands. More often, though, the creator is absent when the column performs its task, in which case it will follow simple courses of action which have been predetermined by the creator.

The caryatid column will 'activate' as soon as any act is committed which its task specifically prohibits — the approach of a potential thief towards the treasure the column has been set to guard, an intrusion into a 'forbidden' area and so on. When it does animate, the caryatid column takes on a fleshy appearance, it reduces to about 5½' height and its form expands slightly so that it now appears as a fair young maiden. The sword, formerly of stone, becomes steel and it is this weapon that the caryatid column will use in melee if necessary, striking as a creature of 5HD to inflict 2–8 hit points of damage.

However the caryatid column will not necessarily enter into combat; its main task is to guard the treasure, prevent intrusion into a particular area or another similar task and if it can carry out this task without combat it will attempt to do so. Its behaviour will depend a great deal on the circumstances and the instructions given by its creator but it might, for example, attempt to divert the attention of intruding adventurers from the forbidden area and lead them to a place where they will be trapped, attacked by a monster or subjected to spell attack by the creator of the column.

If combat is inevitable, however, the caryatid column will initiate it. Normal weapons inflict only half damage on the creature and magical weapons do full damage but without the magical bonus. If a weapon, magical or otherwise, hits the caryatid column, there is a 25% chance (not cumulative) that it will snap, with each 'plus' of a magical weapon reducing that chance by 5% (so a +4 sword would have a 5% chance of snapping); magical weapons with no 'plus' are treated as if +1.

When the caryatid column's task is complete — intruders killed, treasure no longer vulnerable, for example — it will return to its original position and revert to its original stone shape, the sword becoming stone as well. If the column is killed, it returns to stone (as does the sword) on the spot.

CATERWAUL

FREQUENCY: *Rare*
NO. APPEARING: *1*
ARMOUR CLASS: *6 (see below)*
MOVE: *18" or 24" (see below)*
HIT DICE: *4+2*
% IN LAIR: *20%*
TREASURE TYPE: *N,R,S,U*
NO. OF ATTACKS: *3*
DAMAGE/ATTACK:
    1–4/1–4/1–6
SPECIAL ATTACKS:
    Screech; multiple attacks
SPECIAL DEFENCES:
    See below
MAGIC RESISTANCE:
    Standard
INTELLIGENCE: *Low*
ALIGNMENT: *Chaotic evil*
SIZE: *M*
PSIONIC ABILITY: *Nil*
    Attack/Defence Modes: *Nil*
LEVEL/X.P. VALUE:
    IV/170 + 5 per hit point

The caterwaul is a solitary, vicious feline bipedal predator with short midnight-blue fur, yellow eyes and a long tail. Its lair is usually a cave littered with twigs and rushes. Its treasure will consist only of shiny objects and it is particularly fond of gems. The walls of its cave will be covered with raking scratch marks where the caterwaul has honed its claws.

The beast has an uncanny natural agility which varies from individual to individual — roll on the table below when a specimen is encountered, using percentile dice:

% die roll	Armour class bonus	Attacks/round
01–42	0 (AC6)	1/1
43–73	–1 (AC5)	3/2
74–92	–2 (AC4)	3/2
93–00	Roll again on the sub-table below	
01–40	–3 (AC3)	2/1
41–67	–4 (AC2)	2/1
68–85	–5 (AC1)	2/1
86–96	–6 (AC0)	5/2
97–00	–7 (AC–1)	5/2

Armour class bonus: this dexterity bonus also applies to dodging ability and to saving throws against *fireball, lightning bolt* and the like.

Attacks/round: use this table in exactly the same way as the multiple attack table for fighters, rangers and paladins.

The caterwaul can move swiftly on two legs and can reach top speed (24″ rate) in short bursts when dropping to all-fours. As it has the ability to climb almost every surface (base 5% chance of slipping), move silently (75%) and hide in shadows (75%), its preferred method of attack is to lurk high above and spring down on an unsuspecting quarry. It has keen hearing and an exceptional sense of smell and is therefore difficult to surprise (10% chance).

Its initial attack (and this attack only) is always accompanied by a high-pitched keening screech which is of a frequency to do 1—8 hit points of damage to all hearing within 60′ (a character who saves against breath takes no damage).

The caterwaul attacks with two claws (1—4 hit points of damage each) and one bite (1—6 hit points of damage) each round, or more frequently as indicated above.

CIFAL

FREQUENCY: *Rare*
NO. APPEARING: *1—6*
ARMOUR CLASS: *6*
MOVE: *6″ (see below)*
HIT DICE: *8 or 10 (see below)*
% IN LAIR: *15%*
TREASURE TYPE: *Q*
NO. OF ATTACKS: *1*
DAMAGE/ATTACK: *1—12*
SPECIAL ATTACKS: *Nil*
SPECIAL DEFENCES:
*Damage from edged
weapons reduced —
see below*
MAGIC RESISTANCE: *Standard*
INTELLIGENCE: *Non-*
ALIGNMENT: *Neutral*
SIZE: *M*
PSIONIC ABILITY: *Nil*
Attack/Defence Modes: *Nil*
LEVEL/X.P. VALUE:
VII/1,350 + 14 per hit point

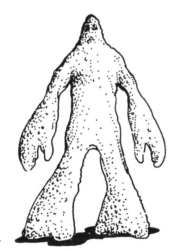

The cifal — the name is acronymic of 'colonial insect-formed artificial life' — is an agglomeration of several swarms of insects (several hundred thousand insects to each swarm) which come together to form a single amorphous creature about man-sized.

The mass as a whole has 8 hit dice while another 2 hit dice are involved in providing the nuclear energy required to keep the constituent swarms locked in a single body. It is from the hit points of the latter 2 hit dice that initial damage is extracted, and if these hit points are lost the mass body will separate into its individual component insects, at which point the insects will fly away at 24″ rate — they will only attack and defend in mass body form. However, the hit points of the binding force may be replaced from the hit points of the remainder of the mass body at the rate of 2 hit points per melee round.

The cifal attacks by an agglomeration of tiny bites which collectively inflict 1—12 hit points of damage.

Edged weapons only cause 1 hit point of damage on the cifal whatever type of weapon is used and whether it is magical or not. Blunt weapons cause full normal damage.

Strictly speaking, this creature does not fly and the movement rate given above refers to movement along the ground, albeit the result of the flying speed of the swarms restricted by the need to maintain coherence of shape. The cifal has no aerial manoeuvrability class, but the constituent insects are of manoeuvrability class A.

CLUBNEK

FREQUENCY: *Uncommon*
NO. APPEARING: *2—8*
ARMOUR CLASS: *8*
MOVE: *12″ (see below)*
HIT DICE: *2*
% IN LAIR: *Nil*
TREASURE TYPE: *Nil*
NO. OF ATTACKS: *3*
DAMAGE/ATTACK:
1—6/1—6/1—8
SPECIAL ATTACKS: *Nil*
SPECIAL DEFENCES: *Nil*
MAGIC RESISTANCE:
Standard
INTELLIGENCE: *Low*
ALIGNMENT: *Neutral*
SIZE: *M*
PSIONIC ABILITY: *Nil*
Attack/Defence Modes: *Nil*
LEVEL/X.P. VALUE:
I/20 + 2 per hit point

These creatures are mutated forms of the ostrich with hard bony beaks which can inflict 1—8 hit points of damage. They also fight with their two claws, each of which inflicts 1—6 hit points of damage.

They can make occasional bursts of high speed and can achieve a movement rate of 24″ one melee round in every five.

Clubneks are coloured varying shades of green and have yellow beaks. They are not normally aggressive unless threatened, but their behaviour is rather erratic and unpredictable. Normally they are herbivorous and are rarely found below the ground, preferring to roam meadowland and woods.

COFFER CORPSE

FREQUENCY: *Rare*
NO. APPEARING: *1*
ARMOUR CLASS: *8*
MOVE: *6″*
HIT DICE: *2*
% IN LAIR: *80%*
TREASURE TYPE: *B*
NO. OF ATTACKS: *1*
DAMAGE/ATTACK:
1—6 or by weapon type
SPECIAL ATTACKS: *Nil*
SPECIAL DEFENCES: *Can
only be hit by magical
weapons*
MAGIC RESISTANCE: *Standard*
INTELLIGENCE: *Low*
ALIGNMENT: *Chaotic evil*
SIZE: *M*
PSIONIC ABILITY: *Nil*
Attack/Defence Modes: *Nil*
LEVEL/X.P. VALUE:
II/36 + 2 per hit point

These foul creatures of the undead class are found in stranded funeral barges or in any other situation in which a corpse has failed to return to its maker. Though the coffer corpse resembles a zombie it is treated as a wraith on the cleric/undead table.

Normal weapons appear to do damage, and if a coffer corpse is struck for more than 6 hit points of damage by normal weapons in a single melee round, it will fall to the ground, apparently finished. However normal weapons do not, in fact, do any damage to the creature, and if it has fallen to the ground one round, it will rise up the next round and continue melee — at which time all involved in melee with the beast must save against *fear* or flee in panic.

A coffer corpse is occasionally (25%) found with a weapon which it

will use in combat, but otherwise it will attack with its bare hands (treat as a single attack inflicting 1—6 hit points of damage). If attacking with bare hands, a hit indicates that the coffer corpse has locked its hands around its victim's throat. Each round thereafter, it will inflict 1—6 hit points of damage on its victim automatically (a 'to hit' roll is not required) until it is killed or its victim is dead. Nothing will release the grasp of the coffer corpse once it has locked its hands in place.

Sleep, charm and other mind-influencing spells do not affect these creatures. Magical weapons can inflict damage on these creatures with the usual bonus.

CRABMAN

FREQUENCY: *Rare*
NO. APPEARING: *2—12*
ARMOUR CLASS: *4*
MOVE: *9"//6"*
HIT DICE: *3*
% IN LAIR: *25%*
TREASURE TYPE: *K*
NO. OF ATTACKS: *2*
DAMAGE/ATTACK: *1—4/1—4*
SPECIAL ATTACKS: *Nil*
SPECIAL DEFENCES: *Nil*
MAGIC RESISTANCE:
   Standard
INTELLIGENCE: *Low to*
   average
ALIGNMENT: *Neutral*
SIZE: *L (9' tall)*
PSIONIC ABILITY: *Nil*
   Attack/Defence Modes: *Nil*
LEVEL/X.P. VALUE:
   II/35 + 3 per hit point

Amphibious creatures usually found in sea-shore caves, crabmen are humanoid in appearance but with a hard, reddish-brown exoskeleton. Instead of hands they have two pincers which they use in combat, each inflicting 1—4 hit points of damage on a victim.

Crabmen greatly value silver and will go to any lengths to obtain it, even attacking a character suspected of carrying any item made of this metal. In normal circumstances, however, they are quite pacific creatures, though from time to time an instinct makes them leave their coastal dwelling to mount a savage raid inland, roaming in bands of 30 or 40 creatures and pillaging all property in their path, not hesitating to attack those who would defend.

Crabmen are often subjected to raids by sahuagin who consider them a tasty delicacy. However the sahuagin's usual net-throwing tactics are ineffective against crabmen since the latter's natural weaponry allows them to cut through nets very quickly.

CRYPT THING

FREQUENCY: *Very rare*
NO. APPEARING: *1*
ARMOUR CLASS: *3*
MOVE: *12"*
HIT DICE: *6*
% IN LAIR: *100%*
TREASURE TYPE: *Z*
NO. OF ATTACKS: *1*
DAMAGE/ATTACK: *1—8*
SPECIAL ATTACKS: *See*
   below
SPECIAL DEFENCES:
   See below
MAGIC RESISTANCE:
   Standard
INTELLIGENCE: *Very*
ALIGNMENT: *Neutral*
SIZE: *M*
PSIONIC ABILITY: *Nil*
   Attack/Defence Modes: *Nil*
LEVEL/X.P. VALUE:
   V/275 + 6 per hit point

A pale, solitary skeletal being which always wears a brown, hooded robe, the crypt thing stays in its lair permanently (at least, none have been encountered elsewhere) and will not attack if it is left undisturbed.

Its special power is its unfailing ability to cast an improved form of a *teleportation* spell on a party (once per party encountered). Those who fail to make their saving throws are instantly *teleported* according to a percentile die roll on the table below:

% die roll	Distance and direction
01—20	100—1000' north
21—40	100—1000' south
41—60	100—1000' east
61—80	100—1000' west
81—90	one dungeon level up
91—00	one dungeon level down

Distance and direction are determined individually for each victim teleported. Victims never arrive in solid material and will arrive in the closest open space to the target spot, if the target spot is solid; however victims need not arrive at floor level.

Those who make their saving rolls may attack the crypt thing, but it can only be hit by magical weapons. The crypt thing will attack in return, using a two-handed clawing movement which inflicts 1—8 hit points of damage.

The crypt thing can communicate in the neutral tongue, but if it is questioned on the disappearance of some members of a party, it will not reveal its power but will instead maintain they have been *disintegrated.*

There are rumoured to be aberrant crypt things in existence which, instead of *teleporting* victims, *paralyse* them and simultaneously turn them *invisible.* Neither this nor the more common type feeds on victims, however — their aim appears to be solely that of obtaining pleasure by creating confusion and dissent.

DAKON

FREQUENCY: *Uncommon*
NO. APPEARING: *6—60*
ARMOUR CLASS: *5*
MOVE: *6"*
HIT DICE: *1+1*
% IN LAIR: *50%*
TREASURE TYPE: *E*
NO. OF ATTACKS: *2*
DAMAGE/ATTACK:
   1—10/1—10
SPECIAL ATTACKS: *Nil*
SPECIAL DEFENCES: *Nil*
MAGIC RESISTANCE: *Standard*
INTELLIGENCE: *Average*
ALIGNMENT: *Lawful neutral*
SIZE: *M*
PSIONIC ABILITY: *Nil*
   Attack/Defence Modes: *Nil*
LEVEL/X.P. VALUE:
   1/20 + 2 per hit point

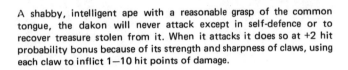

A shabby, intelligent ape with a reasonable grasp of the common tongue, the dakon will never attack except in self-defence or to recover treasure stolen from it. When it attacks it does so at +2 hit probability bonus because of its strength and sharpness of claws, using each claw to inflict 1—10 hit points of damage.

The dakon is usually a light brown colour with green eyes and black hands. It is found in all types of location except near large expanses of water. It is normally on good terms with lawful humans and near-humans, though it has a suspicion of the motives of humanoids and will not communicate with them.

DARK CREEPER

FREQUENCY: *Rare*
NO. APPEARING: *1 (20—80
   see below)*
ARMOUR CLASS:
   0 (or 8 — see below)
MOVE: *9"*
HIT DICE: *1+1*
% IN LAIR: *20%*
TREASURE TYPE: *See below*
NO. OF ATTACKS: *1*
DAMAGE/ATTACK: *1—4*
SPECIAL ATTACKS: *See below*
SPECIAL DEFENCES: *Nil*
MAGIC RESISTANCE: *Standard*
INTELLIGENCE: *Average*
ALIGNMENT: *Chaotic neutral*
SIZE: *S (4' tall)*
PSIONIC ABILITY: *Nil*
   Attack/Defence Modes: *Nil*
LEVEL/X.P. VALUE:
   III/110 + 2 per hit point

The dark creeper (a folk name for the race since the race name is unknown and the race language incomprehensible to linguists) is a humanoid, slightly-built creature about the same height as a dwarf. Members of the race always dress in sombre, dark-coloured clothing, concealing as much of their pallid skin as possible. They detest light and dwell deep underground — usually leading a solitary existence though there have been rumours of underground villages inhabited by

as many as 80 individuals, including 20%—25% females. These villages are always ruled by a dark stalker.

The dark creeper is particularly fond of small magical items such as rings and magic daggers — solitary individuals will carry 25% of their treasure in the copious pockets of their cloaks, so there is a 15% chance of a magic dagger, 5% chance of a magical ring and 10% chance of 1—4 gems *or* 1—2 items of jewellery on any individual encountered. In lair multiply these probable treasure items by the number of male individuals resident, and add 1—100 platinum pieces and 50—500 gold pieces.

The creeper has the abilities of a 4th level thief in addition to the ability to *detect magical items* at a range of 15'. It attacks with a normal (or, if one is possessed, a magical) dagger. The creeper also has the innate power to *create darkness* three times a day — when this power is used, all torches, lanterns and other non-magical sources of illumination within 50' are extinguished and cannot be re-ignited during the next hour (the duration of the creeper's power). During this time the creeper has two main objectives. First, to destroy lanterns and tinderboxes, break flasks of oil and so on — any act which will inhibit the creation of illumination. Secondly, to steal any small magical items detected. Self-preservation ranks marginally above such objectives.

Magical sources of illumination may also be affected by the creeper's *darkness* abilities. In effect, they obtain a saving roll against *magical frost*, and if the item makes such a save it is not affected. If the item fails to save, however, it is extinguished for the next hour, after which its property returns to normal.

During the *darkness,* even infravision becomes useless; however the creeper will not use its power against parties not using artificial illumination, so elves using infravision, for instance, will usually pass unmolested.

The *darkness* power may be countered by spells such as *light*, and if the creeper is attacked in normal illumination its AC is 8.

If a creeper is killed its body undergoes spontaneous combustion of such intensity that all within 10' of the victim are blinded (saving roll against magic permitted) for 1—6 full turns. All traces of the creeper are destroyed though metal items will normally (80% chance) be undamaged; magical items, metal or otherwise, will lose their dweomer if they fail to save against *magical fire*.

DARK STALKER

FREQUENCY: *Very rare*
NO. APPEARING: *1*
ARMOUR CLASS:
   0 (or 8 — see below)
MOVE: *9"*
HIT DICE: *2+1*
% IN LAIR: *20%*
TREASURE TYPE: *See below*
NO. OF ATTACKS: *1*
DAMAGE/ATTACK: *1—6*
SPECIAL ATTACKS: *See below*
SPECIAL DEFENCES: *See below*
MAGIC RESISTANCE: *Standard*
INTELLIGENCE: *Average*
ALIGNMENT: *Chaotic neutral*
SIZE: *M*
PSIONIC ABILITY: *Nil*
   Attack/Defence Modes: *Nil*
LEVEL/X.P. VALUE:
   IV/200 + 3 per hit point

Dark stalkers are the rarely-seen leaders of the dark creepers. They are nearly a race apart, for they breed almost exclusively amongst themselves. They are instantly noticeable amongst a group of dark creepers as they are man-sized and stand head and shoulders above their underlings.

There is an average of one dark stalker to every 25 dark creepers, and each dark creeper village will contain at least one stalker ruler. Stalkers will rarely be encountered on their own, but this has been known to happen as the stalker goes about some mysterious personal mission.

Dark stalkers have all the powers of dark creepers, plus the ability to create a *wall of fog* twice per day.

They fight with short swords if they must, and some of these are magical (25% chance). All of their treasure is carried — there is a 7% chance of a magical ring and a 12% chance of 2—5 gems *or* 1—2 items of jewellery on any given individual encountered. If attacked in normal illumination, the dark stalker has AC8.

If killed, a dark stalker explodes in a blinding flash equal to a 3-dice *fireball*.

DEATH DOG

FREQUENCY: *Very rare*
NO. APPEARING: *5—50*
ARMOUR CLASS: *7*
MOVE: *12"*
HIT DICE: *2+1*
% IN LAIR: *Nil*
TREASURE TYPE: *Nil*
NO. OF ATTACKS: *2*
DAMAGE/ATTACK: *1—10/1—10*
SPECIAL ATTACKS: *Disease*
SPECIAL DEFENCES: *Nil*
MAGIC RESISTANCE: *Standard*
INTELLIGENCE: *Animal*
ALIGNMENT: *Neutral with*
   evil tendencies
SIZE: *M (4' high at shoulder)*
PSIONIC ABILITY: *Nil*
   Attack/Defence Modes: *Nil*
LEVEL/X.P. VALUE:
   III/105 + 3 per hit point

Large black hounds with two heads, the death dogs can attack with each head independently. They usually hunt in packs, in deserts or in dry areas underground.

Each bite delivers 1—10 hit points of damage and the victim of a

bite must save against poison or die as a result of a slow, rotting disease in 4—24 days. *Cure disease* will be an effective remedy.

When attacking, the death dog usually aims for its victim's legs — a natural roll of 19 or 20 on the 'to hit' die against a man-sized or smaller victim means that the victim has been knocked to the ground and attacks at —4 until able to rise again to his feet (which he can do during a single round if he is not knocked down again).

These vicious hounds, which usually attack humans and near-humans on sight (85% chance), are said to be the descendents of Cerberus; their loud penetrating double bark tends to lend support to this theory.

DEATH KNIGHT

FREQUENCY: *Very rare*
NO. APPEARING: *1*
ARMOUR CLASS: *0*
MOVE: *Variable*
HIT DICE: *9 (10-sided dice)*
% IN LAIR: *Nil*
TREASURE TYPE: *Nil*
NO. OF ATTACKS: *1*
DAMAGE/ATTACK:
   By weapon type
SPECIAL ATTACKS: *See below*
SPECIAL DEFENCES:
   See below
MAGIC RESISTANCE:
   75% (see below)
INTELLIGENCE: *Average —*
   genius
ALIGNMENT: *Chaotic evil*
SIZE: *M*
PSIONIC ABILITY: *Nil*
   Attack/Defence Modes: *Nil*
LEVEL/X.P. VALUE:
   VIII/3,700 + 16 per hit point

The death knight — and there are only twelve of these dreadful creatures known to exist — is a horrifying form of lich created by a demon prince (it is thought Demogorgon) from a fallen human paladin. The death knight itself cannot be turned or dispelled (though it is affected by *holy word*) but it has power over undead equivalent to that of a 6th level cleric. It has 75% magic resistance, and if 11 or lower is rolled on percentage dice a magic spell will be reflected back at the caster (roll each time a spell is attempted).

The death knight wears light armour (9" or 12" movement depending on its other encumbrance, if any) but is always treated as armour class 0. It has 18(00) strength and usually attacks with a sword (80% chance of this being a magical sword). It will usually be riding a night-mare (see **ADVANCED DUNGEONS & DRAGONS MONSTER MANUAL** — *Nightmare*) one of which can be summoned to serve a death knight every ten years; the beast will serve a death knight as a paladin's horse serves a paladin. The fearsome powers of the death knight derive largely from its use of magic. It continually generates *fear* in a 5' radius, can create a *wall of ice* at will and has innate powers of *detect magic* and *detect invisibility* Twice a day it can *dispel magic* and *gate* in a demon type I (20%), type II (25%), type III (30%), type IV (20%) or type VI (5%), with a 75% chance of the *gate* opening. Once per day a death knight can use any one of the *power word* spells, a *symbol of pain/fear* and generate a 20-dice *fireball*. Where appropriate, a death knight's magic use is at the 20th experience level.

A death knight will speak 3—6 languages in addition to its alignment tongue and the common tongue.

DEMON

Characteristics and abilities which are common to all demons are reprinted here, in edited form, from ADVANCED DUNGEONS & DRAGONS, MONSTER MANUAL.

Demons are able to move from their own plane into those of *Tarterus, Hades,* or *Pandemonium* or roam the *Astral Plane.* However, they cannot enter the *Material Plane* without aid (conjuration, gate, or by name speaking or similar means).

Demons are chaotic and evil, the smarter and stronger rule those of their kind who are weaker and less intelligent. The less intelligent will attack without question and fight until slain. Demons of type V and above are not actually slain when their material form is killed in combat; their material form being removed from their use, the demon in question is thereby forced back to the plane from whence it originally came, there to remain until a century has passed or until another aids it to go forth again. However, if demons are encountered on their own plane, they can be slain. No demon can ever be subdued. All are able to divide their attacks amongst two or even three opponents if their means allows.

Demons will never willingly serve anyone or anything. If forced to serve through magic or threat they will continually seek a way to slay their master/captor. Those to whom demons show a liking are typically carried off to the demons' plane to become a slave (although a favoured one). Note that demons can be summoned by characters of any alignment, but controlling a demon is another matter entirely. A special pentacle is required for demons of type VI or greater. The threat or reward which the conjuring party uses to attempt gaining a demon's service must be carefully handled by the dungeon master. Demons are repelled by holy (good) relics or artifacts.

Demons frequently roam the *Astral* and *Ethereal Planes.* Their attention is also attracted by persons in an ethereal state. If the name of a particularly powerful demon is spoken there is a chance that he will hear and turn his attention to the speaker. A base 5% chance is recommended to the referee. Unless prepared to avoid such attention — or to control the demon — the demon will thereupon immediately kill, by whatever means are most expeditious, the one pronouncing his name.

Demons' Amulets: Demon lords and princes maintain their vital essences in small containers — their souls, so to speak, are thus at once protected and yet vulnerable if some enterprising character should gain the amulet. Demons with amulets are able to *magic jar* once per day. Demons' amulets cannot be detected as such by any magical means, and they do not otherwise appear unusual in any way. The device need not be with the most powerful princes, although the lesser demons typically need to carry theirs on or near their person.

Possession of an amulet gives the possessor power over the demon to whom it "belongs" for the space of, for example, one adventure, and never more than a day (24 hours). The amulet must then be returned to the demon — or it can be destroyed and thus condemn the prince to abyssment for a year (and it may return thereafter only if summoned). Use of an amulet is very, very dangerous. Possession of one will double chances of calling the attention of another demon, and any demon not controlled by the device will immediately attack the person possessing such an amulet. If the amulet leaves the hand of the one commanding the demon to whom it belongs, that demon attacks him in its most effective fashion, immediately, attempting its utmost to slay and then to carry all that remains to its own domain, i.e. that character is lost and gone forever. On the positive side, however, if the wielder of the amulet carefully repays the demon for aid rendered, adds a considerable sum for having the temerity to dare to command the demon in the first place, and then carefully restores the amulet to the demon, the prince might not bear him a grudge forever afterwards nor seek to hunt him out whenever possible.

Lolth *(Demon Queen of Spiders)* (*Lesser Goddess*)

FREQUENCY: *Very rare*
NO. APPEARING: *1*
ARMOUR CLASS: *−10 (−2)*
MOVE: *1"*9" (15")*
HIT DICE: *66 hit points (16 hit dice)*
% IN LAIR: *25%*
TREASURE TYPE: *Q(x5),R,X(x3)*
NO. OF ATTACKS: *1 and 1 (1)*
DAMAGE/ATTACK:
　4—16 + poison and webs
　(by weapon type)
SPECIAL ATTACKS:
　See below
SPECIAL DEFENCES:
　See below
MAGIC RESISTANCE: *70%*
INTELLIGENCE: *Godlike*
ALIGNMENT: *Chaotic evil*
SIZE *L (M)*
PSIONIC ABILITY: *266*
　Attack/Defence Modes:
　All/all
LEVEL/X.P. VALUE:
　X/12,470*
　(*for destroying Material Plane form only — if actually killed permanently, multiply X.P. figure by 10.)

The demoness Lolth is a very powerful and feared demon lord. She usually takes the form of a giant black widow spider when she is on the *Prime Material Plane* and she sometimes assumes this form on her own plane as well, but she also enjoys appearing as an exquisitely beautiful female dark elf (the statistics for this form are given in parentheses). Little is known about her aims, and only the fact that the drow worship of Lolth causes her to assume form on the earth permits compilation of any substantial information whatsoever.

Lolth enjoys the company of spiders of all sorts — giant species in her arachnid shape, those of normal, large and even huge type in her humanoid form. She is able to converse with all kinds of spiders, and they understand and obey her unquestioningly.

Although Lolth has but 66 hit points, her high armour class prevents most damage and she is able to *heal* herself at will, up to thrice per day. As Lolth enjoys roaming about in one form or another, she will seldom be encountered in her lair no matter what the plane, unless worshippers have invoked her to some special shrine or temple.

In the form of a giant spider, Lolth is able to cast web strands 30' long from her abdominal spinerettes which are equal to those of *web* spell with the addition of 1—4 hit points of damage per round accruing to webbed victims due to a poisonous excretion upon the strands; during the same melee round she is able to deliver a vicious biting attack for 4—16 hit points of damage plus death if the victim is unable to save against poison at a −4 penalty. In her humanoid form, Lolth will use weapons common to drow.

As a giant spider, the demoness can use any one of the following powers, one per melee round, at will: *comprehend languages, confusion* (creature looked at only), *darkness (10' radius), dispel magic;* once per day *gate* in a type I (45%) type II (35%) or type III (20%) demon with 66% chance of the *gate* opening; twice per day use *phase door, read magic, shape change;* once per day *summon* 9—16 large (20%), 7—12 huge (30%), 2—8 giant (40%) or 1—4 phase (10%) spiders, *teleport* with no inaccuracy, *tongues* and *true seeing.* In her humanoid shape, Lolth is a 16th level cleric/14th level magic-user with commensurate abilities. However in the latter form she is unable to wear armour of any sort, and her psionic powers are lost to her (see hereafter).

Lolth is not affected by weapons which are not magical, silver does her no harm (unless magicked to at least +1) and cold, electrical and gas attack forms cause only half damage. Acid, *magic missiles* (if her magic resistance fails her) and poison affect the demoness normally. Lolth is especially susceptible to holy water, taking 6 points of damage from a splash and 6—21 points (3d6 + 3) from a direct hit.

The visual range of the demoness extends into the infrared and ultra violet spectra to a normal distance of 120'. Lolth has limited *telepathy* communication ability, as do demons in general.

Her psionic disciplines are *body equilibrium, clairvoyance, domination* and the major sciences of *dimension walking, mind bar, molecular rearrangement* and *probability travel*. These disciplines (as well as magical powers) are performed at the 16th experience level of ability.

DENZELIAN

FREQUENCY: *Very rare*
NO. APPEARING: *1–2*
ARMOUR CLASS: *0*
MOVE: *1"*
HIT DICE: *6*
% IN LAIR: *100%*
TREASURE TYPE: *Nil*
NO. OF ATTACKS: *Nil*
DAMAGE/ATTACK: *Nil*
SPECIAL ATTACKS: *Nil*
SPECIAL DEFENCES: *Nil*
MAGIC RESISTANCE:
   Standard
INTELLIGENCE: *Semi-*
ALIGNMENT: *Neutral*
SIZE: *S*
PSIONIC ABILITY: *Nil*
   Attack/Defence Modes:
   Nil
LEVEL/X.P. VALUE: *Not applicable*

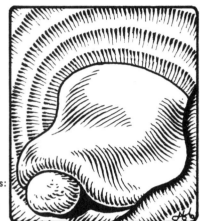

The denzelian is a peaceful rock-eater. Very thin, but of large surface area (about 10'x10'x3"), the denzelian tunnels through solid rock at the rate of 1' per week, slowly wearing it away. Generally one male and one female tunnel near one another. The creatures will avoid metal, making a detour round even small deposits — hence denzelian tunnels tend to follow a meandering course.

Because they look like stone, have a repulsive smell and are indigestible, denzelians are rarely bothered by flesh-eaters.

During its 1,000-year lifespan the denzelian female ovulates once only. If a male is nearby (and one usually is) the resulting litter contains 3–8 eggs which hatch in 100 years. The eggs look like nondescript fist-sized stones. The chance of finding a single egg — for they are not deposited together — in an area frequented by a denzelian female is 1 in 1,000. An egg is worth 1,000 gold pieces or more to certain wealthy mine-owners.

DEVIL

(Full details of the devils are given in the **ADVANCED DUNGEONS & DRAGONS MONSTER MANUAL**. Edited details applicable to the styx devil are reprinted here.)

Devils follow a definite order, a chain of command, which they dare not break for fear of the arch-devils. Still, there is great rivalry, even open antagonism, between the devils of the various planes and between the various arch-devils.

All devils are able to move about the *Planes of Hell* (although they dare not do so without authorization, save for the dukes). They can move to the *Planes of Gehenna, Hades* and *Acheron* at will. They can also move through the *Astral Plane*, although they seldom do so. No devil is able to enter the other planes unless the proper ritual is performed, a gate is opened, or the proper name of a devil is spoken (and heard).

It is possible to destroy the material form of a greater devil or duke of Hell but such creatures can not actually be slain unless encountered and fought in *Hell* or those *Lower Planes* adjacent to it. Devils can never be subdued. The lesser ones will always fight until destroyed. The greater ones will negotiate if seriously threatened. Devils will serve if properly commanded but it is a risky business, for an improper command will break the law which binds them to service. (It also typically requires a contract for the soul of the creature commanding

the infernal power to obey). It is possible for other than lawful evil persons to invoke or otherwise treat with devils (but the long spoon, oft spoken of, had better be used when supping with such monsters). Magic circles will keep devils off for a time if they are properly scribed (and ensymboled in the case of greater and arch-devils). Devils are repelled by holy (good) artifacts or relics.

All devils can direct their attacks against two or more opponents if the means are at hand. If a greater devil has its material form destroyed it is forced to lemure status for nine decades of torment before it resumes its former station. (see **ADVANCED DUNGEONS & DRAGONS MONSTER MANUAL** — *Devil, Lemure).*

All devils have or are able to perform the following:

Charm Person
Suggestion
Illusion
Infravision
Teleportation (no error)
Know Alignment
Cause Fear (effect varies)
Animate Dead

Devils are able to summon their fellows, summoning being similar to a monster summoning spell.

Because they have a special form of telepathy, devils are able to understand and converse with any intelligent creature.

Devils are affected by the listed attack forms as noted below.

Attack	Maximum Damage Will be
acid	full
cold	half
electricity (lightning)	full
fire (dragon, magical)	none
gas (poisonous, etc.)	half
iron weapon	none*
magic missile	full
poison	full
silver weapon	full

*unless affected by normal weapons in which case damage will be according to the weapon type.

Devil's Talismans: Greater devils have a special combination of inscriptions which will bind them to the wielder. The employment of any devil's talisman requires great care and caution. Human sacrifice is required of evil creatures using a talisman. Merely looking at these talismans is dangerous if not properly protected by spells or a magic circle, study of a charm gives a 10% chance of summoning the kind or specific devil to whom the talisman belongs. Speaking the name on the talisman will always call forth the kind or specific devil.

Styx Devil *(Greater Devil)*

FREQUENCY: *Very rare*
NO. APPEARING: *1–2*
ARMOUR CLASS: *–1*
MOVE: *6"/15"*
HIT DICE: *6+6*
% IN LAIR: *60%*
TREASURE TYPE: *Q,R*
NO. OF ATTACKS: *1*
DAMAGE/ATTACK: *2–8*
SPECIAL ATTACKS: *See below*
SPECIAL DEFENCES:
   Cannot be hit by normal weapons — see below
MAGIC RESISTANCE: *50%*
INTELLIGENCE: *High*
ALIGNMENT: *Lawful evil*
SIZE: *M*
PSIONIC ABILITY: *121*
   Attack/Defence Modes:
   B,D/F,G,H
LEVEL/X.P. VALUE:
   *VII/1,275 + 8 per hit point**
   (*for destroying Material Plane form only — if actually killed permanently, multiply X.P. figure by 10)*

Residents of the fifth plane of *Hell*, styx devils are humanoid but with disproportionately large, ugly heads and wings of black trimmed with silver. Their main task is to search for souls to take back to Geryon, but from time to time they will tour the *Material Plane* with intent to destroy all humans they meet.

The styx devil is invulnerable to ordinary weapons but can be damaged by silver weapons and by magical weapons with a bonus of +1 or better.

Their touch causes 2—8 hit points of damage and has a 50% chance of inflicting an *imprisonment* spell on the victim (no saving throw allowed). Treat this as if cast at the 22nd level of magic use and regard the styx devil as having perfect information regarding the victim's name and background.

To dispel a styx devil requires the utterance of *holy word*.

For purposes of aerial combat, the styx devil is manoeuvrability class C.

DEVIL DOG

FREQUENCY: *Rare*
NO. APPEARING: *4—16*
ARMOUR CLASS: *6*
MOVE: *30″ maximum*
HIT DICE: *6*
% IN LAIR: *10%*
TREASURE TYPE: *Nil*
NO. OF ATTACKS: *1*
DAMAGE/ATTACK: *2—8*
SPECIAL ATTACKS:
    Throat attack
SPECIAL DEFENCES: *Nil*
MAGIC RESISTANCE: *Standard*
INTELLIGENCE: *Average*
ALIGNMENT: *Chaotic evil*
SIZE: *M (3′ at shoulder)*
PSIONIC ABILITY: *Nil*
    Attack/Defence Modes: *Nil*
LEVEL/X.P. VALUE:
    V/350 + 6 per hit point

Stark-white hounds with blue eyes, devil dogs live in cold regions and when encountered in snow- or frost-covered areas are invisible beyond a range of 30′. They roam in packs in an endless search for food and will always attack human parties, being sly enough to use their protective colouration to the best advantage.

The devil dog uses a vicious biting attack and always jumps for the throat. Normal damage inflicted is 2—8 hit points, but if the 'to hit' die roll is 4 or more greater than required to hit, or a natural 20 in

any event, a hit is scored on the throat — the victim suffers double damage, is comatose for 2—8 turns and must receive *cure light wounds* (or a stronger ministration of the same nature) during the comatose period to avoid death at the end of that period. (Of course the initial damage may kill the victim anyway).

When attacking or giving chase — and devil dogs move very fast indeed — the creatures emit an intense baying which will cause *fear* in any character of the third experience level or lower unless they save at —4 on their die roll against magic. They can sustain their extraordinarily high (30″) movement rate for three turns, following which they must 'rest' for another three turns during which their maximum movement rate is 12″

DIRE CORBY

FREQUENCY: *Rare*
NO. APPEARING: *1—12*
ARMOUR CLASS: *6*
MOVE: *12″*
HIT DICE: *2*
% IN LAIR: *20%*
TREASURE TYPE:
    Q(x5) — mainly rubies
NO. OF ATTACKS: *2*
DAMAGE/ATTACK: *1—6/1—6*
SPECIAL ATTACKS: *Nil*
SPECIAL DEFENCES: *Nil*
MAGIC RESISTANCE: *Standard*
INTELLIGENCE: *Low*
ALIGNMENT: *Neutral evil*
SIZE: *M*
PSIONIC ABILITY: *Nil*
    Attack/Defence Modes: *Nil*
LEVEL/X.P. VALUE:
    I/20 + 2 per hit point

This subterranean race of huge black bipedal birds contains ferocious fighters which need never check morale. Long ago the dire corbies lost the power of flight; however they make up for this with their great strength and ferocity, always attacking and fighting to the death.

What were once wings have now developed as two powerful arms which end in sharp, rock-hard claws. They fight with these claws and each is capable of inflicting 1—6 hit points of damage on a victim.

They hunt in flocks, running down their hapless victims, at the same time emitting horrifying shrieks. They have rudimentary language (their attack cry can be recognised as 'Doom! Doom!' by those familiar with it).

Dire corbies live in large underground caverns; at one time there was open warfare between them and giant bats, but this has now become an uneasy truce.

DISENCHANTER

FREQUENCY: *Very rare*
NO. APPEARING: *1—2*
ARMOUR CLASS: *5*
MOVE: *12"*
HIT DICE: *5*
% IN LAIR: *Nil*
TREASURE TYPE: *Nil*
NO. OF ATTACKS: *1*
DAMAGE/ATTACK:
    *See below — special
    effect only*
SPECIAL ATTACKS:
    Disenchants — see below
SPECIAL DEFENCES:
    *Can only be hit by
    magical weapons*
MAGIC RESISTANCE:
    Standard
INTELLIGENCE: *Average*
ALIGNMENT: *Neutral*
SIZE: *M (5' high at shoulder)*
PSIONIC ABILITY: *Nil*
    Attack/Defence Modes: *Nil*
LEVEL/X.P. VALUE:
    IV/205 + 5 per hit point

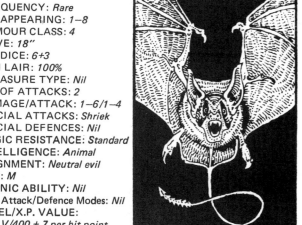

The disenchanter resembles a spindly dromedary-like animal with a long, flexible and muscular snout which can extend as much as 5' from the head in attack. It is a pale electric-blue in colour and slightly translucent; sometimes it may even be seen to shimmer discernably.

The creature has the power to detect magical dweomer — from magical armour, shields, swords and the like — on which it feeds, drawing its sustenance from the powerful enchantments such items carry. It is reasonably discerning in this power, being able for instance to distinguish between *armour of etherealness* and *+1 armour,* and selecting the former as containing stronger radiation. Should the beast encounter a party of adventurers it will be able to detect the most powerful magical item present and will attempt, as its attack, to fasten its snout onto the item in question. If it scores a hit, it will drain the magical power, leaving the item unmarked but non-magical.

Referees will have to consider the ease with which the disenchanter would be able to 'attack' a particular item, despite the dexterity of its snout. Generally speaking it will attempt a relatively simple disenchantment — say on a magical shield in easy reach — rather than attempt a more difficult attack, say on a more powerful magical item hidden in a backpack or sheath.

The disenchanter can only be hit by magical weapons, but these will not lose their enchantment in hitting the beast — only with its snout can the creature disenchant magical items.

No-one has ever discovered a disenchanter lair, nor come to any proven conclusion about its metabolism, which at the least can be described as curious.

DOOMBAT

FREQUENCY: *Rare*
NO. APPEARING: *1—8*
ARMOUR CLASS: *4*
MOVE: *18"*
HIT DICE: *6+3*
% IN LAIR: *100%*
TREASURE TYPE: *Nil*
NO. OF ATTACKS: *2*
DAMAGE/ATTACK: *1—6/1—4*
SPECIAL ATTACKS: *Shriek*
SPECIAL DEFENCES: *Nil*
MAGIC RESISTANCE: *Standard*
INTELLIGENCE: *Animal*
ALIGNMENT: *Neutral evil*
SIZE: *M*
PSIONIC ABILITY: *Nil*
    Attack/Defence Modes: *Nil*
LEVEL/X.P. VALUE:
    V/400 + 7 per hit point

This is a species of giant bat found in dismal underground caverns. The monstrous black creature has a wingspan a full 25' and can pick up and carry off objects weighing up to 300 pounds (3,000 gold pieces weight). At night, it flies into the outer world to hunt, always attacking and seeking to kill any living thing. For the purpose of aerial combat, it is manoeuvrability class C.

The bite of the doombat inflicts 1—6 hit points of damage and it also lashes with its tail for 1—4 hit points of damage. The tail, lined with cruel barbs, stretches a considerable distance from the body, and specimens with tails up to 12' long have been reported.

The normal bat's sonar yip has developed into a terrifying shriek of great sonic power in the doombat. Each doombat can shriek continuously for 2—5 rounds and during the shriek, all within 100' who can hear will not be able to concentrate, making spell use impossible and all attacks at —1. No saving throw is permitted against these effects. The effect of several doombats shrieking at the same time is not cumulative.

Bright light (such as a *light* spell) will keep a doombat at bay, though it is undeterred by torch- or lantern-light.

DRAGON, *Oriental*

Oriental dragons are related to, though different in some respects from, other dragons, and individuals vary as to colour, being possibly white, red, yellow, blue, green or black. Their powers vary with their type, and each sort of dragon is treated individually hereafter. General information and common characteristics are included in this preamble.

As with other dragons, oriental dragons have three general size categories (small, average and huge) according to the size typical of each. This categorisation is determined by rolling d8; 1—2=small; 3—7=average; 8=huge. This size determination also indicates the number of hit dice a dragon has.

Oriental dragons, like other dragons, pass through eight ages in their lives. These growth stages are:

1.	Very young — 1—5 years	1 hit point per die
2.	Young — 6—15 years	2 hit points per die
3.	Sub-adult — 16—25 years	3 hit points per die
4.	Young adult — 26—50 years	4 hit points per die
5.	Adult — 51—100 years	5 hit points per die
6.	Old — 101—200 years	6 hit points per die
7.	Very old — 201—400 years	7 hit points per die
8.	Ancient — 401+ years	8 hit points per die

To determine the age (and thus the number of hit points per die a dragon has) simply roll an 8-sided die, the number rolled indicating the age as shown above.

Oriental dragons never sleep and furthermore they have continual *ESP* (as the spell) at a range in feet equal to 5 times the age-level of the dragon. All except yu lung can *polymorph* into human form and back at will. They can also become *invisible* and visible at will, though they always become visible when attacking. Only yu lung can be subdued.

Certain types have the *scaly command* power. No scaly unintelligent creature which lives in the water (chiefly fishes and reptiles) will ever willingly attack an oriental dragon with the power. In addition, such a dragon can, once per day, control for a half-mile radius the number of unintelligent scaly creatures which live in the water which is specified for each class. This command lasts 2—12 turns and cannot be dispelled. Creatures already under the *scaly command* power of one dragon cannot fall under the power of another. There is no saving throw against *scaly command*.

Certain other types have the power of *water fire*. This unearthly stuff may be created by any oriental dragon with the power whenever it is under or touching water, and may be dispelled by the creator at any time. *Water fire* surrounds the body like the flame of a demon and does damage to anyone touching it at the amount specified for each type. All oriental dragons are themselves immune to *water fire*. The effect will disappear for 20—120 rounds after being contacted by real or magical 'heat' fire, and cannot be recreated until the end of that period.

Like other dragons, oriental dragons (except for yu lung) develop the power to panic enemies as they mature. At *adult* age and older they radiate a powerful aura which causes a *fear* reaction, when a dragon flies overhead or charges, as follows:

1. All creatures under 1 hit die, as well as non-carnivorous creatures of any sort which are not trained for warfare or basically not fearless or aggressive will flee in panic. Such rout will be made at fastest speed possible and it will continue for 4—24 turns.
2. Creatures with fewer than 3 hit dice must save versus magic or be paralysed with fear (50%) or panic as above (50%).
3. Creatures with 3 to 5 hit dice will fight at a penalty of —1 on their 'to hit' roll unless they save versus magic.
4. Creatures with 6 or more hit dice automatically disregard the aura effect.
5. The aura of *adult, old* and *very old* dragons is not as powerful as that of *ancient* dragons, so saving rolls applicable to their auras are at +5, +3 and +1 respectively. Thus, a 2nd level fighter, normally having to score 16 (75%) or better to save against magic (the dragon's aura in this case), would gain a bonus of 5 on his saving roll versus an *adult* dragon's aura; so any score of 11 or more would save him from panic.

Encountering Multiple Dragons: If two or more dragons are encountered outside their lair it will be a mated pair if two are encountered and *sub-adults* if three or more are encountered. If two or more are encountered in their lair it will be a mated pair — with their young if applicable. Mated pairs are always 5th—8th age categories. Any young in lair are eggs (10%) or *very young* (90%). If young are attacked, both adults will automatically breathe and then melee to bite, gaining a ferocity bonus of +2 to hit and +1/+3 in clawing/biting damage. If either of the mated pair is attacked the other oriental dragon will rush to its defence, gaining the ferocity bonuses stated above, unless it is attacked simultaneously.

Treasure: *Very young* oriental dragons will usually have no treasure, but there is a 10% chance that they will have one-quarter the possible listed treasure. *Young* oriental dragons have 25% chance for one-quarter of the listed treasure. *Sub-adults* have a 50% chance for one-half the possible listed treasure. *Young adults, adults* and *old* dragons have normal treasure. *Very old* and *ancient* dragons are 50% and 75% likely to have 150% and 200% respectively of the listed treasure.

Oriental Dragon Saving Throws: When an oriental dragon attains 5 or more hit points per die, its saving throw is calculated by dividing its total hit points by 4, thus giving a higher number of hit dice than it actually has. This reflects the magic resistance and general toughness of the creature. Conversely, even a *very young* oriental dragon gains the benefit of the actual number of its hit dice, even though the hit points/die are but 1 each, for determining scores required. This reflects the same nature of dragonkind, i.e. resistance and toughness.

Li Lung (Earth Dragon)

FREQUENCY: *Rare*
NO. APPEARING: *1—4*
ARMOUR CLASS: *4*
MOVE: *9"/24//6"(1"—6")*
HIT DICE: *7—9*
% IN LAIR: *60%*
TREASURE TYPE: *H*
NO. OF ATTACKS: *3*
DAMAGE/ATTACK:
  2—8/2—8/1—20
SPECIAL ATTACKS:
  Spells — see below
SPECIAL DEFENCES: *Nil*
MAGIC RESISTANCE: *Standard*
INTELLIGENCE: *Average*
ALIGNMENT: *Neutral*
SIZE: *L (18' long)*
PSIONIC ABILITY: *Nil*
  Attack/Defence Modes: *Nil*
LEVEL/X.P. VALUE:
  7HD: VI/575 + 8 per hit point
  8HD: VI/925 + 10 per hit point
  9HD: VII/1,400 + 12 per hit point

The only oriental dragon with wings, these have a lion's body and a dragon's head with human features. They live underground and can swim, though they cannot breathe water. They attack with two claws which inflict 2—8 hit points of damage each and a bite which inflicts 1—20 hit points of damage.

They have no breath weapon, but once a day they can cause an earthquake (as the spell but with no chance of it being dispelled) with a width and length in tens of feet equal to three times the age level of the beast (so a *sub-adult* would produce an effect 30' square). Such a convulsion may bring down the cavern in which the oriental dragon is living, but li lung are never harmed by any earthquake (though they may be inconvenienced by having to dig out of the rubble). Their powerful claws enable them to burrow through solid stone at 1" per turn and through earth at 6 times that rate.

Li lung are manoeuvrability class E in the air.

Lung Wang (Sea Dragon)

FREQUENCY: *Very rare*
NO. APPEARING: *1*
ARMOUR CLASS: *0*
MOVE: *3"//9"*
HIT DICE: *11—13*
% IN LAIR: *60%*
TREASURE TYPE: *H(x2)*
NO. OF ATTACKS: *3*
DAMAGE/ATTACK:
  1—12/1—12/6—36
SPECIAL ATTACKS: *Breath weapon and spells — see below*
SPECIAL DEFENCES: *Nil*
MAGIC RESISTANCE: *Standard*
INTELLIGENCE: *Very*
ALIGNMENT: *Neutral*
SIZE: *L (up to 30' diameter)*
PSIONIC ABILITY: *Nil*
  Attack/Defence Modes: *Nil*
LEVEL/X.P. VALUE:
  11 or 12HD: VIII/4,550 + 16 per hit point
  13HD: IX/6,350 +18 per hit point

These solitary brutes are oriental relatives to the dragon turtle, with a turtle's body, crested neck, and head like a shen lung. They rule large bodies of water and can breathe either water or air. They can lift any ship they come under or ram as the largest warship.

Their ordinary attacks are with two claws which do 1—12 hit points of damage each and a bite which inflicts 6—36 hit points of damage. They can breathe a cone of steam 100' long by 50' wide at the base up to three times a day; this breath weapon does damage equal to the current hit points of the creature.

Lung wang have the *scaly command* power over 4—40 creatures times the age level of the dragon, but no *water fire*. They have no spells other than those general to oriental dragons.

As rulers of the seas, lung wang demand tribute from every passing ship. Regular travellers may work out an arrangement — for example, so much treasure dumped overboard at a given spot.

They have their own language.

Pan Lung (Coiled Dragon)

FREQUENCY: *Rare*
NO. APPEARING: *1—4*
ARMOUR CLASS: *2*
MOVE: *12"/12"//9"*
HIT DICE: *6—8*
% IN LAIR: *60%*
TREASURE TYPE: *H(x½)*
NO. OF ATTACKS: *3*
DAMAGE/ATTACK: *1—3/1—3/2—16*
SPECIAL ATTACKS:
    *Constriction and spells —
    see below*
SPECIAL DEFENCES: *Nil*
MAGIC RESISTANCE: *Standard*
INTELLIGENCE: *High*
ALIGNMENT: *Chaotic neutral*
SIZE: *L (54' long)*
PSIONIC ABILITY: *Nil*
    Attack/Defence Modes: *Nil*
LEVEL/X.P. VALUE:
    6HD: V/475 + 6 per hit point
    7HD: VI/700 + 8 per hit point
    8HD: VII/1,100 + 10 per hit point

A smaller, thinner and longer variety of the shen lung, pan lung live in marshes and swamps. Unlike the shen lung, they have no tail spike, but if they succeed in grasping with their bite (which does 2—16 hit points of damage) they will, on each succeeding round, automatically bite for 1—8 hit points of damage and constrict with their tail for a further 2—12 hit points of damage. They also attack with their two claws, each of which inflicts 1—3 hit points of damage.

Pan lung can fly, breathe air or water at will, have the *scaly command* power over 1—10 creatures times the age level of the dragon, and can use *water fire* for 1—6 points of damage. They have no breath weapon, but may cast *charm monster* three times a day.

Pan lung are manoeuvrability class E for purposes of aerial combat. In their brain they have a magical organ like that of the shen lung which gives them the power of flight — the organ is inextractable.

Pan lung speak their own language which they share with the shen lung.

Shen Lung (Spirit Dragon)

FREQUENCY: *Rare*
NO. APPEARING: *1—4*
ARMOUR CLASS: *1*
MOVE: *12"/12"//9"*
HIT DICE: *9—11*
% IN LAIR: *60%*
TREASURE TYPE: *H*
NO. OF ATTACKS: *4*
DAMAGE/ATTACK:
    1—4/1—4/2—24/1—8
SPECIAL ATTACKS:
    Spells — see below
SPECIAL DEFENCES:
    See below
MAGIC RESISTANCE: *Standard*
INTELLIGENCE: *High*
ALIGNMENT: *Chaotic neutral*
SIZE: *L (48' long)*
PSIONIC ABILITY: *Nil*
    Attack/Defence Modes: *Nil*
LEVEL/X.P. VALUE:
    9HD: VII/1,400 + 12 per hit point
    10HD: VII/2,100 + 14 per hit point
    11HD: VII/3,000 + 16 per hit point

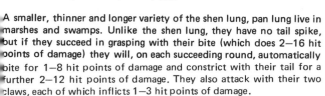

The most common oriental dragon, shen lung are wingless, long and four-footed, with a spiked back and tail, whiskers and two horns on the head. Inside the brain is an inextractable magical organ which gives shen lung the ability to fly.

Shen lung typically attack with two claws for 1—4 hit points of damage each, a bite for 2—24 hit points of damage and a tail spike for 1—8 hit points of damage. The tail is as supple as that of a wyvern, but not poisonous. Shen lung have no breath weapon but can cast *bless* and *curse* once a day each and *control weather* and *ice storm* three times a day each.

These oriental dragons live in rivers and lakes and can breathe air or water. They take no damage from lightning, but take double damage from fire attacks. They have the *scaly command* power over 2—20 creatures times the age-level of the dragon and *water fire* of 2—12 points value.

Shen lung are immune to poison. Another curious power they possess is that no insect, arachnid or arthropod can approach a shen lung within a radius of 60'.

They are manoeuvrability class E as regards aerial combat.

Shen lung speak their own language which they share with the pan lung.

T'ien Lung (Celestial Dragon)

FREQUENCY: *Very rare*
NO. APPEARING: *1*
ARMOUR CLASS: *—2*
MOVE: *9"/48"//6"*
HIT DICE: *11—13*
% IN LAIR: *60%*
TREASURE TYPE: *H(x 2)*
NO. OF ATTACKS: *3*
DAMAGE/ATTACK:
    1—6/1—6/4—40
SPECIAL ATTACKS:
    *Breath weapon and spells —
    see below*
SPECIAL DEFENCES: *Nil*
MAGIC RESISTANCE: *Standard*
INTELLIGENCE: *Exceptional*
ALIGNMENT: *Lawful neutral*
SIZE: *L (48' long)*
PSIONIC ABILITY: *Nil*
    Attack/Defence Modes: *Nil*
LEVEL/X.P. VALUE:
    *11 or 12HD: VIII/4, 550
    + 16 per hit point*
    *13HD: IX/6,350 + 18
    per hit point*

T'ien lung live on high mountain peaks and in cloud castles; they are rulers of the air. Their usual colouration is yellow. Though wingless, they fly by using the same organ in the brain as possessed by shen lung.

Usually they attack with two claws, each of which does 1—6 hit points of damage, and a bite which does 4—40 hit points of damage. They breathe fire in a 90'x30' cone up to six times a day, doing damage equal to the dragon's current hit points. They may also cast *control weather* a number of times per day equal to twice the dragon's age level.

T'ien lung of age *old* and older have a 50% chance of being accompanied by 1—6 wind walkers (see **ADVANCED DUNGEONS & DRAGONS, MONSTER MANUAL** — *Wind Walker*); these fanatically loyal servants cannot be charmed from their purpose and will do their utmost to defend their master and, if necessary, avenge his death.

T'ien lung are very fond of eating opals and pearls and will look favourably on any mortal giving them such delicacies.

In the air, t'ien lung are manoeuvrability class D.

They speak their own language, their alignment language and the common tongue.

Yu Lung (Carp Dragon)

FREQUENCY: *Rare*
NO. APPEARING: *1—4*
ARMOUR CLASS: *3*
MOVE: *6"//18"*
HIT DICE: *5—7*
% IN LAIR: *60%*
TREASURE TYPE: *Nil*
NO. OF ATTACKS: *3*
DAMAGE/ATTACK:
    1—4/1—4/2—16
SPECIAL ATTACKS: *Nil*
SPECIAL DEFENCES: *Nil*
MAGIC RESISTANCE: *Standard*
INTELLIGENCE: *Low*
ALIGNMENT: *Neutral*
SIZE: *L (18' long)*
PSIONIC ABILITY: *Nil*
    Attack/Defence Modes: *Nil*
LEVEL/X.P. VALUE:
    5HD: III/130 + 5 per
        hit point
    6HD: IV/225 + 6 per
        hit point
    7HD: V/350 + 8 per
        hit point

These shy creatures live in fresh water and have a dragon's head, two forelegs and a giant carp's body/tail. They cannot fly, *polymorph* or turn *invisible;* they have no breath weapon and breathe only water, though they can emerge awkwardly onto land for up to one hour.

Their attack is with two claws for 1—4 hit points of damage each and a bite for 2—16 hit points of damage.

When determining the age of yu lung, bring all age levels of 5 or above down to *adult.* There are no older yu lung; when they reach 101 years of age, they are metamorphosed into another kind of oriental dragon (equal probability each type).

DRAGONFISH

FREQUENCY: *Rare*
NO. APPEARING: *1*
ARMOUR CLASS: *4*
MOVE: *6"*
HIT DICE: *2*
% IN LAIR: *Nil*
TREASURE TYPE: *Nil*
NO. OF ATTACKS: *1*
DAMAGE/ATTACK: *1—6*
SPECIAL ATTACKS: *Poison*
SPECIAL DEFENCES: *Nil*
MAGIC RESISTANCE: *Standard*
INTELLIGENCE: *Non-*
ALIGNMENT: *Neutral*
SIZE: *S*
PSIONIC ABILITY: *Nil*
    Attack/Defence Modes: *Nil*
LEVEL/X.P. VALUE:
    III/65 + 2 per hit point

Dragonfish are 2' long, mottled brown flatfish which lurk on the bed of a shallow fresh-water pool or a slow-moving stream or river. They are very difficult to spot (15% chance even if the searchers know what they are seeking) because they merge extremely well with the background.

They have a fringe of horny spines tipped with poison (highly toxic — saving throw is at —1) which snap off in any victim who steps on them or puts his hand on them. The spines are very strong and will penetrate leather boots.

In melee dragonfish bite for 1—6 hit points of damage. The spines themselves do not cause damage other than the poison damage.

DUNE STALKER

FREQUENCY: *Very rare*
NO. APPEARING: *1*
ARMOUR CLASS: *3*
MOVE: *12"*
HIT DICE: *6*
% IN LAIR: *Nil*
TREASURE TYPE: *Nil*
NO. OF ATTACKS: *1*
DAMAGE/ATTACK: *2-12*
SPECIAL ATTACKS:
    Kiss of death
SPECIAL DEFENCES:
    Only damaged by
    magical weapons
MAGIC RESISTANCE: *30%*
INTELLIGENCE: *High*
ALIGNMENT: *Neutral evil*
SIZE: *M*
PSIONIC ABILITY: *Nil*
    Attack/Defence Modes: *Nil*
LEVEL/X.P. VALUE:
    V/400 + 6 per hit point

A vile naked human in appearance, bony and with long sharp fingers and clawed toes, the dune stalker roams desert areas in response to summons from high level evil magicians. It will attack good characters only; any alignment combined with good will attract attack.

It is a faultless tracker, as the invisible stalker (see **ADVANCED DUNGEONS & DRAGONS, MONSTER MANUAL** — *Invisible Stalker*) once set on a particular mission.

The dune stalker's attack is usually by sonic vibration which has range of 60' and delivers 2—12 hit points of damage on a single targe (saving throw not permitted). In close contact the stalker can delive the 'kiss of death' by placing its lips in direct contact with skin. Th sonic vibrations thus set up in the victim's body are of such a intensity that failure to make a saving throw versus spells mean instant death. A successful saving throw negates the effect.

Dune stalkers can only be harmed by magical weapons.

ELEMENTAL PRINCES OF EVIL — ELF — ENVELOPER — ETTERCAP — EYE KILLER — EYE OF FEAR AND FLAME

ELEMENTAL PRINCES OF EVIL

The princes of evil air, cold, earth, fire and water creatures are powerful beings whose principal areas of domination are on the *Elemental Planes* but who also have many followers on the *Prime Material Plane*. Though often at odds with each other (mainly through the actions of their underlings) the elemental princes of evil do share certain common characteristics, each being able to perform *detect invisible, dispel magic* (at 20th level), *infravision* (duration one day), *know alignment, suggestion* (duration 12 hours) and *teleportation* (no error), all at will. They have a special telepathic power which enables them to understand and converse with any intelligent creature. Three times per day (each) they can *read languages* and *read magic;* once per day they can *telekinese* 6,000 gold pieces weight.

The experience point value shown for each prince is for destroying the material form only. If a prince is killed permanently, the XP value is multiplied by 10.

Cryonax *(Prince of Evil Cold Creatures)*

FREQUENCY: *Very rare*
NO. APPEARING: *1*
ARMOUR CLASS: *−6*
MOVE: *9″*
HIT DICE: *90 hit points*
% IN LAIR: *55%*
TREASURE TYPE: *H, V, X.*
NO. OF ATTACKS: *2*
DAMAGE/ATTACK:
 5−20/5−20
SPECIAL ATTACKS: *Cold damage; spells*
SPECIAL DEFENCES: *See below*
MAGIC RESISTANCE: *75%*
INTELLIGENCE: *Genius*
ALIGNMENT: *Neutral evil*
SIZE: *L (15′ tall)*
PSIONIC ABILITY: *200*
 Attack/Defence Modes:
  All/all
LEVEL/X.P. VALUE: *X/28,000*

Cryonax appears as a 15′ tall yeti with tentacles covered with suction cups in place of arms. He radiates 1−6 points of *cold* damage continually, affecting all within 15′ (those with resistance to *cold* take half damage, but there is no saving throw as such against this). He attacks as a 20 hit dice monster with two tentacles, each of which

inflicts 5−20 hit points of damage; in addition the victim must save versus paralysation or be frozen in place for 3−12 full turns. Cryonax can only be damaged by +2 or better weapons.

There is a cumulative 10% chance that any particular weapon hitting Cryonax will shatter; if the weapon does break, damage inflicted by that particular hit is nullified.

As a prince of evil creatures of cold, Cryonax may summon one of the following groups once per day: 1−4 white dragons, 1−4 frost giants or 1−6 yeti. In addition he can, thrice per day, produce a triple-strength *wall of ice*, can *hold person* and can cast an *ice storm* of 4−40 points. Once per day, he can cause a blast of *cold* of 15-dice strength.

Fire attacks against Cryonax are at +2 hit probability and do an additional point of damage per attack die. Cold attacks add to his hit points in an amount equal to the intended damage, up to but not exceeding his original 90 hit points. He is completely immune to poison, nor can he be turned to stone.

This prince lives in a huge castle of ice, quartz and glass, situated at the juncture of the *Planes* of *Air* and *Water* and drawing power from the *Negative Material Plane*.

Imix *(Prince of Evil Fire Creatures)*

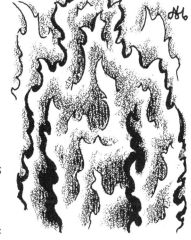

FREQUENCY: *Very rare*
NO. APPEARING: *1*
ARMOUR CLASS: *−4*
MOVE: *18″*
HIT DICE: *90 hit points*
% IN LAIR: *45%*
TREASURE TYPE: *R, U*
NO. OF ATTACKS: *1*
DAMAGE/ATTACK: *6−36*
SPECIAL ATTACKS:
 Fire damage, spells
SPECIAL DEFENCES:
 See below
MAGIC RESISTANCE: *85%*
INTELLIGENCE: *Genius*
ALIGNMENT: *Neutral evil*
SIZE: *L (18′ tall)*
PSIONIC ABILITY: *190*
 Attack/Defence Modes:
  All/all
LEVEL/X.P. VALUE: *X/25,900*

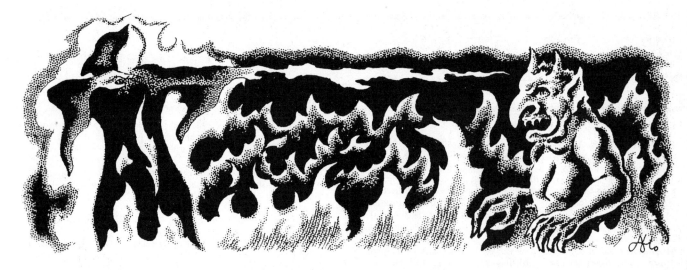

Imix generally appears as an 18' high pillar of fire. He radiates 1—20 points of heat damage constantly, affecting all those within 10' (those with resistance to fire take half damage, but there is no saving throw as such against this). He attacks as a 20 hit dice creature once per round for 6—36 hit points of damage. Only +2 or better weapons can harm him.

As prince of evil fire creatures, Imix may summon one of the following groups once per day: 1—3 efreet, 1—3 fire elementals or 1—3 salamanders. In addition he can perform the following thrice per day: cause painfully bright *continual light,* cast a triple-strength *wall of fire* and initiate *pyrotechnics.* Once a day, Imix can throw a 20-dice *fireball.*

Water attacks on Imix are at +1 hit probability, while cold attacks are at +2 hit probability and add one point of damage to each attack die. Imix is immune to paralysis, poison and petrifaction.

Imix lives in the depths of a monstrous active volcano on the *Elemental Plane of Fire.*

There is great enmity between Imix and Olhydra.

Ogrémoch *(Prince of Evil Earth Creatures)*

FREQUENCY: *Very rare*
NO. APPEARING: *1*
ARMOUR CLASS: *—7*
MOVE: *9"*
HIT DICE: *110 hit points*
% IN LAIR: *65%*
TREASURE TYPE: *H, U, Z*
NO. OF ATTACKS: *2*
DAMAGE/ATTACK: *5—50/5—50*
SPECIAL ATTACKS: *Spells*
SPECIAL DEFENCES: *See below*
MAGIC RESISTANCE: *85%*
INTELLIGENCE: *Exceptional*
ALIGNMENT: *Neutral evil*
SIZE: *L (10' tall)*
PSIONIC ABILITY: *185*
    Attack/Defence Modes:
      All/all
LEVEL/X.P. VALUE: *X/39,450*

Ogrémoch appears in a rough, apparently unfinished bipedal form, 10' tall. He attacks as a 24 hit dice monster, striking twice for 5—50 hit points of damage per attack each round. +3 or better weapons are required to harm him.

As prince of evil earth creatures, Ogrémoch can summon one of the following groups once per day: 1—3 earth elementals, 1—6 evil khargra, 1—4 umber hulks or 1—4 evil xorn. In addition, he can perform the following thrice per day: produce a triple-strength *wall of stone, move earth* (double area, casting time in rounds rather than turns), *flesh to stone.* Once per day he can cause an *earthquake* of 100' diameter.

He cannot be harmed by normal fire or by poison. Cold, lightning and magical fire attacks subtract 1 point of damage per attack die against him. Ogrémoch lives in a great flat-topped mountain on the *Elemental Plane of Earth.*

Olhydra *(Princess of Evil Water Creatures)*

FREQUENCY: *Very rare*
NO. APPEARING: *1*
ARMOUR CLASS: *—5*
MOVE: *6"//18"*
HIT DICE: *90 hit points*
% IN LAIR: *75%*
TREASURE TYPE: *H, S, U*
NO. OF ATTACKS: *1*
DAMAGE/ATTACK: *2—24*
SPECIAL ATTACKS:
    Drowning, spells
SPECIAL DEFENCES: *See below*
MAGIC RESISTANCE: *70%*
INTELLIGENCE: *Genius*
ALIGNMENT: *Neutral evil*
SIZE: *L (20' diameter)*
PSIONIC ABILITY: *210*
    Attack/Defence Modes: *All/all*
LEVEL/X.P. VALUE: *X/23,000*

Olhydra appears only near water as a watery amorphous blob 20' in diameter. She attacks as a 20 hit dice monster once per round with a water wave which inflicts 2—24 points of damage.

She can also attack by enveloping and drowning victims; up to five human-sized creatures may be attacked and enveloped at one time,

and are powerless to do anything (fight, cast spells) while enveloped. All defenders are considered armour class 6 against this attack (with appropriate magical and dexterity modifiers). Victims drown in 2–8 rounds and take 2–12 hit points of damage each round in any case. The only way to save enveloped victims is to kill or drive away the princess since she cannot move enveloped bodies.

Olhydra can ram ships with the force of two heavy galleys. She can only be hit by +1 or better weapons, and edged weapons only do half damage on her when they hit.

As princess of evil water creatures, Olhydra may summon one of the following groups once per day: 1–3 water elementals. 1–2 sea hags. 2–5 water weirds or 20–200 sahuagin (salt water only). She can also perform the following thrice per day: produce a triple-strength *wall of fog, lower* and *part water* (at 20th level), *transmute rock to mud, ice storm*.

Fire attacks are at +2 hit probability against her and do an additional 1 point of damage per attack die. Cold attacks cannot damage her, but if over 20 points in value, they act as a *slow* spell upon her (her magical resistance is ineffective in this case, nor does she get a saving throw). Any normal fire within 10' of Olhydra is automatically extinguished. She cannot be paralysed or turned to stone.

Olhydra lives in a great undersea castle on the *Elemental Plane of Water.* There is great enmity between her and Imix.

Yan-C-Bin *(Prince of Evil Aerial Creatures)*

FREQUENCY: *Very rare*
NO. APPEARING: *1*
ARMOUR CLASS: *–6*
MOVE: *48″*
HIT DICE: *85 hit points*
% IN LAIR: *15%*
TREASURE TYPE: *U, Z*
NO. OF ATTACKS: *2*
DAMAGE/ATTACK: *2–20/2–20*
SPECIAL ATTACKS: *Spells,*
    whirlwind, monk's abilities
SPECIAL DEFENCES:
    See below
MAGIC RESISTANCE: *90%*
INTELLIGENCE: *Genius*
ALIGNMENT: *Neutral evil*
SIZE: *L (10' diameter)*
PSIONIC ABILITY: *220*
    Attack/Defence Modes:
    All/all
LEVEL/X.P. VALUE: *X/25,650*

Yan-C-Bin is naturally invisible, creating a slight disturbance in the air as he flies which may be detected by high-level characters (see **ADVANCED DUNGEONS & DRAGONS DUNGEON MASTERS GUIDE** – *Invisibility*). He is about 10' in diameter but has no definite shape. He attacks as a 19 hit dice monster twice per round for 2–20 hit points of damage each attack, with the same chance as that of an 8th level monk to stun or kill an opponent outright. +2 or better weapons are required to harm him. For purposes of aerial combat, he is manoeuvrability class A.

As Prince of evil aerial creatures, Yan-C-Bin can summon one of the following groups once per day: 1–3 air elementals, 1–4 cloud giants, 1–4 invisible stalkers or 1–3 wind walkers.

Lightning attacks are ineffective against Yan-C-Bin, but fire attacks against him are at a hit probability bonus of +1 for every four levels of the attacker (so a 3rd level character would get a bonus of +1, a

seventh level character +2 and so on). Yan-C-Bin cannot be harmed by any object cast into the air and is immune to petrifaction. He can form a whirlwind – a truncated reverse cone, with a 2″ bottom diameter, a 6″ top diameter and a height of 16″. If the full height of the whirlwind cannot be attained due to some overhead obstruction the whirlwind is only half strength. A full strength whirlwind sweeps away and kills all creatures under three hit dice and causes 4–32 hit points of damage on all non-aerial creatures which it fails to kill outright. (A half strength whirlwind does 2–16 hit points of damage). Yan-C-Bin can sustain this form for 2-5 rounds. Formation of this whirlwind or dissipation of it requires one full round.

Yan-C-Bin lives in a great airy palace on the *Elemental Plane of Air.*

ELF
Drow *(Dark Elf)*

FREQUENCY: *Very rare*
    (at best)
NO. APPEARING: *5–50*
ARMOUR CLASS: *4 (and better)*
MOVE: *12″ (females 15″)*
HIT DICE: *2 (and better)*
% IN LAIR: *0*
TREASURE TYPE:
    Individuals: N(x5),Q(x2)
NO. OF ATTACKS: *1 or 2*
DAMAGE/ATTACK: *By*
    weapon type
SPECIAL ATTACKS: *See below*
SPECIAL DEFENCES: *See below*
MAGIC RESISTANCE:
    50 % (and better); all
    saving throws at +2
INTELLIGENCE: *Mean:*
    highly intelligent
ALIGNMENT: *Chaotic evil*
SIZE: *M(5' tall)*
PSIONIC ABILITY: *Unknown*
    Attack/Defence Modes:
    Unknown
LEVEL/X.P. VALUE:
    II and up/Variable

Ages past, when the elvenfolk were but new to the face of the earth, their number was torn by discord and those of better disposition drove from them those of the elves who were selfish and cruel. However constant warfare between the two divisions of elvenkind continued, with the goodly ones ever victorious, until those of dark nature were forced to withdraw from the lands under the skies and seek safety in the realm of the underworld. Here, in lightless caverns and endless warrens of twisting passages and caves hung with icicles of stone, the dark elvenfolk – the drow – found both refuge and comfort. Over the centuries they grew strong once again and schooled themselves in arcane arts. And though they were strong enough to face and perhaps defeat their former brethren in battle, the drow no longer desired to walk upon the green lands under the sun and stars. They no longer desired a life in the upper world, being content with the gloomy fairyland beneath the earth that they had made their own. Yet they neither forgave nor forgot, and even now, above all else, they bear enmity for all of their distant kin – elves and faeries – who drove them down beneath the earth and now dwell in the meadows and dells of the bright world. Though they are seldom if ever seen by any human or demi-human, the drow still persist, occasionally entering lower dungeon levels and consorting with other creatures in order to work out their schemes and inflict revenge upon those who inhabit the world above.

Regardless of the number of drow appearing, there will always be one of higher level than the main body. Drow males are all at least 2nd level fighters – some are as high as 7th level in fighting ability. Males can also be magic-users, some as high as 12th level. Female drow are also at least 2nd level fighters and some have attained 9th level as fighters. Most drow clerics are female, and no upper limit to their level of ability is known; however no male drow cleric has been known to be higher than 4th level.

Drow wear a fine mesh armour of exquisite workmanship. It is made of an alloy of steel containing adamantite. Even the lowliest fighters

have in effect +1 chainmail, with higher level drow having +2, +3, +4 or even +5 chainmail. Small bucklers are also used — shields of unusual shape — those drow of greater experience level and importance in drow society having bucklers fashioned of adamantite so as to be +1, +2 or even +3 value.

As will be described later, all drow move silently and with graceful speed, even when wearing their black mesh of armour. Each drow carries a small amount of personal wealth in a soft leather bag worn around the neck beneath the mail. In addition they arm themselves with long dagger and short sword of adamantite alloy (+1 to as high as +3 or even +4 borne by noblefolk); 50% or more carry small cross-bows which are held in one hand (6″ range light crossbow) and shoot darts coated with a poison which renders the victim unconscious (save is at —4). These darts also inflict 1—3 points of damage on a victim. A few drow also carry adamantite maces (+1 to +5) and/or small javelins (also poisoned with the same substance as the darts) with atlatls (9″ range, +3/+2/+1 to hit at short/medium/long range).

Drow have superior infravision of the 12″ range variety and move with silence. The black boots and cloaks that Drow wear are similar to *cloaks* and *boots of elvenkind*, except that the wearer has only a 75% chance of surprising enemies or blending into shadows. The material will not cut easily and cloaks have a +6 to saving throws vs. fire attacks; however, any alteration to the cloak has a 75% chance of unraveling the material and making it useless. Drow themselves are only 12½% (1 in 8) likely to be surprised by opponents. Drow are also both intelligent and highly co-ordinated, being able to use either or both hands/arms for attack and defence. They make saving throws versus all forms of magic (clerical included) spells, whether from a caster or from a device, at +2. Drow magic resistance increases by 2% for each level of experience they have gained, with multi-classed individuals gaining this bonus for but one of their classes (the highest). Thus, a 7th level Drow is 64% resistant to any magic and will save at +2 against any magic which could have an effect.

Because the drow have dwelled so long in the dark labyrinthine places under the surface of the earth, they dislike bright light. They will not venture forth into daylight except on the cloudiest, gloomiest days. If within the radius of a *light* or *continual light* spell the dark elves are 90% likely to be seen, they lose 2 from their dexterity and all attacks made by them are at —2 on the 'to hit' roll (+2 on saving rolls against such attacks as applicable). If they are attacking targets inside the radius of *light* or *continual light* spells, the bright illumination causes them to suffer a 'to hit' penalty of —1 and the converse +1 on saving throws against such attacks is awarded to the target creatures. If bright light exists, it is 75% likely that drow will retire from the situation because of the illumination, unless such a retreat would imperil one of their number, would otherwise be harmful to their desired ends or would expose some important feature to the light-bringing intruders. In any event, such dimmer light sources as torches, lanterns, magic weapons, fire beetle essence or *faerie fire* do not adversely affect the performance of the dark elves.

Drow are able to speak the subterranean trade language common to most intelligent dwellers in the underworld, the common tongue, gnome, elven and their own language in addition to the other tongues which their level of intelligence allows. Many know the languages of the various races which speak and dwell underground. All of the dark elves also have a *silent language* composed of hand movements, and this means of communication is highly sophisticated, being able to convey much information to a considerable degree of complexity. When drow are within 30′ of each other, they use facial and body expression, movement and posture; these latter means of communication alone are capable of conveying considerable information, and when coupled with hand/finger movements the whole is as erudite as any spoken speech.

All the dark elves can use the following spells once per day: *dancing lights, faerie fire, darkness.* Those above 4th level are also able to *detect magic, know alignment* and *levitate* once per day. Drow females can, in addition, use the following spells once per day: *clairvoyance, detect lie, suggestion, dispel magic.* Drow have powers which are the same as those of dwarves with respect to stone and things underground. They also detect hidden or secret doors as elves do.

Drow abilities are determined as follows: Strength 8 + 1—6 (6 + 1—6 for males); Intelligence 12 + 1—6 (10 + 1—8 for males); Wisdom 8 + 1—10 (8 + 1—4 for males); Dexterity 12 + 2—8; Constitution 4—16; Charisma 10 + 1—8 (8 + 1—8 for males).

If more than 10 drow are encountered there will be in addition a male who is a fighter/magic-user of at least 3rd level. If more than 20 are encountered, there will be a female fighter/cleric of at least 6th level clerical ability in addition to the male fighter/magic-user. If more than 30 drow are encountered, 11—16 will be females, the leader will be a female cleric/fighter of at least 8th/7th ability level, the male fighter/magic-user will be at least of 5th/4th ability level and each will have an assistant of level as previously indicated for the ones present with

Special Note Regarding Drow Treasure: Cloaks, armor, and weapons made by the Drow have special properties, although they do not radiate magic. The items are made in the strange homeland of the Drow: vast underground cities of carven stone and minerals, places of weird and fantastic beauty inundated with unknown radiations which impart the special properties to their items. When these are exposed to direct sunlight, irreversible decay starts and the items will become totally useless in 2—12 days. If protected from sunlight, they will retain their special properties for 31—50 days before becoming normal items; and if exposed to the radiations of the Drow homeland for a period of 1 week out of every 4 weeks, the items could remain potent indefinitely. Drow sleep poison decays instantly in sunlight, and will lose its effectiveness after 60 days in any event after being exposed to air, although unopened packets of the poison will remain potent for up to one year.

Description: Drow are black-skinned and pale-haired. They are slight of build and have long, delicate fingers and toes.

ENVELOPER

FREQUENCY: *Very rare*
NO. APPEARING: *1*
ARMOUR CLASS: *4*
MOVE: *9″*
HIT DICE: *3, 5, 7 etc.*
% IN LAIR: *85%*
TREASURE TYPE: *E*
NO. OF ATTACKS: *2*
DAMAGE/ATTACK: *1—8/1—8*
SPECIAL ATTACKS:
    See below
SPECIAL DEFENCES: *Nil*
MAGIC RESISTANCE: *Variable*
INTELLIGENCE: *Variable*
ALIGNMENT: *Variable*
SIZE: *L*
PSIONIC ABILITY: *Variable*
    Attack/Defence Modes:
        Variable
LEVEL/X.P. VALUE:
    III and up/Variable

The enveloper is basically a mass of malleable flesh in the form of a rough cylinder 8′ tall and 3′ in circumference. It can form up to five appendages at will by reshaping flesh in the appropriate areas, and when in view of humans or near-humans it will adopt approximate human form (the appendages being head, arms and legs). It is basically of animal intelligence, of neutral alignment, with standard magic resistance and no psionic abilities.

In melee the enveloper strikes with two 'fists', each capable of delivering 1—8 hit points of damage.

If the enveloper kills a victim — monster or character — its first act is to fall on the body which in one melee round is totally consumed, leaving all clothes, weapons etc. behind. After a further delay of three melee rounds (during which time the beast can fight as normal — it cannot attack in its consuming round') the beast can use any of the victim's abilities; for example, it gains the victim's experience and knowledge, can speak with the victim's voice, can cast spells memorised by the victim and so forth. For each hit die of the victim, the enveloper gains 1—3 hit points (though it continues to attack with the same hit probability as before, no matter how many extra points it gains).

As the enveloper consumes additional victims it will gain additional abilities and powers. In the case of mutual conflict (for example in terms of alignment) of attributes or powers, one is discarded at random until the conflict is removed. The beast will tend towards the alignment of its most recently-consumed victim, and alignment language will vary accordingly.

The enveloper gains hit dice as it ages, in steps of 2 dice; theoretically there is no limit to the number of hit dice, or hit points, an old enveloper may possess.

ETTERCAP

FREQUENCY: *Rare*
NO. APPEARING: *1—2*
ARMOUR CLASS: *6*
MOVE: *12"*
HIT DICE: *5*
% IN LAIR: *30%*
TREASURE TYPE: *Nil*
NO. OF ATTACKS: *3*
DAMAGE/ATTACK:
   1—3/1—3/1—8
SPECIAL ATTACKS: *Poison*
SPECIAL DEFENCES:
   Traps — see below
MAGIC RESISTANCE:
   Standard
INTELLIGENCE: *Low*
ALIGNMENT: *Neutral evil*
SIZE: *M*
PSIONIC ABILITY: *Nil*
   Attack/Defence Modes: *Nil*
LEVEL/X.P. VALUE:
   IV/165 + 5 per hit point

A biped, roughly man-sized, with very long arms, protruding pot-belly, short legs and hairy skin, the ettercap has clawed hands and two poison fangs protruding one on each side of the mouth. Ettercaps are cruel, cunning and treacherous.

The ettercap attacks with its claws for 1—3 hit points of damage each and also inflicts a poisonous bite for 1—8 hit points of damage.

The creature has silk glands like those of a spider located near the anus. These glands secrete a thin, very tough, silvery cord which the beast uses to make assorted weapons and devices — lariats, nets, garottes, tripwires and so forth. Each ettercap has its preferred weapons and trap devices, so an encounter will vary according to an ettercap's preference, though they will always lay traps and prepare an ambush if there is time to do so.

Ettercaps get along well with all forms of spider.

EYE KILLER

FREQUENCY: *Very rare*
NO. APPEARING: *1—4 or 2—8*
ARMOUR CLASS: *5*
MOVE: *9"*
HIT DICE: *4*
% IN LAIR: *25%*
TREASURE TYPE: *Nil*
NO. OF ATTACKS: *1*
DAMAGE/ATTACK: *1—6*
SPECIAL ATTACKS:
   Death stare
SPECIAL DEFENCES: *Nil*
MAGIC RESISTANCE: *Standard*
INTELLIGENCE: *Animal*
ALIGNMENT: *Chaotic evil*
SIZE: *M*
PSIONIC ABILITY: *Nil*
   Attack/Defence Modes: *Nil*
LEVEL/X.P. VALUE:
   III/150 + 4 per hit point

At birth, the eye killer is limbless and almost spherical; later it develops a bat-like upper torso on the body of a large snake. Its stunted wings cannot support flight. The upper part of its body is a dark grey-green while the lower part is a medium green flecked with dull yellow. Its eyes are disproportionately large and apparently lidless.

The creature dislikes daylight and hates bright naked flame. It dwells in dark places underground, where 2—8 may also (10% chance) be found.

The behaviour of the creature depends almost entirely on the illumination. If approached and attacked by creatures relying solely on infravision or on low-level natural ambient illumination, the eye killer will attack with its coils only, crushing its victim for 1—6 hit points of damage (a hit indicates that it has managed to wrap its coils round a victim; each melee round thereafter it automatically delivers crushing damage of 1—6 hit points without a 'to hit' roll).

If an approaching party is carrying lanterns or torches, however, the eye killer can use the dreaded *Death Stare* up to a range of 50'. Its eyes gather the illumination falling on them, amplify it enormously and project it back at the light-bearer in a powerful, narrow ray of intense light. This ray strikes a victim as though he were AC10; the victim must make his saving throw against death ray or die instantly. Victims who make their saving throw take 3—18 hit points of damage. The *stare* can be reflected though it does not harm the eye killer — it will simply gather the illumination, amplify it still more, and project it in the same round at another victim. Fortunately for adventurers, the *Death Stare* can only be used once per day.

If torch- or lantern-bearers come close to the eye killer, it will not face the light and will try to flee if the illumination becomes intense (equivalent to three torches at a range of 10'). If the illumination is not strong enough to force its flight, it will attack with its coils as previously described.

EYE OF FEAR AND FLAME

FREQUENCY: *Very rare*
NO. APPEARING: *1*
ARMOUR CLASS: *2*
MOVE: *9"*
HIT DICE: *12*
% IN LAIR: *Nil*
TREASURE TYPE: *Nil*
NO. OF ATTACKS: *See below*
DAMAGE/ATTACK: *See below*
SPECIAL ATTACKS: *See below*
SPECIAL DEFENCES: *See below*
MAGIC RESISTANCE: *See below*
INTELLIGENCE: *High*
ALIGNMENT: *Chaotic evil*
SIZE: *M*
PSIONIC ABILITY: *Nil*
   Attack/Defence Modes: *Nil*
LEVEL/X.P. VALUE:
   VII/2,850 + 16 per hit point

The eye of fear and flame is a hooded man-sized figure; the face is always invisible, the interior of the hood being seen as an opaque black screen. It constantly stalks the underworld seeking lawful or lawful/neutral parties or individuals. It will command an individual, or a member of a party, to perform evil deeds (speaking in the alignment tongue appropriate to the individual addressed since it has permanent *know alignment* power and can speak all alignment languages). The nature of the deeds will vary but they will be uniformly evil. If the eye is attacked, or its commands are not obeyed, it will cast back the hood to reveal a bare skull with a red jewel in one eye-socket and black jewel in the other.

The red gem unleashes a 12-dice *fireball* once every three melee rounds, while the black gem acts as a *fear* wand every melee round. The gems are worth 1,000-2,000 gold pieces each, though they lose their properties when removed from the skull or when the creature is killed.

If melee is going against the creature it has the power to transfer to the *Ethereal Plane*, taking two melee rounds to do so, where it will try to make its escape. It has no means of fighting hand-to-hand.

If the spells *blindness* or *power word: blind* are cast on the eye, they will be reflected back to the caster with no loss of power.

It is said that the eyes of fear and flame were either created by the chaotic evil gods for the destruction of lawfuls, or by the lawful/neutral gods for their testing. The truth is hidden. It is rumoured that only about twenty of these creatures exist.

FIREDRAKE — FIRENEWT — FIRE SNAKE — FIRETOAD — FLAIL SNAIL — FLIND — FLUMPH — FORLARREN — FROST MAN

FIREDRAKE

FREQUENCY: *Rare*
NO. APPEARING: *2–8*
ARMOUR CLASS: *5*
MOVE: *6"/18"*
HIT DICE: *4*
% IN LAIR: *80%*
TREASURE TYPE: *Nil*
NO. OF ATTACKS: *1*
DAMAGE/ATTACK: *2–8*
SPECIAL ATTACKS:
  Breath weapon
SPECIAL DEFENCES: *Nil*
MAGIC RESISTANCE: *Standard*
INTELLIGENCE: *Semi-*
ALIGNMENT: *Neutral*
SIZE: *S (4' long)*
PSIONIC ABILITY: *Nil*
  Attack/Defence Modes: *Nil*
LEVEL/X.P. VALUE:
  III/125 + 4 per hit point

Found only in rocky areas, this small dragonet (4' long or thereabouts) resembles a miniature red dragon in appearance if not in temperament. If it is disturbed even with peaceful intent there is a 50% chance it will attack. Its claws are not used in combat but its bite will cause 2–8 hit points of damage.

The firedrake also has a breath weapon which it can use five times daily. This is a cone of fire 60' long by 10' base diameter which delivers 2–16 hit points of damage (halved if a saving throw is made).

Firedrakes have a short lifespan compared with their larger cousins, the dragons — the age-incremental hit point steps do not apply.

The dragonet's blood burns fiercely in air (the breath weapon is in fact a jet of blood) though it is inert if kept in a container under water. Swords dipped in the blood immediately become *flaming swords* for 3–6 melee rounds though there is a 2% cumulative chance during this time of the sword breaking when a blow is struck with it. It the sword 'survives' this 3–6 round period, it reverts to its original powers after it ceases to flame.

For purposes of aerial combat, the firedrake is manoeuvrability class C.

FIRENEWT

FREQUENCY: *Rare*
NO. APPEARING: *10–100*
ARMOUR CLASS: *5*
MOVE: *9"*
HIT DICE: *2+2*
% IN LAIR: *75%*
TREASURE TYPE:
  Individuals K, M; in lair F.
NO. OF ATTACKS: *1*
DAMAGE/ATTACK:
  By weapon type
SPECIAL ATTACKS: *Breathe fire*
SPECIAL DEFENCES: *See below*
MAGIC RESISTANCE: *Standard*
INTELLIGENCE: *Low*
ALIGNMENT: *Neutral evil*
SIZE: *M*
PSIONIC ABILITY: *Nil*
  Attack/Defence Modes: *Nil*

LEVEL/X.P. VALUE:
  Normal: III/90 + 3 per hit point
  Elite: III/125 + 4 per hit point
  Priest: IV/190 + 4 per hit point
  Overlord: IV/165 + 5 per hit point

These distant relatives of the lizard men live in sun-baked rocky hills, volcanic regions or any other locale which tends to be hot, dry and sometimes sulphurous, whether above or below ground. They are sometimes known as salamen.

Firenewt warriors (the most common variety) are typically armoured in chainmail and carry normal weapons — pike and sword (45%), sword only (25%), pike and hand-axe (20%) or battle-axe (10%).

For every ten warriors encountered there will be one elite warrior with 3+3 hit dice and of AC3 (chain plus dexterity bonus). For every 30 encountered there will, in addition to three elite warriors, be one 'priest' with 3+3 hit dice, AC5 and the following druidic powers, each usable once per day: *animal friendship, faerie fire, predict weather, produce flame, heat metal* and *pyrotechnics*. Elite warriors always carry battle-axes, while priests use a mace in melee.

33% of all firenewts encountered above ground (90% of elite warriors, all priests) will be mounted on giant striders; these beasts are trained by the priests and are highly skilled in melee even if the firenewt 'master' dismounts.

All firenewts have a limited breath weapon. Once per turn they can breathe fire on a foe immediately in front of them and within a 5' range for 1–6 points of damage (a successful saving throw indicates half damage).

Firenewts have high resistance to fire-based attacks, saving with a bonus of +3. Additionally, all fire-based attacks which affect them are reduced by 1 hit point of damage per attack die. Conversely, firenewts save at −3 against cold attacks and damage inflicted on them by these attacks is increased by 1 hit point per attack die.

Firenewts are cruel marauders — if firenewts are encountered they will usually be the members of a hunting party. They delight in torturing and roasting victims alive before feasting on them.

In a firenewt lair there will be an additional 70% females and 150% young as well as a secret, closely-guarded hatching ground containing 200% eggs. The hatching ground will be under the priests' control and will be guarded by 1–3 young fire lizards (see **ADVANCED DUNGEONS & DRAGONS MONSTER MANUAL** — *Lizard, Fire*). The lair will be ruled by an overlord firenewt of 4+4 hit dice and AC3 who will have a close retinue of four elite warriors.

Description: A typical firenewt is a mottled sepia colour, darkest along the spine and fading to near-white on the belly. The smooth flesh and features are eel-like, though the flesh is dry. The eyes are deep crimson. Females are slightly shorter than males (about 5½' tall) and are a duller brown. The young are light in colour, darkening progressively as they approach maturity.

FIRE SNAKE

FREQUENCY: *Uncommon*
NO. APPEARING: *1–6*
ARMOUR CLASS: *6*
MOVE: *4″*
HIT DICE: *2*
% IN LAIR: *100%*
TREASURE TYPE: *Q*
NO. OF ATTACKS: *1*
DAMAGE/ATTACK: *1–4*
SPECIAL/ATTACKS: *Paralysation*
SPECIAL DEFENCES:
    Immune to fire
MAGIC RESISTANCE: *Standard*
INTELLIGENCE: *Semi-*
ALIGNMENT: *Neutral*
SIZE: *S(2′-3′ long)*
PSIONIC ABILITY: *Nil*
    Attack/Defence Modes: *Nil*
LEVEL/X.P. VALUE:
    III/73 + 2 per hit point

Fire snakes — coloured in shades from blood-red to orange — are always found in fires. Some large permanent fires will contain 1–6 of these creatures, though in smaller, semi-permanent fires such as fire-pits and oil bowls there may be one snake. Beneath the snakes will be the gems they accumulate.

Since their colour matches well with their surroundings they strike with a 60% chance of gaining surprise. Their bite inflicts 1–4 hit points of damage and injects a mild venom which causes paralysation of the victim for 2–8 turns unless the victim makes a saving throw against poison.

It is conjectured that fire snakes are larval salamanders.

FIRETOAD

FREQUENCY: *Rare*
NO. APPEARING: *1–6*
ARMOUR CLASS: *10*
MOVE: *6″*
HIT DICE: *4+1*
% IN LAIR: *20%*
TREASURE TYPE: *C*
NO. OF ATTACKS: *1*
DAMAGE/ATTACK: *Variable*
SPECIAL ATTACKS: *Nil*
SPECIAL DEFENCES: *Nil*
MAGIC RESISTANCE: *Standard*
INTELLIGENCE: *Low*
ALIGNMENT: *Chaotic neutral*
SIZE: *S*
PSIONIC ABILITY: *Nil*
    Attack/Defence Modes: *Nil*
LEVEL/X.P. VALUE:
    IV/165 +5 per hit point

A large red toad about 4′ high and covered with warty purple excrescences, this beast shuns water and inhabits dry regions above and below ground. Throwing liquid — even ordinary water — at it will cause it to retreat, though in doing so it will concentrate two *fireball* attacks, in the single melee round of its retreat, on the person performing this act.

The firetoad has the power of breathing small *fireballs* with a range of 30′ and a blast radius of 5′ at will. This is its only mode of attack, the *fireball* doing damage equivalent to the number of hit points the firetoad has remaining. A normal saving throw is permitted against this attack, success indicating half damage.

The firetoad will rarely (20% chance) attack unless threatened, molested or in defence of its treasure.

FLAIL SNAIL

FREQUENCY: *Very rare*
NO. APPEARING: *1*
ARMOUR CLASS: *4*
MOVE: *3″*
HIT DICE: *4–6*
% IN LAIR: *Nil*
TREASURE TYPE: *Nil*
NO. OF ATTACKS: *1 per tentacle*
DAMAGE/ATTACK: *1–8 per*
    tentacle
SPECIAL ATTACKS: *Nil*

SPECIAL DEFENCES: *See below*
MAGIC RESISTANCE: *See below*
INTELLIGENCE: *Low*
ALIGNMENT: *Neutral*
SIZE: *L*
PSIONIC ABILITY: *Nil*
    Attack/Defence Modes: *Nil*
LEVEL/X.P. VALUE:
    4HD: III/150 +4 per hit point
    5HD: IV/205+ 5 per hit point
    6HD: V/350+6 per hit point

This silicon-based mollusc averages 8′ high at the crown of its shell and keeps its club-tentacles (of which it has 4–6) in constant motion, flailing everything in its path. In combat each tentacle has its own hit points and when 'dead' ceases to attack. After all the tentacles have been killed the beast withdraws its head and the rest of its body into its shell; it will die in 1–3 turns, during which time it utters pitiful, wailing cries which have a 50% chance per turn of attracting a wandering monster. The creature's body also has hit points, but it is so adept at withdrawing it into the shell at high speed that it can be regarded as AC –8; any hit on the body will, however, kill the creature outright even if some tentacles survive.

In melee each of the tentacles will strike for 1–8 hit points of damage. Each tentacle represents 1HD of the creature, so a snail with 5 tentacles has 5 hit dice.

The flail snail is immune to fire (normal or magical) and poison, but is hypersensitive to bright illumination and hence is always encountered at night or underground.

The highly-coloured shell affords the flail snail partial protection against magic, acting as a type of *robe of scintillating colours*. Whenever it is attacked by magic the effects are variable — 40% chance of the spell malfunctioning, 30% chance of it functioning normally, 20% of it failing to work at all and 10% chance of it being reflected onto the person casting it. If a spell malfunctions its effects will alter (at the total discretion of the referee, who will not permit more than minor alteration) and the altered effect will be deviated from the snail to the nearest person or creature.

The shell weighs 250 pounds (2,500 gold pieces weight) and retains its magical properties for 1–6 months after its occupant's death. It can be sold for as much as 5,000 gold pieces.

FLIND

FREQUENCY: *Rare*
NO. APPEARING: *2—24*
ARMOUR CLASS: *5*
MOVE: *12"*
HIT DICE: *2+3*
% IN LAIR: *20%*
TREASURE TYPE: *A*
NO. OF ATTACKS: *1*
DAMAGE/ATTACK:
    1—6 or 1—4 — see below
SPECIAL ATTACKS:
    Disarming — see below
SPECIAL DEFENCES: *Nil*
MAGIC RESISTANCE: *Standard*
INTELLIGENCE: *Average*
ALIGNMENT: *Lawful evil*
SIZE: *M(6½' tall)*
PSIONIC ABILITY: *Nil*
    Attack/Defence Modes: *Nil*
LEVEL/X.P. VALUE:
    Normal: II/35 + 3 per hit point
    Leader: III/60 + 4 per hit point

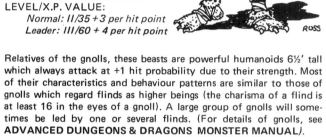

Relatives of the gnolls, these beasts are powerful humanoids 6½' tall which always attack at +1 hit probability due to their strength. Most of their characteristics and behaviour patterns are similar to those of gnolls which regard flinds as higher beings (the charisma of a flind is at least 16 in the eyes of a gnoll). A large group of gnolls will sometimes be led by one or several flinds. (For details of gnolls, see **ADVANCED DUNGEONS & DRAGONS MONSTER MANUAL***).*

The normal flind usually attacks with a club which delivers 1—6 hit points of damage. 25% of a group encountered will instead carry chain-linked iron bars which they use in attack, moving so swiftly with these devices that they gain two attacks per round. If either attack hits, the victim will receive 1—4 hit points of damage and in addition must save (as against wands) or his weapon will have become entangled with the chains and he is disarmed.

This disarming device — the flindbar — can be used by any character with both strength and dexterity of 13 or better, providing he practices with it and selects it as a weapon of proficiency.

Leader-types (one for every 15 flinds encountered) are 3+3 hit dice, have 17 strength and high intelligence, with 18 charisma so far as gnolls are concerned. Leaders all use the flindbars in melee.

Flinds speak the same tongues as do gnolls and are on friendly terms with orcs, hobgoblins, bugbears and ogres. However, they dislike trolls and will not co-operate with them.

FLUMPH

FREQUENCY: *Rare*
NO. APPEARING: *2—16*
ARMOUR CLASS:
    Upper surface 0;
    underside 8
MOVE: *6"*
HIT DICE: *2*
% IN LAIR: *Nil*
TREASURE TYPE: *Nil*
NO. OF ATTACKS: *1*
DAMAGE/ATTACK:
    1—8 plus 1—4 (acid)
SPECIAL ATTACKS: *Nil*
SPECIAL DEFENCES: *See below*
MAGIC RESISTANCE: *Standard*
INTELLIGENCE: *Average*
ALIGNMENT: *Lawful good*
SIZE: *S (2' diameter)*
PSIONIC ABILITY: *Nil*
    Attack/Defence Modes: *Nil*
LEVEL/X.P. VALUE:
    II/36 + 2 per hit point

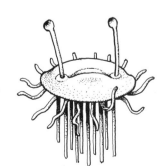

These strange creatures are saucer shaped and pure white in colour. The mouth is at the centre of the upper surface which is AC0; either side of the mouth is a 4" long eyestalk. The underside is AC8 and carries a mass of small spikes and numerous small tentacles.

The flumph 'flies' by sucking air into its mouth and expelling it through its underside. Normally it floats about 4" above the ground but can fly up to 10', particularly for attack purposes. It is manoeuvrability class D.

Normally the flumph repels an attack with a squirt of foul-smelling liquid; this can strike anyone within a 60° arc up to a range of 20' — any victim who fails his saving throw (versus poison) will flee in disgust. The liquid is squirted through an aperture on the creature's 'equator' — the horizontal line of maximum diameter. For 1—4 hours afterwards, a victim struck by this liquid will be shunned by his companions who will not be able to tolerate his presence within 100' until the effects wear off.

If this method of repulsion fails the flumph will rise above its target and drop vertically on its chosen victim. The spikes collectively inflict 1—8 hit points of damage and the tentacles fill the wounds with an acid which does an additional 1—4 hit points of damage, the latter damage recurring for the next 2—8 rounds unless magical means are used to negate the acid (alchemists have so far failed to create an effective antidote).

A flumph is helpless if turned over.

The creature can communicate in the lawful alignment tongues, though its vocabulary is severely limited.

FORLARREN

FREQUENCY: *Very rare*
NO. APPEARING: *1*
ARMOUR CLASS: *2*
MOVE: *9"*
HIT DICE: *3*
% IN LAIR: *Nil*
TREASURE TYPE: *Nil*
NO. OF ATTACKS: *2*
DAMAGE/ATTACK: *1—4/1—4*
SPECIAL ATTACKS:
    Heat metal — see below
SPECIAL DEFENCES: *Nil*
MAGIC RESISTANCE: *Standard*
INTELLIGENCE: *Semi-*
ALIGNMENT: *Neutral evil*
SIZE: *M*
PSIONIC ABILITY: *Nil*
    Attack/Defence Modes: Nil
LEVEL/X.P. VALUE: *III/90 + 3 per hit point*

These creatures are descendents of the offspring of a good nymph and the greater devil who enslaved her. They wander alone, seeking vengeance on good and evil alike, as they detest their own existence in a limbo. They attack characters on sight, using their fists as cudgels for 1—4 points of damage each fist.

The forlarren also has the ability to *heat metal* once a day by contact and will use this mode of attack on the first opponent wearing metal armour they encounter in melee. All armour classes are treated as AC10 for the purpose of this attack. If the heating of the metal succeeds (i.e. if a 'hit' is scored) the victim will take 3—18 hit points of damage each round contact is maintained if wearing plate mail, 2—16 hit points of damage per round if wearing lighter types of metal armour (the latter category including all types of magical metal armour). Once contact has been made it will be maintained until the forlarren or its victim is dead. A successful saving throw (versus dragon breath) will halve the damage.

As soon as it has killed one character the ambivalent nature of the forlarren is revealed. It will show great remorse and will offer any survivors its services and powers (the blood of its ancestral mother still runs through its veins). After a time the dominant evil part of the forlarren resumes control and it will leave the party it is aiding. From that time on, the forlarren will again attack on sight, including the party it earlier befriended if it encounters that party again.

The period of friendship is variable and cannot be forecast with accuracy. As an approximation the referee may select 1—6 days, though there is a 10% chance of the period being shorter (13-24 hours) or longer (7-10 days)..

The creature can speak a rudimentary form of the common tongue.

FROST MAN

FREQUENCY: *Very rare*
NO. APPEARING: *1*
ARMOUR CLASS: *5*
MOVE: *12"*
HIT DICE: *4*
% IN LAIR: *20%*
TREASURE TYPE: *C*
NO. OF ATTACKS: *1*
DAMAGE/ATTACK:
    By weapon type
SPECIAL ATTACKS: *Ice blast*
SPECIAL DEFENCES: *Nil*
MAGIC RESISTANCE: *Standard*
INTELLIGENCE: *Average*
ALIGNMENT: *Lawful evil*
SIZE: *M*
PSIONIC ABILITY: *Nil*
    Attack/Defence Modes: *Nil*
LEVEL/X.P. VALUE: *III/125 + 4 per hit point*

Because of the deadly talent of these creatures, native tribes are greatly fearful of them and call them 'ice demons', though frost men are in most respects very like normal humans and can have the abilities of fighters, clerics, thieves or even magic-users. They will carry weapons appropriate to their class.

Frost men also have the power, three times per day, of radiating a freezing cone of ice mist, 35' long and with 10' base diameter, from one eye (when not in use that eye is usually covered by a patch). The other eye is focusing so there is no reduction in hit probability due to monocular vision.

Any creature caught in the mist cone takes 3—18 hit points of damage (halved if a saving throw versus dragon breath is made).

To date, these creatures have only been encountered singly and the location of their lair, its type and their pattern of living are unknown. It is thought that there are villages of frost men, with females and children, buried in deep caves in mountains, mainly in cold regions. None have yet ventured to establish the veracity of these rumours.

Frost men appear like normal human males. However they radiate cold — readily discernable from as far away as 30' though not of sufficient power to inflict damage. They dress in loose animal skins and carry their personal treasure in leather sacks.

Based on the limited evidence available, the majority (75%) of frost men are of the fighter class. 15% are thieves, about 8% clerics and only 2% magic-users. Clerics and magic-users appear only to have developed spell-use to the second experience level in comparison with humans.

GALLTRIT — GAMBADO — GARBUG — GIANT — GIANT STRIDER — GIBBERLING — GITHYANKI — GITHZERAI — GOLDBUG — GORBEL — GORILLA BEAR — GRELL — GRIMLOCK — GRYPH — GUARDIAN DAEMON — GUARDIAN FAMILIAR

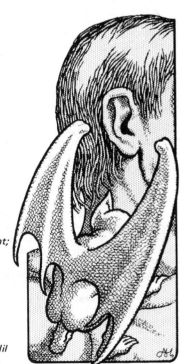

GALLTRIT

FREQUENCY: *Very rare*
NO. APPEARING: *1—4*
ARMOUR CLASS: *2*
MOVE: *3"/18"*
HIT DICE: *2 hit points*
% IN LAIR: *20%*
TREASURE TYPE: *1—3 gems*
NO. OF ATTACKS: *1*
DAMAGE/ATTACK: *1—2*
SPECIAL ATTACKS:
    Blood drain; anti-coagulant;
    anaesthesis
SPECIAL DEFENCES: *Nil*
MAGIC RESISTANCE:
    Standard
INTELLIGENCE: *Average*
ALIGNMENT: *Chaotic evil*
SIZE: *S (½' tall)*
PSIONIC ABILITY: *Nil*
    Attack/Defence Modes: *Nil*
LEVEL/X.P. VALUE: *II/32*

The galltrit is a small (½' tall) winged gremlin with a nasty disposition. It is coloured a stone grey, which combined with its small size makes

it difficult to detect — humans and most demi-humans detect them 1 chance in 8, elves 1 chance in 6.

A galltrit will be found in areas containing dung, carrion or offal. It will attack if disturbed (e.g. by noise) by flying onto a victim — preferably unnoticed — and biting for 1—2 hit points of damage, locking its teeth into the victim's skin. If the galltrit gains surprise prior to attacking, this initial attack will be at +3 hit probability. It is manoeuvrability class B for purposes of aerial combat.

The saliva of the galltrit has an anaesthetic effect, deadening the nerves and skin local to the bite for a full turn, during which the galltrit sucks blood at the rate of one hit point of damage per melee round. Every four melee rounds the anti-coagulant in the saliva reduces the victim's constitution by one point for as many days as the number of hit points drained (e.g. after 10 melee rounds the galltrit has drained 10 points of blood and the victim has lost two points of constitution which will be restored after 10 days).

A galltrit will rarely remain in contact with a victim for more than one full turn even if not noticed, and will try to flee as soon as its presence is detected (note that, if the creature is not noticed in its initial attack, it will not be noticed by the victim of that attack thereafter because of the anaesthesis; the victim will sense the loss of blood after a time and will feel his constitution waning, but only then will he be conscious enough of the effects of the attack to consider searching for the cause).

If a victim loses three constitution points (albeit temporarily) he will collapse and the galltrit's presence is almost certain to be revealed at that time. After collapse the victim will take two full turns to recover (and 12 days to regain the lost constitution).

GAMBADO

FREQUENCY: *Rare*
NO. APPEARING: *1–8*
ARMOUR CLASS: *6*
MOVE: *See below*
HIT DICE: *4*
% IN LAIR: *100%*
TREASURE TYPE: *P, R*
NO. OF ATTACKS: *3*
DAMAGE/ATTACK:
    1–8/1–4/1–4
SPECIAL ATTACKS: *Nil*
SPECIAL DEFENCES: *Nil*
MAGIC RESISTANCE: *Standard*
INTELLIGENCE: *Low*
ALIGNMENT: *Chaotic neutral*
SIZE: *M*
PSIONIC ABILITY: *Nil*
    Attack/Defence Modes: *Nil*
LEVEL/X.P. VALUE: *III/85 + 4
    per hit point*

These extraordinary-looking creatures are man-sized, with a powerful human torso and two arms ending in very sharp claws. Supported on the thin (but very strong) neck is the creature's head which is a skull — usually of an animal but sometimes of primitive man. The lower part of the creature's body consists of a cylinder of muscle and skin which can be compressed spring-style and released, below which are three long and thin single-toed feet. Its manner of locomotion — since it lacks legs as such — is a series of springs; if jumping vertically it can just reach a 14' high ceiling with its head, and when moving horizontally it has speed equivalent to a 12" movement rate.

A gambado's normal form of attack is to stand upright in its lair, which is a pit some 6' deep, with its head just at ground level. By shoring up the sides of the pit it can create a 'cover' of rock, wood, rags and old bones, so that to an approaching adventurer the pit is hidden and only the skull is seen, apparently simply lying on the ground. If a living creature comes within 2' of the edge of the pit. (i.e. within 4' or so of the skull-head) the creature will spring out and attack, in the first instance with bite only for 1–8 hit points of damage and thereafter with bite and its claws, each of which inflicts 1–4 hit points of damage. If melee is going against it, it will flee rather than fight to the death.

If a gambado kills a victim it will ignore all booty except coins, gems and small pieces of jewellery. These are taken into the pit and stored either on the pit floor or hidden in a cache-hole in the pit side, packed tightly with earth. Though essentially solitary creatures, a gambado will often dig its pit nearby those of others of its kind; in places where bones are common, as many as 8 of the creatures may be found to have dug pits quite close together, although they do not appear actually to communicate with each other.

GARBUG

	Black	Violet
FREQUENCY:	*Rare*	*Rare*
NO. APPEARING:	*1–3*	*1–3*
ARMOUR CLASS:	*5*	*5*
MOVE:	*6"/9"*	*6"/9"*
HIT DICE	*2+2*	*3+1*
% IN LAIR:	*40%*	*40%*
TREASURE TYPE:	*C*	*C*
NO. OF ATTACKS:	*1 and 6*	*2 and 6*
DAMAGE/ATTACK:	*1–4 and special*	*1–6/1–6 and special*
SPECIAL ATTACKS:	*Paralysation*	*Paralysation*
SPECIAL DEFENCES:	*Nil*	*Nil*
MAGIC RESISTANCE:	*Standard*	*Standard*
INTELLIGENCE:	*Animal*	*Animal*
ALIGNMENT:	*Neutral*	*Neutral*
SIZE:	*L (9' long)*	*L (9' long)*
PSIONIC ABILITY:	*Nil*	*Nil*
Attack/Defence Modes:	*Nil*	*Nil*
LEVEL/X.P. VALUE:	*III/145 + 3 per hit point*	*IV/190 + 4 per hit point*

Both types of garbug resemble wasp-bodied lobsters. They can fly in rather a cumbersome manner on flimsy wings but their more normal means of locomotion is on their six legs. They have six tentacles surrounding their mouths which flail at prey; each tentacle is 2' long and exudes a paralysing secretion (save versus paralysation or it takes effect).

In melee each type of garbug will attack with its tentacles as well as its 'specialist' weapon. The tentacles only have the paralysing effect — they do not inflict hit points of damage as such.

For purposes of aerial combat, both types of garbug are manoeuvrability class D.

Black Garbug: The black garbug is a uniform glossy black. It has, in addition to its tentacles, a proboscis which it uses to strike at a victim within a 5' range. If a hit is scored, the victim suffers 1–4 hit points of damage. The creature may deliver this attack at the same time as flailing with its tentacles.

Violet Garbug: The violet garbug differs from its black cousin in that it has no attacking proboscis. Instead — and in addition to the flailing attacks from its tentacles — it attacks with two large pincers, placed in a position similar to those of a lobster; each of these can inflict 1–6 hit points of damage.

The violet garbug is a uniform violet of striking hue except for its claws which are deep yellow.

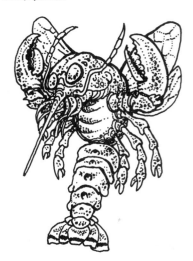

GIANT

Giants are huge humanoids. In addition to the six major races of giants (see **ADVANCED DUNGEONS & DRAGONS MONSTER MANUAL** — *Giant),* there are at least these two sub-races. Common characteristics are given here, while the unique features of each sub-race is detailed under the heading appropriate to each.

All giants are very strong, with strengths ranging from 21 to 30 as compared with humans. Because of this strength, they are able to pick up rocks and hurl them as if the missile were shot from a catapult, but without the minimum range restriction of the device.

Whenever they leave their lair, giants of all sorts will always have a huge sack with them. Giant's bags contain various odds and ends of things precious only to the giant: a large rock or two, and from 1,000 to 6,000 coins of some type — usually gold.

Although giants are often stupid, they are usually cunning, too. They can sometimes be tricked and will be likely to bargain if approached from a position of strength. It is not unusual for giants to agree to share in an undertaking with a group of creatures of similar alignment to that of the giant, for these huge monsters are eager for treasure.

Young giants will have hit points and do damage according to the percentage of a normal adult male indicated by the dice roll.

Each race of giants speaks its own particular dialect which is unintelligible to other races. They also speak their appropriate alignment tongue.

Fog Giant

FREQUENCY: *Very rare*
NO. APPEARING: *1–4*
  (rarely 1–6)
ARMOUR CLASS: *1*
MOVE: *15"*
HIT DICE: *14*
% IN LAIR: *50%*
TREASURE TYPE: *E*
NO. OF ATTACKS: *1*
DAMAGE/ATTACK: *4–24*
SPECIAL ATTACKS:
  *Hurling rocks for 2–20
  points of damage*
SPECIAL DEFENCES: *See below*
MAGIC RESISTANCE: *Standard*
INTELLIGENCE: *Average to high*
ALIGNMENT: *Neutral (good 50%
  evil 50%)*
SIZE: *L (18' tall)*
PSIONIC ABILITY: *Nil*
  Attack/Defence Modes: *Nil*
LEVEL/X.P. VALUE:
  VIII/3,950 + 18 per hit point

Fog giants are cousins to the cloud giants and if on very rare occasions as many as six fog giants are encountered, they will always be accompanied by a cloud giant.

Fog giants have very keen hearing and a highly-developed sense of smell. For these reasons, they are surprised only on a 1 (d6). They also have the ability to blend into fog, thus gaining surprise on their opponents (80% chance). They inhabit foggy areas such as marshes, swamps, dense forests and places near the sea coast.

Fog giants have milk-white skin, silvery white hair and black, penetrating eyes. They love massive ornate swords and prefer armour made from white dragon hides studded with silver. In melee they fight either with the swords they love or with their fists, in either case inflicting 4–24 hit points of damage on their victim. Their armour, if worn, has no effect on their AC which is always treated as 1.

Adult fog giants, like their cloud giant cousins, can hurl rocks from 1" to 24" distance, inflicting 2–20 hit points of damage if they hit. They have a 45% chance of catching similar missiles.

Fog giants speak their alignment language and their own particular dialect of the giant language, unintelligible to all other giants except cloud giants.

Mountain Giant

FREQUENCY: *Very rare*
NO. APPEARING: *1–4*
ARMOUR CLASS: *4*
MOVE: *12"*
HIT DICE: *12*
% IN LAIR: *90%*
TREASURE TYPE: *E*
NO. OF ATTACKS: *1*
DAMAGE/ATTACK: *4–40*
SPECIAL ATTACKS:
  *Hurling rocks for 2–16 points
  of damage*
SPECIAL DEFENCES: *Nil*
MAGIC RESISTANCE: *Standard*
INTELLIGENCE: *High*
ALIGNMENT: *Chaotic neutral*
SIZE: *L (14' tall)*
PSIONIC ABILITY: *Nil*
  Attack/Defence Modes: *Nil*
LEVEL/X.P. VALUE:
  VII/2,850 + 16 per hit point

Mountain giants are rarely encountered outside their lair — a huge cavern carved out of the heart of a rocky mountain. In addition to their normal tongue, they can all speak the ogre language.

Like their cousins the hill giants they can hurl rocks from 1" to 20" distance, inflicting 2–16 hit points of damage if they hit. They are able to catch similar missiles 30% of the time. In melee they strike with huge clubs, inflicting 4–40 hit points of damage.

The mountain giant can summon and control other monsters — usually (70%) 6–15 ogres, but sometimes (20%) 4–9 trolls or even (10%) 1–4 hill giants. If a mountain giant is encountered in its lair, it is 75% probable that these creatures will be there, acting as servants and guards.

Giantesses and young mountain giants are rarely encountered — if four mountain giants are encountered in their lair, there will be in addition one female and one young giant (each has hit dice of 8+ 1–2 and 1 attack doing 2–16 hit points of damage; otherwise mountain giants encountered will always be adult males.

Mountain giants have light tan to light reddish-brown skin and dress in rough hides or skins, as do the hill giants.

GIANT STRIDER

FREQUENCY: *Rare*
NO. APPEARING: *1–6*
ARMOUR CLASS: *4*
MOVE: *15"*
HIT DICE: *2*
% IN LAIR: *Nil*
TREASURE TYPE: *Nil*
NO. OF ATTACKS: *2*
DAMAGE/ATTACK: *1–8/1–10*
SPECIAL ATTACKS: *Fireball*
SPECIAL DEFENCES: *See below*
MAGIC RESISTANCE: *Standard
  but +2 bonus on saving roll
  and immune to magical fire*
INTELLIGENCE: *Animal*
ALIGNMENT: *Neutral evil*
SIZE: *L (6'-7' tall at shoulder)*
PSIONIC ABILITY: *Nil*
  Attack/Defence Modes: *Nil*
LEVEL/X.P. VALUE:
  III/73 + 2 per hit point

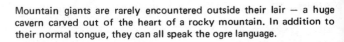

These large flightless, featherless birds appear as heavy ostriches. Beside each of their two dully-glowing red eyes is a small duct from which the beast can project a small *fireball* which does 1–6 hit points of damage. The beast can project these *fireballs* at the rate of two per hour (one from each duct) with accuracy as a +4 longbow, a maximum range of 50' and a burst radius of 10'.

In addition, the giant strider can attack to its front or flank with a bite for 1–8 hit points of damage or deliver a kick to its rear for 1–10 hit points of damage. It cannot, however, co-ordinate both attacks simultaneously in the same melee round and will generally launch its attack in the direction from which it was last hit.

These birds are immune to fire, magical or otherwise, and in fact their bodies have adapted to derive sustenance from warmth; consequently they are most at home in desert and volcanic regions. Intense heat, flames, *fireballs* and so on act as a *cure light wounds* spell on them once every three rounds. As a result, giant striders are often found wading in lava-beds or standing in the flames of a forest fire (it is possible that the phoenix legend derived from such a sight).

Conversely, *cold* spells and the like do an additional 2–7 hit points of damage and water (if drunk) is poison to them. Even if a cold liquid is thrown over their bodies, they will take some damage (at the discretion of the referee according to the circumstances, but normally 1–2 hit points of damage).

These creatures are used as steeds by the firenewts. They are generally fearless and never check morale.

GIBBERLING

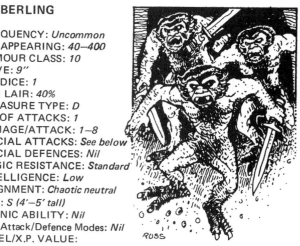

FREQUENCY: *Uncommon*
NO. APPEARING: *40–400*
ARMOUR CLASS: *10*
MOVE: *9″*
HIT DICE: *1*
% IN LAIR: *40%*
TREASURE TYPE: *D*
NO. OF ATTACKS: *1*
DAMAGE/ATTACK: *1–8*
SPECIAL ATTACKS: *See below*
SPECIAL DEFENCES: *Nil*
MAGIC RESISTANCE: *Standard*
INTELLIGENCE: *Low*
ALIGNMENT: *Chaotic neutral*
SIZE: *S (4′–5′ tall)*
PSIONIC ABILITY: *Nil*
   Attack/Defence Modes: *Nil*
LEVEL/X.P. VALUE:
   I/14 + 1 per hit point

Pale, hunched, naked humanoids with short legs and long arms, gibberlings are usually found in desolate woods or dark caverns underground. The subterranean variety loathe bright light and are particularly afraid of fire.

Gibberlings attack in great numbers, uttering ghastly howls and insane chattering noises which cause even the boldest hirelings to check morale each round, though player-characters are not affected. They attack with normal swords and such is their skill in using these weapons that they strike with a +1 hit probability bonus. In all circumstances they will fight to the death, relying on sheer weight of numbers to defeat their enemies (which means virtually any creature which dares to venture into their territory, for gibberlings are highly aggressive).

Though they clearly have a primitive means of communicating among themselves, they have no discernable language. Curiously, though it might be expected that creatures who attack in such great numbers would have leader-types to control them and determine their policy, no such leader-types have yet been encountered. Nor are there, apparently, gibberlings of other than the fighter class.

GITHYANKI

FREQUENCY: *Very rare*
NO. APPEARING: *1–4*
ARMOUR CLASS: *Variable*
MOVE: *Variable*
HIT DICE: *Variable (upper*
   limit of 11)
% IN LAIR: *40%*
TREASURE TYPE: *Individuals N;*
   lair A, Z(x2)
NO. OF ATTACKS: *Variable*
   (as human)
DAMAGE/ATTACK:
   By weapon type
SPECIAL ATTACKS: *Nil*
SPECIAL DEFENCES: *Nil*
MAGIC RESISTANCE: *Standard*
INTELLIGENCE: *Exceptional or*
   genius
ALIGNMENT: *Variable but*
   always evil
SIZE: *M*
PSIONIC ABILITY: *150–250*
   Attack/Defence Modes:
      All/all but J
LEVEL/X.P. VALUE:
   IV and up/variable

Millenia ago the mind flayers (see **ADVANCED DUNGEONS & DRAGONS MONSTER MANUAL** — *Mind Flayer*) conquered a race of evil humans and bound them to service, usually employing them as slaves but from time to time selecting particularly choice victims for food. The humans harboured deep resentment for centuries but could not summon up sufficient strength to free themselves from the mind

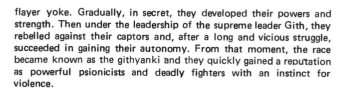

flayer yoke. Gradually, in secret, they developed their powers and strength. Then under the leadership of the supreme leader Gith, they rebelled against their captors and, after a long and vicious struggle, succeeded in gaining their autonomy. From that moment, the race became known as the githyanki and they quickly gained a reputation as powerful psionicists and deadly fighters with an instinct for violence.

The githyanki now dwell in the *Astral Plane* but from time to time project themselves to the *Prime Material Plane* (an innate ability now common to all members of the race) and set up temporary refuges underground, using these as bases from which they mount raids on humans and mind flayers alike. (If githyanki encounter humans and mind flayers simultaneously they will destroy the mind flayers first and may appear to be co-operating with the humans, but as soon as the mind flayers are killed, the githyanki will turn on the humans and attempt to destroy them too.)

The githyanki worship a lich-queen said to have powers at the 24th level of magic-use or even higher.

Githyanki progress as fighters, magic-users or fighter/magic-users; they have no ranger, monk, druid or assassin class though illusionists are infrequently (5%) met and there is a form of anti-paladin class — the knight. They have never been known to progress beyond the 11th level of experience and rarely above the 9th — it is assumed that the lich-queen destroys any githyanki who becomes powerful enough to risk challenging her supremacy.

The githyanki dwell in huge castles on the *Astral Plane,* each castle being ruled by a supreme leader — a fighter/magic-user of 10th/8th or 11th/9th level. The supreme leaders have power of life and death over all under their rule. Each castle will also contain 40 knights (anti-paladins of 9th level) — the supreme leader's elite supporting force and personal guard — and up to 1,000 githyanki of lower status.

They use armour and weapons as men do, though the ornateness of their design is often a distinguishing feature. When on war expeditions they wear +4 splint mail (AC0) but do not carry shields. Fighters and fighter/magic-users of 5th level and above will usually (50% chance) carry two-handed swords of +1 bonus, otherwise using normal two-handed swords. A githyanki fighter of 7th level and above will usually (60%) carry a +2 or +3 longsword, while a knight of 7th level and above will have (100%) a *silver sword* — a +3 two-handed sword which, if used astrally, has a 20% chance per melee round of cutting the *silver cord* (this does not affect *mind barred* victims). A supreme leader will wield a *special silver sword* which is +5, fully *vorpal* and affects *mind barred* victims. The *silver swords* are non-aligned, though they have intelligence of 8 or more and appropriate powers. Githyanki will go to almost any lengths to prevent any of these *silver swords* from falling into human hands and the loss of a *special silver sword* will promote the immediate formation of a very powerful raiding party of githyanki whose task is to recover the sword — failure to do so means instant death.

Outside their *Prime Material Plane* lairs, githyanki will rarely be encountered in parties larger than 4, a typical party consisting of two trainees of any of the three classes (level 1-3), one fighter of level 4-6 and a leader fighter/magic-user of 7th/6th level. Rarely (10%) the githyanki parties encountered will have a special mission in which case there will only be one trainee and the party will be led by a knight of 8th level.

If a lair is found it will house 21-30 githyanki with typical distribution as follows:—

1 supreme leader:	11th level fighter or 7th/8th level fighter/magic-user
2 captains:	8th level fighter and 7th/6th level fighter/magic-user
1 knight:	8th level anti-paladin
2 warlocks:	magic-users of 4th-7th level
3 sergeants:	fighters of 4th-7th level
2 'gish':	fighter/magic-users of 4th/4th level
10–19 lower levels:	evenly distributed between the three possible classes and with experience levels 1st-3rd.

Very infrequently, githyanki parties larger than four in number will be encountered (5% chance). These will be on particularly purposeful missions (though not in search of a lost *silver sword* — that activity promotes an even larger and stronger party) and will be stronger than normal; 5-10 individuals can be expected, led by the supreme leader of the lair, supported by one of the captains, the knight and 2—7 'lower ranks', evenly distributed. Both in the lair and in a large party, there is a 5% chance that there will be an illusionist of 6th level instead of one of the lower level types.

Githyanki have normal human chances for magic item distribution other than swords.

A *Prime Material Plane* lair will contain 5—10 magical items, selected as being particularly appropriate to the mission. In a small githyanki party there will usually (75%) be one magical item and a larger party will have 1—10.

Githyanki have a pact with a group of red dragons (see **ADVANCED DUNGEONS & DRAGONS MONSTER MANUAL** — *Dragon, Red*) which, in return for shelter, food and treasure, assist the githyanki when on the *Prime Material Plane* by acting as steeds. The dragons transport 4—6 and 1—5 githyanki each according to size/age (above *sub-adult*); thus a small *young adult* dragon could transport 5 githyanki (4 for size, 1 for age), an average-sized *old* dragon could transport 8 (5 for size, 3 for age) and a huge *ancient* dragon could transport 11 (6 for size, 5 for age). These red dragons will obey only githyanki when the latter are on the *Prime Material Plane*.

Githyanki move at 96" movement rate on the *Astral Plane*.

GITHZERAI

FREQUENCY: *Very Rare*
NO. APPEARING: *1—4*
ARMOUR CLASS: *Variable*
MOVE: *Variable*
HIT DICE: *Variable (upper limit of 9)*
% IN LAIR: *50%*
TREASURE TYPE: *A*
NO. OF ATTACKS: *Variable (as human)*
DAMAGE ATTACK:
   By weapon type
SPECIAL ATTACKS: *Nil*
SPECIAL DEFENCES: *Nil*
MAGIC RESISTANCE: *50%*
INTELLIGENCE: *Exceptional*
ALIGNMENT: *Chaotic neutral*
SIZE: *M*
PSIONIC ABILITY: *121—250*
   Attack/Defence Modes:
   All/all
LEVEL/X.P. VALUE:
   II and up/Variable

The githzerai are a race of inhabitants of limbo, co-existing with the slaadi, roaming the *Prime Material Plane* like the githyanki and constantly at war with the latter race. The githyanki-githzerai warfare is curious since they are both offshoots of the original race released from mind flayer bondage under the leadership of Gith — yet the war is vicious and long-enduring. Githzerai are generally slightly weaker than githyanki, but their magic resistance appears to compensate and neither side holds supremacy for long over the other.

The githzerai and the mind flayers hold to an uneasy truce, but this is constantly being broken in isolated skirmishes.

The same class limitations apply to githzerai as apply to githyanki, though some githzerai have been known to specialise as monks and the githzerai have no counterpart to the githyanki anti-paladin class. They fight with *silver swords* and other weapons as do the githyanki, with the same probability of possession of a particular item. Githzerai appear not to have developed the *special silver swords* as have the githyanki. They have the same sort of political organisation as have the githyanki and are ruled by an undying wizard-king said to be of 16th/23rd level of fighting/magic-use who prevents githzerai progression beyond the 9th level of experience.

Whereas the githyanki are users of baroque armour and ornate weapons and are generally florid in their magic-use, githzerai are monastic creatures, their weapons are very plain and their magic-use economic of movement and direct in effect.

Githzerai hold a few fortresses on the *Prime Material Plane* but these are particularly strong holdings, with walls of adamantite rising as huge squat towers from dusty plains. Each houses about 500 githzerai.

All githzerai have the following psionic abilities at the 6th level of mastery: *astral projection, mind bar, probability travel* and *energy control*. Their psionic powers are highly developed, with all attack/defence modes.

Like the githyanki, githzerai will rarely be encountered outside their lair in parties greater than 4, a typical party consisting of two trainees of any of the three main classes (fighter, magic-user or fighter/magic-user, levels 1—2), one fighter of level 3—5 and a leader fighter/magic-user of 5th/5th level. The chance of a character with monkish abilities is only 5%, but if one is encountered it will be of 6th—8th experience level since the monks' main training takes place in the githzerai fortresses.

If a lair is found it will be a temporary base for hunting/warring activities and will house 21—30 githzerai, with distribution approximately as follows:—

1 supreme leader:	9th level fighter or 4th/7th level fighter/magic-user
1 captain:	6th level fighter or 5th/5th level fighter/magic user
2 warlocks:	magic-users of 3rd-5th level
3 sergeants:	fighters of 3rd-6th level
3 'zerths':	fighter/magic-users of 3rd/3rd level
11—20 1st-2nd levels:	evenly distributed between the three possible classes.

If a monk is present (10% chance) it will replace one of the lower-level githzerai and will be of the 6th-8th experience level.

Githzerai have normal human chances for possession of magic items (except for swords). A lair will contain 2—16 magical items.

A large githzerai party will be organised on much the same lines as a large githyanki party, depending to a certain extent on the importance of the mission. A typical large party would contain the supreme leader, both warlocks, 2 of the sergeants, a zerth and 4—7 1st or 2nd levels. If a monk is present in the lair, it will always accompany a large party.

GOLDBUG

FREQUENCY: *Rare*
NO. APPEARING: *1–20*
ARMOUR CLASS: *9*
MOVE: *1"*
HIT DICE: *1*
% IN LAIR: *100%*
TREASURE TYPE: *Nil*
NO. OF ATTACKS: *1*
DAMAGE/ATTACK: *1–4*
SPECIAL ATTACKS: *Poison*
SPECIAL DEFENCES: *Nil*
MAGIC RESISTANCE: *Standard*
INTELLIGENCE: *Non-*
ALIGNMENT: *Neutral*
SIZE: *S*
PSIONIC ABILITY: *Nil*
    Attack/Defence Modes: *Nil*
LEVEL/X.P. VALUE:
    II/45 +1 per hit point

The goldbug is a beetle with a flattened, circular body and a golden shell, the size and shape of a gold piece. It is a very sluggish creature and spends most of its time asleep, often choosing a pile of gold coins as its bed. Only a very close examination will distinguish it from the coins on which it lies. Thus, though it has no treasure of its own, it inhabits that of others.

When disturbed it inflicts a poisonous bite like that of a large spider, inflicting 1–4 hit points of damage on the victim who must also save versus poison or die.

GORBEL

FREQUENCY: *Uncommon*
NO. APPEARING: *1–20*
ARMOUR CLASS: *3 (10–see below)*
MOVE: *18"*
HIT DICE: *See below*
% IN LAIR: *Nil*
TREASURE TYPE: *Nil*
NO. OF ATTACKS: *1*
DAMAGE/ATTACK: *1–4 or 1–6*
SPECIAL ATTACKS: *Nil*
SPECIAL DEFENCES: *Nil*
MAGIC RESISTANCE: *Standard*
INTELLIGENCE: *Non-*
ALIGNMENT: *Neutral with*
    chaotic tendencies
SIZE: *S (3' diameter)*
PSIONIC ABILITY: *Nil*
    Attack/Defence Modes: *Nil*
LEVEL/X.P. VALUE:
    II/32 + 2 per hit point

A curious creature, the gorbel appears as a red globe of thin rubbery material about 3' in diameter (its high armour class is due to its high dexterity) with a tiny mouth, six tiny eyes on short retractable stalks equally spaced around the upper hemisphere and two clawed legs which it uses to move at remarkable speed.

When attacking (which it usually does), it attempts to attach itself to its victim's back with its claws; a successful initial hit means it has done so, delivering 1–4 hit points of damage. Thereafter it cannot be detached until dead and it automatically hits its victim each round for 1–6 points of clawing damage. Initially, it attacks as a creature of 2HD.

A hit with a blunt weapon will not harm the gorbel, but a hit with a pointed or edged weapon causes it to burst asunder, killing it and doing 1–4 hit points of blast damage to anyone within 5'.

Naturally, when the gorbel is attached to a victim it loses its dexterity bonus and its AC is then 10.

Gorbels are mischievous, fickle and irritable creatures.

GORILLA BEAR

FREQUENCY: *Uncommon*
NO. APPEARING: *2–7*
ARMOUR CLASS: *4*
MOVE: *9"*
HIT DICE: *4*
% IN LAIR: *50%*
TREASURE TYPE: *Nil*
NO. OF ATTACKS: *2*
DAMAGE/ATTACK: *1–8/1–8*
SPECIAL ATTACKS: *Hugs for*
    2–12 hit points of damage
SPECIAL DEFENCES: *Nil*
MAGIC RESISTANCE: *Standard*
INTELLIGENCE: *Low*
ALIGNMENT: *Neutral*
SIZE: *L (9' tall)*
PSIONIC ABILITY: *Nil*
    Attack/Defence Modes: *Nil*
LEVEL/X.P. VALUE:
    III/85 + 4 per hit point

These monsters have the head, body and legs of a gorilla with the sharp teeth and powerful arms of a bear. They have the aggressive disposition of the grizzly bear and the carnivorous tendencies of the cave bear. They have excellent hearing, smell and eyesight so are rarely (15%) surprised. Their dexterity is also high, accounting for their improved AC.

The beast attacks with its two paws for 1–8 hit points of damage each; a paw hit scored with an 18 or better indicates that the beast also hugs for 2–12 hit points of additional damage. If a roll of 18 is insufficient to hit the victim, the hug only occurs on a roll of 19 or, if that too is insufficient, on a roll of 20. A roll of 20 means a hug whatever the AC of the victim.

The gorilla bear does not have the normal bear's ability of continuing to fight after its hit points are reduced below zero.

GRELL

FREQUENCY: *Rare*
NO. APPEARING: *1*
ARMOUR CLASS: *4*
MOVE: *12"*
HIT DICE: *5*
% IN LAIR: *Nil*
TREASURE TYPE: *Nil*
NO. OF ATTACKS: *11*
DAMAGE/ATTACK:
    10x1—4/1—6
SPECIAL ATTACKS:
    Paralysation
SPECIAL DEFENCES:
    Immune to lightning
MAGIC RESISTANCE:
    Standard
INTELLIGENCE: *Average*
ALIGNMENT:
    Neutral evil
SIZE: *M*
PSIONIC ABILITY: *Nil*
    Attack/Defence Modes: *Nil*
LEVEL/XP.-VALUE:
    VI/840 + 5 per hit point

The appearance of this dreadful creature is fearsome indeed — a body like a giant exposed brain approximately 5' in diameter and with a frontal beak, below which trail ten 6' long tentacles. The beast 'flies' by a *levitation* process, small inflections of the tentacles controlling horizontal movement. It is manoeuvrability class D.

Grell are usually found underground but are occasionally seen in ruined/abandoned buildings. They are particularly dangerous and vicious, dropping on their victims from above whenever circumstance permit.

All ten tentacles are brought to bear on a single victim. Each inflicts 1—4 hit points of damage and carries small spines which can inject a venom into the victim; this will paralyse the victim unless he makes his saving throw against paralysation at +4. If any one of the tentacles succeeds in paralysing a victim, each melee round thereafter two tentacles will remain anchored on his body, the grell lashing with the other eight tentacles (for 1—4 hit points of damage each) and rending with its beak for 1—6 hit points of damage. None of these attacks, after the initial paralysation, requires a 'to hit' roll — once the grell has grasped its victim, lucky is he who escapes alive.

Any hit on a tentacle will render it inoperative (though if the creature survives, the tentacle will regenerate in 1—2 days) but the damage is not subtracted from the creature's hit points — only by hitting the body can the grell be damaged in the usual way. The body and tentacles all have AC4.

Grell are immune to lightning but otherwise have standard resistance to normal and magical attacks.

The body of the grell is a drab olive colour streaked with white; the tentacles are pale olive-green.

GRIMLOCK

FREQUENCY: *Uncommon*
NO. APPEARING: *20—200*
ARMOUR CLASS: *5*
MOVE: *12"*
HIT DICE: *2*
% IN LAIR: *50%*
TREASURE TYPE: *Individuals K, L, M; in lair B*
NO. OF ATTACKS: *1*
DAMAGE/ATTACK: *1—6 or by weapon type*
SPECIAL ATTACKS: *Nil*
SPECIAL DEFENCES: *See below*
MAGIC RESISTANCE: *Save as 6th level fighter (and see below)*
INTELLIGENCE: *Average*
ALIGNMENT: *Neutral evil*
SIZE: *M*
PSIONIC ABILITY: *Nil*
Attack/Defence Modes: *Nil*
LEVEL/X.P. VALUE:
Warriors: II/28 + 2 per hit point
Leaders: II/50 + 3 per hit point
Champions: III/85 + 4 per hit point

These fierce subterranean humanoid warriors dwell in deep caverns, only emerging in raiding parties to maraud across the earth's surface late at night, searching for humans to butcher and devour. Their eyes are blank and sightless; however they have highly developed senses of hearing and smell, these giving them effective 'vision' within 20'.

They are immune to the effects of spells affecting the visual nerves such as *phantasmal force, darkness, invisibility, mirror image* and so on. However spells such as *audible glamer* will partially 'blind' them, reducing their effective range of 'vision' to 10' and reducing their hit probability by 2. Substances such as snuff have the same effects if inhaled by a grimlock.

For every 10 grimlocks encountered there will be a 'leader' of 3 hit dice and AC4, while for every 40 there will also be a 'champion' of 4 hit dice and AC3. In the grimlock lair there will be females (an additional 80% of the number of males, each with 1 hit die and AC6) and young (an additional 100% of the number of males, each with 1 hit point, AC6 and non-combatant).

Grimlocks rarely consort with other beings, though there is a small (10%) chance that they will allow medusae to share their lair and a 2% chance that a wandering group of grimlocks will be accompanied by 1—2 mind flayers. For the latter reason, grimlocks are particularly hated by githyanki.

Grimlocks prefer edged blood-letting weapons and though they can fight with their bare hands (for 1—6 hit points of damage) they will usually be armed (90% chance) with weapons as follows:

hand-axe	20%
battle-axe	15%
two-handed sword	15%
bastard sword	15%
broad sword	15%
long sword	20%

Leaders and champions will wield a battle-axe or two-handed sword.

If encountered in rocky terrain, grimlocks are able to blend with their surroundings; so long as they remain motionless, they cannot be detected other than by *detect invisibility* (unless someone actually bumps into them).

All grimlocks — whether warrior, leader or champion — make all saving throws as if they were 6th level fighters.

Description: Powerfully-built humanoids with thick, scaly grey skin, they are usually clad in dark rags. Their hair is long, black and usually unkempt. Their teeth are white and particularly sharp.

GRYPH

FREQUENCY: *Very rare*
NO. APPEARING: *1—6*
ARMOUR CLASS: *6*
MOVE: *21"*
HIT DICE: *2—4*
% IN LAIR: *Nil*
TREASURE TYPE: *Nil*
NO. OF ATTACKS: *1*
DAMAGE/ATTACK: *2—12*
SPECIAL ATTACKS: *See below*
SPECIAL DEFENCES: *Nil*
MAGIC RESISTANCE: *Standard*
INTELLIGENCE: *Animal*
ALIGNMENT: *Neutral evil*
SIZE: *S*
PSIONIC ABILITY: *Nil*
Attack/Defence Modes: *Nil*
LEVEL/X.P. VALUE:
2HD: II/28 + 2 per hit point
3HD: II/50 + 3 per hit point
4HD: III/85 + 4 per hit point

The gryph is a bird with multiple legs — usually four, but specimens with six or even eight have been seen. It approximates to the size of an eagle and has a razor-sharp beak with powerful jaws. Its bite will inflict 2—12 hit points of damage and it will normally attack at high speed from high up in the shadows of an underground cavern. For purposes of aerial combat, it is manoeuvrability class B.

If 3 or more of these birds are encountered, one will be female and there is a 35% chance that she will be ready to lay her eggs. If such a female gryph attacks it will attempt to grapple its victim with its legs, and if a hit is scored, it will inject its small eggs into the bloodstream. Note that in such an instance, the beak is not used in the attack and the victim receives no damage — the eggs are injected through a thin tube which projects from the bird's abdomen.

If these eggs remain alive they will hatch in 1–3 days, killing the victim immediately and releasing 1–4 baby gryphs. During this period the victim will feel slight discomfort and swelling of the abdomen, this increasing to an agonising intensity just prior to the hatching. In fact there are far more than 1–4 eggs in the victim — it is simply that number which survive the 1–3 day period.

Between the time the eggs are injected and the time of the hatching, the casting of *cure disease* or *dispel evil* on the victim will kill the eggs. Of course, a *wish* or similar spell will also have this effect, if used properly.

GUARDIAN FAMILIAR

FREQUENCY: *Very rare*
NO. APPEARING: *1*
ARMOUR CLASS: *8*
MOVE: *12"*
HIT DICE: *1 (9)*
% IN LAIR: *Nil*
TREASURE TYPE: *See below*
NO. OF ATTACKS: *3*
DAMAGE/ATTACK:
    1–6/1–4/1–4
SPECIAL ATTACKS: *Nil*
SPECIAL DEFENCES: *See below*
MAGIC RESISTANCE: *See below*
INTELLIGENCE: *Animal*
ALIGNMENT: *Any (see below)*
SIZE: *S (see below)*
PSIONIC ABILITY: *Nil*
    Attack/Defence Modes: *Nil*
LEVEL/X.P. VALUE:
    VII/1,800 + 12 per hit point

The guardian familiar takes the form of a small black cat set to guard the treasure of a high-level wizard (thus the guardian familiar may be of any alignment — the same as that of its summoner). It will never leave its position on top of the treasure or chest, nor does it attack unless it is itself attacked or attempts are made to get at the treasure. If it attacks, it does so with two raking claws (1–4 hit points of damage each) and by biting with its sharp teeth for 1–6 hit points of damage. During its attack, the creature grows progressively larger, eventually resembling a bobcat; it reverts to normal size if melee is suspended — this appears to be a power of the creature designed to deter robbers.

The guardian familiar will have magic resistance which varies according to the experience level of its master. The familiar of a 10th level magic-user will have 50% magical resistance and the incremental variation will be 5% per level in either direction, so the familiar of a 6th level magic-user will have 30% magic resistance and the familiar of a 15th level magic-user will have 75% magic resistance. Note that a magic-user of 4th level or below will not be able to secure the services of a guardian familiar.

The guardian familiar has nine lives (and is the creature upon which the traditional 'cat with nine lives' legend is built). Each time it is slain, up to the 9th time, it is instantaneously reborn, stronger than before. At each rebirth, add 1 to its number of hit dice (re-rolling hit points), add 2" to its movement, improve its AC by 1 and add one point of damage to each of its attacks. Thus when the guardian familiar has been slain four times it will be reborn at '5th level' — it will have AC4, a movement rate of 20", 5 hit dice and will deliver 5–8/5–8/5–10 hit points of damage with its attacks. This 'pyramiding of powers' can be stopped by the following spells (or powers which duplicate their effects) so long as the creature's magic resistance is overcome:— *disintegrate*, *flesh to stone*, *temporal stasis* and of course *wish* and *alter reality* (if used properly). *Holy (Unholy) word* will banish the creature back to its plane of origin.

If attackers choose to break off melee at any time, the guardian familiar will not pursue but will return to continue its duties.

The guardian familiar should not be confused with the normal familiar, as delineated in the first level magic-user spell *find familiar* (see **ADVANCED DUNGEONS & DRAGONS PLAYERS HANDBOOK** *Character Spells*). Its means of summoning, though they involve the casting of the *find familiar* spell, are known only to a small group of arcane magicians (and those few who they train in their specialist art) and are believed to involve bargaining with the denizens of the *Outer Planes* on which the guardian familiars dwell.

Naturally, the guardian familiar will, if killed a ninth time, remain dead and will not rise again.

GUARDIAN DAEMON

FREQUENCY: *Very rare*
NO. APPEARING: *1–3*
ARMOUR CLASS: *1*
MOVE: *9" (but see below)*
HIT DICE: *8*
% IN LAIR: *Nil*
TREASURE TYPE: *See below*
NO. OF ATTACKS: *3*
DAMAGE/ATTACK:
    1–6/1–12/1–12
SPECIAL ATTACKS: *See below*
SPECIAL DEFENCES: *See below*
MAGIC RESISTANCE: *See below*
INTELLIGENCE: *Very*
ALIGNMENT: *Neutral*
SIZE: *Variable*
PSIONIC ABILITY: *Nil*
    Attack/Defence Modes: *Nil*
LEVEL/X.P. VALUE:
    VII/1,275 + 10 per hit point

These daemons vary in size and form — examples encountered have resembled type II or type IV demons, large bears and wild cats. They are summoned by evil high priests to guard treasure and though their movement for melee purposes is 9" they are constrained never to leave the treasure they guard, unless released by the summoner.

Despite their variation in size and form they always exhibit certain characteristics in common:

)   immunity to *charm, hold, sleep, polymorph* and *fear;*

)   immunity to non-magical weapons and to magical weapons with a bonus less than +2;

)   ability to speak and understand all languages; and

)   ability to breathe fire in a cone 30' long with a 10' base diameter inflicting 5–30 hit points of damage (saving throw will halve damage).

In melee the daemon attacks with a bite for 1–6 hit points of damage and two claws, each inflicting 1–12 hit points of damage, since they are unable to use their breath weapon on a target within 10'.

The nature of their summoning usually (80%) leaves them invulnerable to one other particular form of attack (e.g. fire or swords) in addition to those specified above.

Guardian daemons have no treasure of their own (on the *Prime Material Plane* — they may well own treasure in their natural home) and will always be guarding the treasure of their summoner, so treasure must be determined by reference to the summoner. In that treasure there will usually be at least one clerical scroll and/or a magical device of clerical nature.

HELLCAT

FREQUENCY: *Rare*
NO. APPEARING: *1*
ARMOUR CLASS: *6*
MOVE: *12″*
HIT DICE: *7+2*
% IN LAIR: *30%*
TREASURE TYPE: *Nil*
NO. OF ATTACKS: *3*
DAMAGE/ATTACK:
  2–5/2–5/2–12
SPECIAL ATTACKS: *Nil*
SPECIAL DEFENCES: *Special
  invisibility and see below*
MAGIC RESISTANCE: *20% and
  immune to charm, sleep and
  similar spells*
INTELLIGENCE: *Average*
ALIGNMENT: *Lawful evil*
SIZE: *L*
PSIONIC ABILITY: *Nil*
  Attack/Defence Modes: *Nil*
LEVEL/X.P. VALUE:
  VI/1,000 + 10 per hit point

Hellcats are the associates and familiars of devils, and as such can usually be found upon their native levels of *Hell*. They will occasionally journey to the *Prime Material Plane*, where they seek to serve the ends of *Hell* by becoming servants to powerful characters of lawful evil alignment.

The hellcat is invisible in the presence of any light-source, but in darkness it can be seen as a faintly-glowing wraith-like outline with blazing crimson eyes, in form resembling a domestic cat the size of a tiger.

It can only be harmed by magical weapons, and even then the magical damage bonuses do not apply (so, for example, a +2 dagger would do 1–4 hit points of damage rather than 3–6 if it hit). It has a base 20% magic resistance and is completely immune to the effects of all mind-controlling spells (such as *charm*, *hold*, *sleep*, *suggestion* etc.)

If a hellcat is encountered which is not already attached to a character or a creature, the hellcat will select the most powerful member of the party with lawful evil alignment and will serve him. If there are two or more members of the party with that alignment and of equally high experience levels, the hellcat will choose a cleric over other classes, then a magic-user or illusionist, followed by a fighter and then other classes. Once it has selected a master, the hellcat will serve that person in the performance of evil deeds, will protect and defend that person and communicate only with him, using *telepathy* of range 9″. It will only serve intelligent creatures of the lawful evil alignment.

The attachment of the hellcat to its master can be broken in two ways. First, a hellcat will always give up its current master for a new, more powerful, master of the lawful evil alignment whenever such is encountered, providing the potential new master will have the hellcat (if not, the hellcat's bond with the existing master will remain intact). The creature, if it selects and is received by a new master, will have no compunctions about attacking its former master if ordered to do so. It is therefore possible for a character to 'steal' a hellcat from one monster only to have it 'stolen' from him, in turn, by another.

Secondly, the hellcat can only remain on the *Prime Material Plane* in the service of a master for a year and a day, after which it must return to its home in *Hell*. It may return again subsequently, but its bond with its former master is not automatically re-established. If the master encounters the creature again he may acquire its services in the same manner as before.

The only demand the hellcat makes in return for its service is the payment of one living human victim per week as its meal. The master must supply the victim — if he fails to do so, he will fill that role personally.

A hellcat attacks with two claws for 2–5 hit points of damage each and a bite for 2–12 hit points of damage.

If a party encounters a hellcat which is already in the service of a person or creature, the hellcat may switch its allegiance as described above or it may remain in the service of its existing master.

If a hellcat is encountered by a party of which no member is of the lawful evil alignment there are two possibilities. If the party contains one or more persons or creatures of evil disposition (i.e. neutral evil or chaotic evil) the hellcat will flee. However if the party contains no person or creature with an evil alignment, in any combination, the hellcat will attack.

HOAR FOX

FREQUENCY: *Rare*
NO. APPEARING: *1–6*
ARMOUR CLASS: *6*
MOVE: *15″*
HIT DICE: *2*
% IN LAIR: *20%*
TREASURE TYPE: *See below*
NO. OF ATTACKS: *1*
DAMAGE/ATTACK: *1–6*
SPECIAL ATTACKS: *Breath weapon*
SPECIAL DEFENCES: *Nil*
MAGIC RESISTANCE: *Standard*
INTELLIGENCE: *Animal*
ALIGNMENT: *Neutral*
SIZE: *S (4′ long)*
PSIONIC ABILITY: *Nil*
  Attack/Defence Modes: *Nil*
LEVEL/X.P. VALUE:
  II/28 + 2 per hit point

Inhabitants of cold regions, hoar foxes are usually encountered in small packs and are rarely (10% chance) aggressive unless threatened. However their pelts, of beautiful silver-grey fur, are regarded as very valuable — an undamaged specimen will command 100 gold pieces on the open market — and for this reason they are often threatened by adventurers.

Though they bite in attack for 1–6 hit points of damage, their main weapon is a breath weapon — a cone of *cold* with a range of 30′, only wide enough to catch one victim. The *cold* does 2–12 hit points of damage (a saving throw will halve the damage). For the purpose of the breath attack, the victim's AC is treated as 10 (though modifiers for dexterity are permitted).

The hoar fox is immune to cold-based attacks but takes double damage from fire (and fire will, of course, render the pelt valueless).

50

HOOK HORROR

FREQUENCY: *Rare*
NO. APPEARING: *2–12*
ARMOUR CLASS: *3*
MOVE: *9″*
HIT DICE: *5*
% IN LAIR: *20%*
TREASURE TYPE: *P*
NO. OF ATTACKS: *2*
DAMAGE/ATTACK: *1–8/1–8*
SPECIAL ATTACKS: *Nil*
SPECIAL DEFENCES: *Nil*
MAGIC RESISTANCE: *Standard*
INTELLIGENCE: *Low*
ALIGNMENT: *Neutral*
SIZE: *L (9′ tall)*
PSIONIC ABILITY: *Nil*
    Attack/Defence Modes: *Nil*
LEVEL/X.P. VALUE:
    IV/90 + 5 per hit point

Large, powerful bipeds, hook horrors have vulture-like heads and a hard plated exoskeleton which is mottled grey in colour. They inhabit deep underground corridors and chambers.

Though their vision is very poor, their hearing is extremely acute and there is only a 10% chance of surprising a hook horror. The creature's arms end in sharp hook-like talons which it uses in melee, each inflicting 1–8 hit points of damage.

A hook horror cannot speak but communicates with others of its kind by making clacking noises with the exoskeleton — an eerie sound which can alarm the unwary as it echoes around dungeon corridors.

HORNET, *Giant*

FREQUENCY: *Uncommon*
NO. APPEARING: *1*
ARMOUR CLASS: *2 in flight*
    4 when settled
MOVE: *24″*
HIT DICE: *5*
% IN LAIR: *70%*
TREASURE TYPE: *Nil*
NO. OF ATTACKS: *1*
DAMAGE/ATTACK: *1–4*
SPECIAL ATTACKS:
    Poison, incapacitation
SPECIAL DEFENCES: *Nil*
MAGIC RESISTANCE: *Standard*
INTELLIGENCE: *Semi*
ALIGNMENT: *Neutral*
SIZE: *M*
PSIONIC ABILITY: *Nil*
    Attack/Defence Modes: *Nil*
LEVEL/X.P. VALUE:
    IV/165 + 5 per hit point

This very aggressive creature has a 5′ long body and wings with a span of 10′ or more. It will attack on sight with a vicious sting which has the following effects if it hits:

  1)   1–4 hit points of damage;
  2)   5–30 poison damage (save negates); and
  3)   incapacity for 2–12 hours (save also negates).

One saving throw is rolled for each of the poison and incapacitation effects.

The natural habitat of the giant hornet is coniferous forest, though from time to time one will be encountered underground.

Smoke and flame will reduce the effectiveness of the hornet's attack, causing it to strike at −2 and −4 hit probability respectively. Fortunately for its potential victims, the creature's buzz is loud and can be heard 150′ away in dungeon corridors (this range is halved for each intervening door up to three doors).

For purposes of aerial combat, the giant hornet is manoeuvrability class B.

HOUND OF ILL OMEN

FREQUENCY: *Very rare*
NO. APPEARING: *1*
ARMOUR CLASS:
    Not applicable
MOVE: *Not applicable*
HIT DICE: *Not applicable*
% IN LAIR: *Nil*
TREASURE TYPE: *Nil*
NO. OF ATTACKS: *1*
DAMAGE/ATTACK: *Special*
SPECIAL ATTACKS: *Nil*
SPECIAL DEFENCES: *Nil*
MAGIC RESISTANCE: *Standard*
INTELLIGENCE: *Non-*
ALIGNMENT: *Neutral*
SIZE: *M (5′ tall)*
PSIONIC ABILITY: *Nil*
    Attack/Defence Modes: *Nil*
LEVEL/X.P. VALUE: *Not applicable*

One of the legendary beasts whose appearance traditionally portends death, this creature appears in the form of a dark, shadowy wolf-hound, 5′ tall at the shoulder. It appears instantaneously and remains in view only for a few seconds during which time it is only visible to one member of a party of adventurers. Because of its brief appearance and shadowy form, it cannot be harmed in any way, and it is rumoured that only one of these creatures exists.

The person sighting the hound will hear it emit a booming howl before it vanishes again. The character has no saving throw against the effects of the howl, though if *remove curse* is cast on the victim within one turn the effects of the howl will be halved.

The howl has this effect: the next 1–10 wounds suffered by its victim (1–5 if *remove curse* has been cast) do quadruple damage on him. If he survives, the victim will take no further effect from the howl, but until the requisite number of wounds has been taken no healing (*cure wounds* spells, for instance) will have any effect on him.

It is said that the hound only appears if a character has seriously offended his deity, for example by a flagrant act out of alignment.

HUECUVA

FREQUENCY: *Very rare*
NO. APPEARING: *1–10*
ARMOUR CLASS: *3*
MOVE: *9″*
HIT DICE: *2*
% IN LAIR: *10%*
TREASURE TYPE: *C*
NO. OF ATTACKS: *1*
DAMAGE/ATTACK: *1–6*
SPECIAL ATTACKS: *Disease*
SPECIAL DEFENCES:
    Can only be hit by silver
    and magical weapons
MAGIC RESISTANCE: *See below*
INTELLIGENCE: *Semi-*
ALIGNMENT: *Chaotic evil*
SIZE: *M*
PSIONIC ABILITY: *Nil*
    Attack/Defence Modes: *Nil*
LEVEL/X.P. VALUE:
    III/81 per hit point

The huecuva is an undead spirit, similar in appearance to a robed skeleton, which is treated as a wight on the cleric/undead matrix. It is resistant to all mind-influencing spells. It is able to *polymorph self* three times a day.

The touch of the huecuva inflicts 1–6 hit points of damage and unless the victim makes his saving throw against poison he will be infected with an acute cardiovascular-renal disease (as in the **ADVANCED DUNGEONS & DRAGONS DUNGEON MASTERS GUIDE** under *disease*).

ICE LIZARD

FREQUENCY: *Very rare*
NO. APPEARING: *1—4*
ARMOUR CLASS: *1*
MOVE: *9"/15"*
HIT DICE: *3+3*
% IN LAIR: *30%*
TREASURE TYPE: *G*
NO. OF ATTACKS: *3*
DAMAGE/ATTACK: *1—6/1—3/1—3*
SPECIAL ATTACKS:
 Spells; breath weapon
SPECIAL DEFENCES: *See below*
MAGIC RESISTANCE:
 80% (but see below)
INTELLIGENCE: *Low*
ALIGNMENT: *Chaotic evil*
SIZE: *S (3' long)*
PSIONIC ABILITY: *Nil*
 Attack/Defence Modes: *Nil*
LEVEL/X.P. VALUE:
 V/255 + 4 per hit point

The ice lizard appears as a small (3' long) winged lizard, though it can *polymorph self* twice per day (for a duration of two hours each time) into the form of a white dragon (see **ADVANCED DUNGEONS & DRAGONS MONSTER MANUAL** — *Dragon, White*). It can also cast *sleep* and *fear* twice per day each.

Although highly resistant to most forms of magic, it is somewhat susceptible to *charm* and *hold* (—2 on saving throw in each case).

It can use a cold breath weapon (as the white dragon) for 2—16 hit points of damage up to three times per day. Otherwise it attacks with its two claws (1—3 hit points of damage each) and a bite which inflicts 1—6 hit points of damage.

The ice lizard lives in cold regions underground and is dull silver in colour. In its natural form it is manoeuvrability class C, but in white dragon form it becomes class E.

IMORPH

FREQUENCY: *Very rare (at best)*
NO. APPEARING: *1*
ARMOUR CLASS: *5 (see below)*
MOVE: *6" (see below)*
HIT DICE: *5 (see below)*
% IN LAIR: *10%*
TREASURE TYPE: *Nil*
NO. OF ATTACKS: *2*
DAMAGE/ATTACK: *1—4/1—4*
SPECIAL ATTACKS: *Nil*
SPECIAL DEFENCES: *See below*
MAGIC RESISTANCE: *Standard*
INTELLIGENCE: *Animal*
ALIGNMENT: *Neutral*
SIZE: *M*
PSIONIC ABILITY: *Nil*
 Attack/Defence Modes: *Nil*
LEVEL/X.P. VALUE:
 III/130 + 5 per hit point

The natural form of this beast is a grey-green lumpy cylinder about 4' high and 2' average diameter. A short single leg trails behind the main body and has a suction cup like that of a snail. Other similar suction cups under the main body itself permit the beast a jerky mode of locomotion. Two 5' long tentacles emerge from the top of the body but there are no apparent eyes, ears or other features — indeed the whole creature is a constantly-changing mass of a rubbery, dough-like substance the same colour as bilious human flesh.

The creature will not normally attack unless threatened, but when it does so it strikes with its tentacles for 1—4 hit points of damage each.

When engaged in melee the creature exhibits a startling power of *imorphism*. At the beginning of each melee round (except the first) it changes its hit dice and armour class by 1 point each towards the values of its opponent, at the same time gradually changing its shape to resemble its opponent's shape. When hit dice and armour class (and hence appearance) are the same as those of its opponent, the creature instantly alters its attack and movement to fit the subject.

Note that the imorph assumes only the physical appearance of its opponent; though it will grow various appendages to copy its opponent's weapons and limbs, it will still strike with the equivalent of two tentacles each round for 1—4 hit points of damage each (even though one tentacle may look like an arm wielding a sword and the other an arm holding a shield, for example). The hit points of the imorph remain the same even when the hit dice value changes. However, the creature will change its hit probability to conform to its new hit dice value.

When the imorph is exactly the same shape as its opponent, has the same hit dice and the same armour class, it changes to the appropriate attack matrix for its hit probability (the fighter table, for example if it is attacking a human fighting man). It remains attacking on that table until it starts to change back again towards its original form.

When the melee is over, or when the imorph is down to 8 hits or fewer, it will revert to its original form by the reverse process, changing armour class and hit dice by 1 point each per melee round.

If faced with more than one attacker, the imorph will select one at random to attack and to emulate. If the original 'model' dies during melee, or retreats, the imorph will immediately start to alter in order to emulate another opponent.

Within the creature's body there is a small organ, corresponding to the human liver, made of a rubbery green substance. Within the organ is a liquid of similar colour which, when mixed with water in equal quantity, serves as a potion of *polymorph self*. There will be sufficient liquid in a single imorph to make 1—3 draughts of such a potion, and it is for this reason that the imorph is attacked by adventurers.

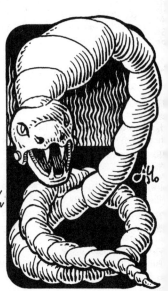

IRON COBRA

FREQUENCY: *Very rare*
NO. APPEARING: *1*
ARMOUR CLASS: *0*
MOVE: *12"*
HIT DICE: *1*
% IN LAIR: *Nil*
TREASURE TYPE: *See below*
NO. OF ATTACKS: *1*
DAMAGE/ATTACK: *1—3*
SPECIAL ATTACKS: *Poison*
SPECIAL DEFENCES: *See below*
MAGIC RESISTANCE: *See below*
INTELLIGENCE: *Non-*
ALIGNMENT: *Neutral*
SIZE: *S (3' long)*
PSIONIC ABILITY: *Nil*
 Attack/Defence Modes: *Nil*
LEVEL/X.P. VALUE:
 III/88 + 1 per hit point

The invention of some great magic-user or minor deity, this segmented automaton is made of an unknown metal and shaped in imitation of a snake. It is believed that there are only a dozen or so of these creatures in existence and they are quite valuable (high-level magic-users rate their value at 2,000 gold pieces if deactivated and the control words are known).

The cobra is activated and deactivated by key words set by its creator; when activated, it can obey simple verbal commands. When immobile it is absolutely silent but when moving it usually emits a soft rustling noise not unlike that made by a normal snake.

It has no mind so is not affected by spells affecting the mind (for example *sleep* or *charm*) nor is it affected by *webs*. Non-magical weapons inflict only half damage on it. It has the ability of an 8th level thief to hide in shadows (in which case it is not detected by infravision since it emits no body heat) and can also strike with surprise from behind, moving in utter silence for short periods as necessary. Its bite delivers a deadly poison (which also inflicts 1–3 hit points of damage) against which a victim must save at −2. The capacity of the fangs is, however, limited; after three poisonous bites the poison supply runs dry and the fangs simply inflict 1–3 hit points of damage. (If the controller of the snake is at hand, of course, the fangs can be re-charged with poison when an opportunity arises).

Against magical spell attacks, other than those mentioned above, the iron cobra makes a saving throw as would a 12th level magic-user.

The iron cobra may be set to guard a treasure or to act as a bodyguard. Alternatively it can be ordered to track down and destroy

anyone whose name is known providing that person is within one mile. In the latter case, the creature tracks down its quarry by homing in on his psychic vibrations (the victim can block these, if he is aware of the pursuit of the cobra, by *mind blank* or a similar spell).

It is said that some iron cobras contain in their fangs paralysing, sleep-inducing drugs instead of poison; against these a victim would need to make a normal saving throw.

JACULI – JERMLAINE

JACULI

FREQUENCY: *Rare*
NO. APPEARING: *11–20*
ARMOUR CLASS: *6*
MOVE: *9"*
HIT DICE: *1*
% IN LAIR: *Nil*
TREASURE TYPE: *Nil*
NO. OF ATTACKS: *1*
DAMAGE/ATTACK: *1–6*
SPECIAL ATTACKS: *Nil*
SPECIAL DEFENCES: *Nil*
MAGIC RESISTANCE: *Standard*
INTELLIGENCE: *Animal*
ALIGNMENT: *Neutral*
SIZE: *L (8'–12')*
PSIONIC ABILITY: *Nil*
  Attack/Defence Modes: *Nil*
LEVEL/X.P. VALUE
  1/10 + 1 per hit point

The jaculi (singular and plural) are agile serpents with chameleon-like camouflage abilities. They are usually found in woods and forests for they are basically arboreal in nature and feed on tree mosses and insects, but some swarms have adapted their habitat to pillared halls and the like. Although not naturally vicious, jaculi swarms are highly territorial and excitable, resenting more than a transient intrusion into what they regard as their territory. Because of their camouflage abilities (only 1 chance in 4 of detection even when they are in clear view) it is unlikely they will be seen before attack.

The serpent has a long muscular body and a broad, flat head with a ridge of razor-edged bone projecting at either side. It can project itself from any high point with the force and accuracy of a javelin, surprising its victim unless previously detected. Its 'flying speed' is thus high (51" rate), but once it has attacked in this manner it can make no further attack from ground level and must crawl away up another tree or pillar before it can attack again.

JERMLAINE *(Jinxkins)*

FREQUENCY: *Uncommon*
NO. APPEARING: *12–48*
ARMOUR CLASS: *7*
MOVE: *15"*
HIT DICE: *1–4 hit points*
% IN LAIR: *Special*
TREASURE TYPE:
  Per 10 individuals O, Q;
  in lair C, Q (x5), S, T
NO. OF ATTACKS: *1*
DAMAGE/ATTACK: *1–2 or 1–4*
SPECIAL ATTACKS: *See below*

SPECIAL DEFENCES: *See below*
MAGIC RESISTANCE: *See below*
INTELLIGENCE: *Average*
  (with genius level cunning)
ALIGNMENT: *Neutral evil (with*
  slight lawful tendency)
SIZE: *S (1' + tall)*
PSIONIC ABILITY: *Nil*
  Attack/Defence Modes: *Nil*
LEVEL/X.P. VALUE:
  Normal 1/7 + 1 per hit point
  Elder II/32 + 1 per hit point

Jermlaine, or jinxkins, sometimes known as bane-midges, dwell in elaborate tunnel and den warrens beneath the ground — often very deep beneath the surface. As they mix freely with rats of all sorts, even the giant variety, they are often (75%) found in company with such rodents and are 50% likely to be sharing an integrated system of burrows, tunnels and holes. (If jermlaine are encountered, a percentile die roll of 01—75 indicates that rats (25%) or giant rats (50%) are with them. If the jermlaine are in their lair, it is 50% probable that there will be connecting rat tunnels). This cohabitation extends to all forms of mutual co-operation and defence.

These evil runts are cowardly and will attack only when it seems probable that they can overwhelm victims without serious opposition. Jinxkins thus waylay weakened and wounded parties or single individuals who are unwary, asleep etc. While strong groups or alert adventurers will not be physically attacked, jermlaine bands will certainly seek to cause them harm and otherwise injure them out of sheer maliciousness. This injury to the adventurers brings both personal gain to the jermlaine and the possibility of eventual gain of new victims.

Jermlaine are very fast, moving with a scuttling gait, very quiet, and are masters of remaining unseen. On occasion, however, if a party or individual suddenly becomes still and listens carefully, their movement or twittering, squeaking speech can be detected.

It is 60% probable that bane-midges will be within 60' of their lair at any time they are encountered, but the tunnels which give access to such places are twisting mazes and passage is impossible for any creature larger than a gnome — even the latter having to creep and crawl to get through, and of course this exposes the intruder to attack.

Jermlaine typically arm themselves with needle-sharp darts which they can hurl up to 12' and cause 1—2 hit points of damage. In addition to a dart, each minimus carries a pike-like weapon — a 1½' long wand of supple wood with a sharp metal tip. This instrument is used as a spear or pike to inflict 1—4 hit points of damage. Their favoured attack method is ambush with pit or net, however, taking victims alive.

In little-used passages, these nasty creatures will laboriously prepare pits covered by camouflaged trapdoors, or string overhead nets entwined with silk from the webs of giant spiders, and lay in wait for passing prey. In more travelled ways, jermlaine will stretch thin but strong cords (often woven of human hair) to trip the unwary. Victims not stunned by the trap are pummelled senseless by bane-midges wielding leathern clubs filled with sand or lead shot while others entwine the prone creatures with ropes and cords. Note that beating with the clubs has a 2% cumulative chance per blow of knocking the victim unconscious, but those protected by splint, banded or plate mail will not be so attacked. Well-armoured victims who cannot be bound fast are attacked to kill — possibly with flaming oil missiles or acid. Some victims will be devoured by the jermlaine (or their rat-friends) but most humans will be stripped naked, shaved and left

trussed and helpless in the passageway. The jermlaine will usually watch such victims from a safe hide, awaiting the 'fun' of seeing some passing monster come and devour the bound victims.

If alert creatures should happen to pause near a hidden group of jermlaine, the spiteful things will steal forth and cut belts and straps, packs and seams — typically one such vandalistic act per jinxkin, for they act with haste in order to escape unnoticed and unharmed. Their vandalism will usually be noticed only 1—12 turns later, when a weakened strap parts, a seam opens fully etc. Worse still, if packs and other goods are placed out where jinxkins can reach them, these monstrous atomites will pollute the water, sour the wine and turn it into vinegar, spoil food, desecrate holy water, steal small items (gems, coins, garlic buds, herbs etc.) wedge daggers or swords so that they are difficult to draw out quickly, cut bow strings, blunt arrows, puncture oil flasks and so on.

If more than 35 of these creatures are encountered, there will be one very old and exceptionally evil one who has a very wicked power; this individual bane-midge will be able to drain all magic properties from any magical item (except an artifact or relic) which he can handle for 1—4 rounds.

The grey-brown warty hide of jermlaine blends with earth and stone, and they always dress in scraps and rags of the same colouration so that they can remain concealed from view. Coupled with their ability to move quietly, the jinxkins are likely to surprise opponents on a roll of 1—5 (d6) and they are 75% undetectable if looked for or listened for, unless the action is done suddenly so as to catch them off their guard.

Jermlaine are treated as 4 hit dice creatures with respect to the effects of magical attacks and saving throws. Because of their size and quickness, jinxkins which save versus attacks which would normally inflict half damage will escape unscathed.

Although they have weak eyes and their infravision extends only 30', jermlaine have keen hearing and smell, so even invisible creatures are 50% likely to be detected by them under normal dungeon conditions.

Jermlaine speak their own tongue and their alignment language, and can converse with rats of all sorts. 1 in 10 can speak the common tongue, and the same probability exists with respect to the languages of dwarves, gnomes, goblins and orcs.

Description: Jinxkins look as if they are diminutive humans wearing baggy clothing and ill-fitting leather helmets. Closer inspection will show that the baggy 'garments' are actually the creatures' lumpy and many-folded skins, while the 'helmets' are in reality the pointed and evilly-visaged heads — all leathery and smooth. The limbs of these creatures are knotty and bowed, with hands and feet tipped with thick nails which are always filthy but nimble.

KAMADAN – KELPIE – KENKU – KHARGRA – KILLMOULIS – KUO–TOA

KAMADAN

FREQUENCY: *Rare*
NO. APPEARING: *1*
ARMOUR CLASS: *4*
MOVE: *18"*
HIT DICE: *4+2*
% IN LAIR: *20%*
TREASURE TYPE: *C*
NO. OF ATTACKS:
   3 plus number of
   snake heads
DAMAGE/ATTACK:
   1–3/1–3/1–6 plus 1–4
   per snake head
SPECIAL ATTACKS: *Breath*
   weapon
SPECIAL DEFENCES: *Nil*
MAGIC RESISTANCE: *Standard*
INTELLIGENCE: *Low*
ALIGNMENT: *Neutral*
   (chaotic evil)
SIZE: *L*
PSIONIC ABILITY: *Nil*
   Attack/Defence Modes: *Nil*
LEVEL/X.P. VALUE:
   IV/240 + 5 per hit point

This greatly feared beast resembles a large leopard with 4-7 snakes sprouting from its shoulders — it is clearly a relative of the displacer beast (see **ADVANCED DUNGEONS & DRAGONS MONSTER MANUAL** – *Displacer Beast*) though how it became such a curious cross-mutation is a matter for speculation.

In melee the creature attacks with two claws for 1–3 hit points of damage each and bites for 1–6 hit points of damage. Each snake will also bite for 1–4 hit points of damage, though the snake bites are not poisonous.

It also has a breath weapon — a cone of *sleep* 30' long and with base diameter 10'. This puts creatures of 4 dice and below to sleep — no saving throw allowed; creatures with more hit dice are permitted a saving throw as against dragon breath.

Kelpies are a form of intelligent aquatic plant life that, in their own shape, rather resemble a pile of wet seaweed. They are able to shape their bodies into any form they choose, and will often assume the aspect of a beautiful human woman in order to lure men into deep waters. They have also been known to take the shape of a horse. However, though the form may be changed, the substance still resembles green seaweed and the effect is somewhat grotesque.

To counter this, the kelpie can cast one powerful *charm* spell per day. If the victim does not save against spells (at −2) he will perceive the kelpie as the most wonderful, perfect and desirable woman (or steed, perhaps) and will willingly leap into the water to join her (or gain it). The kelpie will wrap itself around the charmed man, he will attempt to inhale water and sink with the kelpie in an ecstasy of drowning. If left alone, he will happily drown and be dragged off to the kelpie's lair to be consumed. Even if the kelpie cannot physically reach the charmed victim, he will still try to swim downward and breathe water. If the charming kelpie is killed, the spell will be broken immediately. Charmed victims attempting to drown themselves will suffer 2–20 hit points of damage per melee round until they either surface for air or perish.

For some reason, females are immune to the spell of the kelpie. Legend has it that this is so because kelpies were created by the sea-god as punishment for those men who are rash enough to sail the oceans without paying their lord his proper respect. Women were not involved in these transgressions and thus did not incur the sea-lord's ill will. Others say that Olhydra, the Elemental Princess of Evil Water Creatures, created the kelpies and rendered females immune in proper regard for her own gender.

Besides the oceans and the seas, kelpies will also be found in dismal swamps and stagnant subterranean grottos; occasionally they will be found in almost any deep body of water, even man-made. They can leave the water to walk on land for short periods of time (1-3 hours maximum).

Due to their slimy wetness, fire attacks do only half damage on kelpies (none if a saving throw is made).

Kelpies are very cunning and will try to pick off stragglers, lone watchmen or tail-end members of groups if at all possible.

KELPIE

FREQUENCY: *Very rare*
NO. APPEARING: *1–4*
ARMOUR CLASS: *3*
MOVE: *9"//12"*
HIT DICE: *5*
% IN LAIR: *70%*
TREASURE TYPE: *D*
NO. OF ATTACKS: *Nil*
DAMAGE/ATTACK: *Nil*
SPECIAL ATTACKS: *See below*
SPECIAL DEFENCES: *See below*
MAGIC RESISTANCE: *Standard*
INTELLIGENCE: *Low-average*
ALIGNMENT: *Neutral evil*
SIZE: *M*
PSIONIC ABILITY: *Nil*
   Attack/Defence Modes: *Nil*
LEVEL/X.P. VALUE:
   IV/165 + 5 per hit point

KENKU

FREQUENCY: *Uncommon*
NO. APPEARING: *2—8*
ARMOUR CLASS: *5*
MOVE: *6"/18"*
HIT DICE: *2—5*
% IN LAIR: *20%*
TREASURE TYPE: *F*
NO. OF ATTACKS: *3 or 1*
DAMAGE/ATTACK:
   1—4/1—4/1—6 or
   by weapon type
SPECIAL ATTACKS: *Nil*
SPECIAL DEFENCES: *See below*
MAGIC RESISTANCE: *30%*
INTELLIGENCE: *Average*
ALIGNMENT: *Neutral*
SIZE: *M*
PSIONIC ABILITY: *Nil*
   Attack/Defence Modes: *Nil*
LEVEL/X.P. VALUE:
   2HD: II/28 + 2 per hit point
   3HD: III/120 + 3 per hit point
   4HD: IV/240 + 4 per hit point
   5HD: V/420 + 5 per hit point

ROSS

Bipedal humanoid birds with wings, clawed hands and feet, and the head of a hawk with a sharp beak, kenku are mischievous creatures which habitually use their limited magical powers to annoy and inconvenience humans, though their intent is not usually to kill. Every kenku has thieving abilities at the 4th level of experience and they are also expert fighters, usually wielding a quarterstaff or a samurai sword. If unarmed they fight with two claws (1—4 hit points of damage each) and a vicious bite for 1—6 hit points of damage.

If a group of kenku is encountered, its members will depend on the group size. A small group will contain two creatures of 2HD and two of 3HD or three and two respectively; a group of 6 or 7 will contain a leader of 4HD, two creatures of 3HD and three or four of 2HD, while a group of 8 will contain a supreme leader of 5HD.

Kenku of 3HD or more have certain magical powers. A 3HD creature will have one first-level magic-user spell — often *magic missile*. They also have the innate ability of *shape change* once in every 30 days; after 7 days in the changed shape, they must resume normal form. Particularly adventurous kenku have been known to use this power to assume the form of a god and accept offerings from credulous worshippers, and this is but one example of the bizarre uses to which kenku, and particularly the younger of the species, have put this power.

Kenku of 4HD have all the powers of those with 3HD plus an additional first-level magic-user spell — usually *shocking grasp*. They also have the innate ability of *invisibility* with no limitations on frequency of use or duration of effects. Again, these powers are sometimes put to unusual uses, but 4HD kenku tend to be older than the 3HD birds (the innate abilities develop with age and suitable training) and less reckless in their activities.

Kenku with 5HD have all the powers of those with 4HD plus a second-level magic-user spell — usually *mirror-image* or *web*. They may also *call lightning* — an innate ability which has the same effects as the 3rd level druidic spell.

All kenku have well-developed disguise abilities and can pass for human with only a 50% chance of detection (though the length of the nose usually gives away the deception).

Kenku favour kidnapping as a source of funds. They will freely give treasure but this is rarely genuine and will crumble to a valueless dust within a day. They will appear helpful to humans and will offer non-verbal advice, though this is usually carefully designed to mislead and to tempt the party into danger and/or difficulties. As a rough guide, the approximate chance of a kenku actually aiding humans is 5%, though this will vary with the circumstances.

Kenku do not speak; they appear to communicate with each other on the telepathic level.

It is rumoured that kenku of more than 5HD exist with even greater magical powers. Kenku lairs so far discovered have been small underground caverns but it is believed that larger caverns, deeper underground, contain larger numbers of the beasts in a formalised social structure.

For purposes of aerial combat, they are manoeuvrability class D.

KHARGRA

FREQUENCY: *Very rare (at best)*
NO. APPEARING: *1—6*
ARMOUR CLASS: *—3*
MOVE: *3"(15")*
HIT DICE: *6*
% IN LAIR: *Nil*
TREASURE TYPE: *See below*
NO. OF ATTACKS: *1*
DAMAGE/ATTACK: *3—18*
SPECIAL ATTACKS:
   Surprise on 1—7(d8)
SPECIAL DEFENCES: *See below*
MAGIC RESISTANCE: *Standard*
INTELLIGENCE: *Low*
ALIGNMENT: *Neutral*
SIZE: *S (3½' long)*
PSIONIC ABILITY: *Nil*
   Attack/Defence Modes: *Nil*
LEVEL/X.P. VALUE:
   V/300 + 6 per hit point

Creatures from the *Elemental Plane of Earth*, the khargra occasionally venture onto the *Prime Material Plane* in search of high-grade ores which they digest and use as food. They 'swim' along the layers of rock in small schools, riding on earth movements and the shifting of geological strata as if swimming — or surfing — in the sea. When they find a suitable vein of ore, they settle down to feed and ingest the material, grinding it up and, through their curious metabolic and digestive processes, actually separating out and refining the metal. The slaggy waste material is excreted and the metal is deposited in the khargra's internal reservoirs, there to be assimilated slowly into the body.

Naturally a khargra prefers refined metal to unrefined ore, and if the former is sensed reasonably close to hand, it will forego its normal diet for this new rich source of food. Khargra consider armour and weaponry a tasty meal indeed and are particularly fond of 'eating' metallic treasure.

Khargra will leap from the wall or floor of a cavern or subterranean passage like fish leaping from water, flying as far as 10'. They then attempt to fasten themselves with their clawed arms onto large metallic objects, which they will devour. Such attacks will surprise nearby adventurers on a roll of 1—7 (d8), or 1—5 (d6) if dwarves or gnomes are present. A single khargra can swallow up to 5 pounds (50 gold pieces weight) of metal per melee round and has a capacity of 100 pounds or sometimes more.

When khargra have emerged into the air from their normal rock environment, they must crawl, pulling themselves along with their arms.

If assaulted, the khargra will fight back, annoyed at having its meal disturbed. When attacked with a metal weapon, a khargra will bite the end off and swallow it on any roll of 16 or better. They fight non-metallic opponents by delivering a powerful bite for 3—18 hit points of damage, but their attack will be merely incidental to their main objective of eating metal. They use their three strong clawed arms to grasp and pull themselves towards their prey, and at least one of the three arms must 'hit' a victim before a successful bite can be inflicted on him, though the arms themselves do no damage. Once an arm has grasped, however, it will not let go until the way is clear for it to reach the metal it desires or its victim has been killed. Khargra have been known to bite right through large flesh creatures in order to reach a concentration of metal beyond. Each arm 'hits' as if a creature of 12HD.

Fortunately, khargra are very rarely seen on the *Prime Material Plane* and can usually be appeased by the immediate surrender of all metallic items.

If a dead khargra is cut open — far from an easy task — there will be found, inside its unique digestive system, up to 500 gold pieces weight of non-assimilated pebbles of metal. These pebbles will reflect the creature's most recent diet and may be any kind of metal, including precious metal.

Though a khargra can emerge from rock instantaneously, it takes a full melee round to re-integrate its structure back into its native substance, and if a *phase door* spell is cast on the creature during this re-integration, it is killed instantly and the body will remain out of phase until the magic is *dispelled. Transmute metal to wood* will also kill a khargra, though they are immune to fire- and cold-based spells except for *heat metal*, which always does maximum damage. *Lightning* does full damage and *move earth* will stop a khargra in its tracks, stunning and confusing it for 1—3 melee rounds.

Description: Khargra are about 3½' long and shaped like a cylinder, tapering towards the rear. They sport three large flexible metal fins, spaced equi-angularly around their body and radially orientated with respect to their longitudinal axis. Between the fins, also equally spaced, are three conical sheaths from which emerge extensible clawed arms, capable of reaching out 3' from the creature's body. Small eye-bulges protrude on either side of the top fin. The mouth is fully a foot in diameter and lined with curved, razor-sharp metal teeth which operate like an iris to open and close the mouth aperture. Their bodies are covered in large metallic scales. Khargra weigh about 300 pounds.

KILLMOULIS

FREQUENCY: *Uncommon*
NO. APPEARING: *1—3*
ARMOUR CLASS: *6*
MOVE: *15"*
HIT DICE: *½ (1—4 hit points)*
% IN LAIR: *60%*
TREASURE TYPE: *K*
NO. OF ATTACKS: *Nil*
DAMAGE/ATTACK: *Nil*
SPECIAL ATTACKS: *See below*
SPECIAL DEFENCES: *See below*
MAGIC RESISTANCE: *20%*
INTELLIGENCE: *Average*
ALIGNMENT:
    Neutral (chaotic good)
SIZE: *S*
PSIONIC ABILITY: *Nil*
    Attack/Defence Modes: *Nil*
LEVEL/X.P. VALUE:
    I/9 + 1 per hit point

Killmoulis always dwell where some industry is in progress, preferably one involving grain or other foodstuffs. They inhabit the areas under floors, in cracks in walls or amidst the dark rafters, only coming out when the human workers leave. Brownie-like, the killmoulis then work and otherwise make themselves useful, at the same time devouring prodigious amounts of meal, flour, grain or whatever other foodstuffs are available.

It is also an integral part of their nature to play tricks and practical jokes — certain to be destructive or harmful if the inhabitants of the place molest any of the killmoulis, but otherwise of merely bothersome and irksome nature without undue destruction.

Killmoulis are very fast and are able to blend with their surroundings and conceal themselves in shadowy places so as to be virtually undetectable (10% chance only). They hate dogs and cats almost as much as they do rats, for these animals will attack killmoulis. While the latter are snared or killed with long pins, the former are typically poisoned if they prove a threat, the killmoulis gaining access to whatever poison is available nearby. If the killmoulis are unable to kill the cats, dogs and rats which threaten them, they will certainly move to another locale.

A killmoulis is typically quite small, usually under a foot in height. Each has a thin body and limbs, but a large head with proportionate ears. There is no mouth in the head, food being drawn into the huge nose. Killmoulis appear to communicate with each other on the telepathic level.

KUO—TOA

FREQUENCY: *Very rare*
NO. APPEARING: *2—24*
    (40—400)
ARMOUR CLASS: *4*
MOVE: *9"//18"*
HIT DICE: *2 or more*
% IN LAIR: *See below*
TREASURE TYPE: *Individuals*
    L, M, N; in lair, Z.
NO. OF ATTACKS: *1 or 2*
DAMAGE/ATTACK: *By weapon*
    type and/or 2—5
SPECIAL ATTACKS: *See below*
SPECIAL DEFENCES: *See below*
MAGIC RESISTANCE: *See below*
INTELLIGENCE: *High and up*
ALIGNMENT: *Neutral evil*
    (with chaotic tendencies)
SIZE: *M (higher levels L)*
PSIONIC ABILITY: *Nil*
    Attack/Defence Modes: *Nil*
LEVEL/X.P. VALUE:
    II and up/variable

The ancient kuo-toa people once inhabited the shores and islands of the upper world, but as the race of mankind and its associate species grew more and more numerous and more powerful, the 'men-fish' were slowly driven to remote regions. Continual warfare upon these evil, human-sacrificing creatures threatened to exterminate the species, for a number of powerful beings were aiding their sworn enemies — mankind. Some kuo-toans sought refuge in sea caverns and secret subterranean waters, and while their fellows above were being slaughtered, these few prospered and developed new characteristics to match their lightless habitats. However, the seas contained other fierce and evil creatures with designs of their own, and the deep-dwelling kuo-toans were eventually wiped out leaving only those in the underworld to carry on the species. These survivors were unknown to men, and mankind eventually forgot the men-fish entirely. Even the word *goggler*, a derisive term for their ichthyoid foes, lost its meaning to humans. But the kuo-toans remaining in their underworld places did not allow memory of the past to lapse — and woe to the hapless human who falls into the slimy clutches of the kuo-toans.

Now the kuo-toans are haters of sunlight and are almost never encountered on the surface of the earth. This, and their inborn hatred of discipline, prevent the resurgence of these creatures, for they have become numerous once again and have gained new powers. However, they have also become somewhat unstable, and insanity is not uncommon amongst the species.

Sometimes the kuo-toans are encountered in small groups journeying in the upper world to kidnap humans for slaves and sacrifice. Such parties are also found occasionally in the dungeon labyrinths which connect to the extensive system of underworld passages and caverns which honeycombs the crust of the earth. Only far below the earth's surface will the intrepid explorer find the natural caverns and spaces hewn from living rock over the ages in which the kuo-toa people build their underground communities.

These creatures normally travel in well-armed bands. If more than 20 kuo-toans are encountered it is 50% likely that they will be within 1—6 miles of their lair. For every four normal warriors in an encountered band there will be an additional fighter of 3rd or 4th level. For every eight normal fighters encountered there will be an additional fighter of 5th or 6th level. For every 12 in the group there will be a cleric/assassin of equal levels, either 4th/4th, 5th/5th, 6th/6th or 7th/7th (d4 + 3 for determination of level). If more than 20 normal (2nd level) fighters are in the group, it will be a *war party* — i.e. a full-scale raiding/fighting detachment. A *war party* will include:

    1 10th level fighter as 'captain'
    2 8th level fighters as 'lieutenants'
    4 3rd/3rd level fighter/assassin 'whips'
    1 'monitor' (see hereafter)
    1 slave per 4 kuo-toans

The 'whips' are fanatical devotees of the Sea Mother goddess of the kuo-toans. They inspire the troops to stand firm and fight without quarter for the glory of their ruler and their deity.

If a kuo-toan lair is found it will contain 40—400 2nd level males. In addition, there will be higher level fighters in the same ratio as noted above for outside groups, *war parties*, and:

1 priest-king of 12th/12th level, a cleric/assassin, if 350 or more normal kuo-toans are indicated, or
1 priest-duke of 11th/11th level if 275—349 normal kuo-toans are indicated, or
1 priest-prince of 10th/10th level if fewer than 275 normal kuo-toans are indicated, together with
8 'eyes' of the priest-king, priest-duke or priest-prince, 8th/8th (or 7th/7th or 6th/6th) level cleric/assassins
1 'chief whip'—6th/6th level fighter/assassin
2 'whips' of 4th/4th or 5th/5th level
1 'monitor' per 20 2nd level male kuo-toans
females equal to 20% of the male population
young (non-combatant) equal to 20% of the total kuo-toans
slaves equal to 50% of the total male population.

In special religious areas there will also be a number of kuo-toan clerics. For every 20 individuals in the community there will be a 3rd level cleric, for every 40 there will be a 4th level cleric, for every 80 there will be a 5th level cleric, all in addition to the other individuals. These clerics will be headed by:

1 6th level cleric if the group is 160 or fewer, or
1 7th level and 1 6th level cleric if the group is between 161 and 240, or
1 8th level, 1 7th level and 1 6th level if the group numbers between 241 and 320, or
1 9th level, 2 7th level and 3 6th level if the group numbers 321 and 400, or
1 10th level, 2 8th level and 4 6th level if the group numbers in excess of 400.

It is 50% probable that any kuo-toan cleric above 6th level will be armed with a *pincer staff*. This is a 5' long pole topped by a 3' long "claw". It corresponds to a medieval man-catcher, and if the user scores a hit the claw end has closed upon the opponent, making it impossible for the trapped individual to get free. (Naturally, this weapon can be employed only against creatures of a girth about that of a small-to-large human — a size range between the elf and the gnoll). It is 10% probable that both arms will be pinned by the claw, 40% probable that only one arm will be trapped (if the victim is right-handed, the claw will trap the left hand with 75% probability, the right with 25% probability). Trapped opponents lose all shield and dexterity protections (or weapon attack potential if it is their weapon-bearing arm which is trapped, in which case dexterity protections are still lost but the shield is still effective) and nearby kuo-toans will always strike at such trapped individuals.

Kuo-toans spawn as do fish, and hatchlings — 'fingerlings' as they are usually called — are raised in pools until their amphibian qualities develop about one year after hatching. The young — now 1' or so high — are then able to breathe air, and they are raised in gens according to their sex and fitness.

The number of hit dice possessed by this hardy race is not indicative of their possible variation in hits, since their breeding gives them exactly the same number of hit points per die, varying by level:

Number of hit dice	Hit points for	
	males	females
2	12	10
3	18	15
4	28	24
5	35	30
6	42	36
7	56	49
8	64	56
9	72	—
10	90	—
11	99	—
12	120	—

Typical arms carried by kuo-toan fighters are:

dagger, spear and shield	40%
dagger, spear and weighted throwing net	30%
dagger and harpoon*	10%
dagger and short bow (half female population)	20%

*The harpoon is generally used only by higher-level fighters. It is a wickedly barbed throwing weapon with a range of 30'. It inflicts 2—12 hit points of damage, exclusive of bonuses. Creatures struck must attempt a saving throw of 13 or better (d20) to avoid being snagged by the weapon. Creatures of man-size or less who are thus caught will be jerked off their feet and stunned for 1—4 rounds. The harpooning kuo-toan will haul in his victim and attempt to slay him with a dagger thrust, since the harpoon is fastened to the hurler by a stout cord.

The shields employed by these creatures are fashioned of special boiled leather, and just before battle they are treated with a special, particularly sticky, glue-like substance. There is a 25% chance that any frontal attack on a shield-bearing warrior will strike this glue and stick fast until the wielder is able to pull it free (same chance as that of individual has of opening a dungeon door).

Kuo-toans wear no clothing — only leather harnesses for their weapons and a small amount of personal gear, as any other garments would hinder their swimming. Their skin is tough, scaled and very slimy. Coupled with their dexterity, their slimy tough skin gives them a high natural armour class. Note that shields do not add to their armour class — they are used as weapons.

Hit probability for these creatures is the same as a human of the same level but males gain a +1 bonus on their 'to hit' roll and on damage, due to their strength. This bonus applies only to weapons, not to their natural biting attack mode (which causes 2—5 hit points of damage). When fighting with a dagger only, these creatures are also able to bite at an opponent.

When two or more kuo-toan clerics or cleric-assassins operate together, by joining hands they can generate a stroke of lightning. The bolt is very narrow, so that only the specific target victim will be affected unless, by mischance, another creature gets into the 2' wide path of the stroke. The bolt of electrical energy causes 6 hit points of damage per cleric or cleric/assassin to any creature struck — half that if a saving throw is made. The chance of generating such a stroke of lightning is 10% cumulative per round per kuo-toan involved. (Check each round when priests are acting in conjunction).

The special defences of these creatures include their skin secretion which makes it only 25% probable that an attempt to grapple, grasp, tie or *web* a kuo-toan will succeed. Although their eyes are set on the sides of their heads, kuo-toans have excellent independent monocular vision, a very wide degree of field (180°), and they are able to detect movement even though a creature is normally invisible due to magic,

astrally projected or ethereal. Thus, only complete motionlessness can avoid visual detection by a kuo-toan. They see into the infrared and ultraviolet spectra, and vibrations within 10' can be felt by these creatures, so they are only surprised on a 1 (in 6).

Kuo-toans are totally immune to poison and are not affected by paralysis. Spells which generally affect only humanoid-type creatures (*charm person, hold person, sleep* and so on) have no effect on these creatures. Electrical attacks cause only half damage (or none if a saving throw is made). A *magic missile* will cause only 1 hit point of damage to a kuo-toan, and all forms of illusion are useless against them. However, kuo-toans hate bright light — such as from a *light* spell — and fight at −1 on 'to hit' rolls when exposed to such illumination. They suffer full damage from all fire-based attacks and saving throws against such attacks are at −2 on the die.

Especially fit fingerlings, usually of noble spawning, are trained for the priesthood — as clerics, cleric/assassins or as special celibate monks. The latter are 'monitors' whose role it is to control the community members who become violent or go insane. The monitor is capable of attacking to subdue or to kill. A monitor has 56 hit points, attacks at 7th level, and has the following characteristics:

twice normal movement rate

surprised only on a 1 in 10

armour class 1

4 attacks per round, 2 bare-handed doing 2–8 hit points of damage (double if attacking to subdue), 2 with teeth doing 2–5 hit points of damage; one hands/bite routine in the forepart of a round and the second in the last portion.

Subdued creatures cannot be larger than man-sized or slightly larger (up to 8' tall/500 pounds). Subduing attacks cause only half actual damage, but when hit points scored equal the total for the creature it is rendered unconscious for 3–12 rounds.

Kuo-toans do not generally co-operate from community to community, although they have special religious places in common. These places are usually for intergroup trade, councils and worship of Sea Mother, so they are open to all kuo-toans. These religious communities, as well as other kuo-toan settlements, are open to the drow and their servants, for the dark elves provide useful goods and services as slave-traders and merchants, but the drow are both feared and hated by the kuo-toan people, so there are frequent kidnappings and

minor skirmishes between the peoples. The illithids (mind flayers — see **ADVANCED DUNGEONS & DRAGONS MONSTER MANUAL** — *Mind Flayer*) are greatly hated by the kuo-toans and they and their allies are attacked on sight. Despite their common hatred of mind-flayers, the kuo-toans and githyanki are not on good terms with each other; the kuo-toans entertain deep mistrust of githyanki and do their best to avoid them. Kuo-toans will always attack githzerai.

Slaves obtained by the kuo-toans are used for labour, food and sacrifice. The composition of any slave group can be determined at random from the following table:

Die roll	Race of slave	Die roll	Race of slave
1	dwarf	8	half-orc
2	elf*	9	hobgoblin
3	gnoll**	10–14	human
4–5	gnome (svirfneblin)	15–16	lizard man
6	goblin	17–18	orc
7	half-elf	19–20	troglodyte

*25% chance for bugbear in community isolated from drow
**50% chance for drow in community isolated from drow.

The kuo-toans speak the strange subterranean trade language common to most intelligent dwellers in the underworld. In addition, they speak their own arcane tongue and can communicate with most fish by empathic means. Their religious speech is a corruption of the language used on the *Elemental Plane of Water* and if a cleric is near it is 75% improbable that any creature from this plane will attack kuo-toans, for the cleric will speak and request that they be spared in the name of Sea Mother (Blibdoolpoolp).

Description: A kuo-toan presents a cold and horrid appearance. A typical specimen looks much as if a human body, albeit a paunchy one, had been covered with scales and topped with a fish's head squarely on the shoulders. The huge fish eyes tend to swivel in different directions when observing an area or creature. The hands and feet are very long, with three fingers and opposing digit, partially webbed. The legs and arms are short for the body size. Their colouration is pale grey, with undertones of tan or yellow in males only, and the whole skin has a sheen from its slime covering. The colour darkens when the individual is angry and pales when the creature is badly frightened.

LAMIA NOBLE — LAVA CHILDREN — LIZARD KING

LAMIA NOBLE

FREQUENCY: *Very rare*
NO. APPEARING: *1*
ARMOUR CLASS: *6*
MOVE: *9"*
HIT DICE: *10+1*
% IN LAIR: *60%*
TREASURE TYPE: *D*
NO. OF ATTACKS: *1*
DAMAGE/ATTACK: *1–6*
SPECIAL ATTACKS:
 Spells — see below
SPECIAL DEFENCES: *Nil*
MAGIC RESISTANCE: *Standard*
INTELLIGENCE: *High*
ALIGNMENT: *Chaotic evil*
SIZE: *M*
PSIONIC ABILITY: *Nil*
 Attack/Defence Modes: Nil
LEVEL/X.P. VALUE:
 VII/2,550 + 14 per hit point

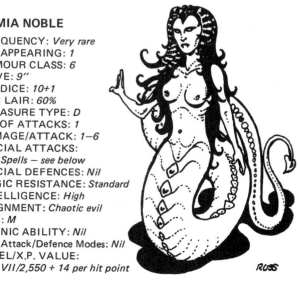

RUSS

These beings have rule over other lamias and the wild, lonely areas they inhabit. They differ from the normal lamia (see **ADVANCED DUNGEONS & DRAGONS MONSTER MANUAL** — *Lamia*) in that the lamia noble's lower body is that of a giant serpent and the upper body can be either male or female. If male, they wield short swords and have magical ability at experience level 1–6 in addition to the spells *charm person, mirror image, suggestion* and *illusion*. Those with female upper bodies are unarmed and only attack by means of spells; however they are more experienced magically and will have abilities at experience level 2–8 together with the spells listed above. The lamia noble's touch permanently drains 1 point of wisdom from a victim, and when wisdom drops below 3 the victim will willingly do whatever the lamia noble tells him to do.

All lamia nobles are able to assume human form (though intelligent humanoids will always be able to penetrate the disguise) and in this guise attempt to penetrate human society to wreak acts of evil. They speak all the languages of the man-like races.

When in human form they will be recognised as lamias only by humans and demi-humans of the 7th experience level or above (10% cumulative chance per level above 6th with clerics receiving a flat 15% extra chance).

Lamia nobles are given to outbursts of senseless violence.

LAVA CHILDREN

FREQUENCY: *Very rare*
NO. APPEARING: *3—18*
ARMOUR CLASS: *4*
MOVE: *9"*
HIT DICE: *4 or more*
% IN LAIR: *Nil*
TREASURE TYPE: *Q*
NO. OF ATTACKS: *3*
DAMAGE/ATTACK:
 1—6/1—6/2—12
SPECIAL ATTACKS:
 Spells — see below
SPECIAL DEFENCES:
 *'Immune' to metal — see
 below*
MAGIC RESISTANCE:
 Standard, but see below
INTELLIGENCE: *Average*
ALIGNMENT: *Neutral*
SIZE: *M*
PSIONIC ABILITY: *Nil*
 Attack/Defence Modes: *Nil*
LEVEL/X.P. VALUE:
 4HD: III/150 + 4 per hit point
 5HD: IV/205 + 5 per hit point
 Spell-casters: V/280 + 5 per hit point
 Double-classed: V/475 + 6 per hit point
 Triple-classed: VI/700 + 7 per hit point

These humanoids are approximately the same size as a broadly-built man; however, they have a curious child-like appearance, with pinkish-white skin and a permanent smile on their faces. They are the unnatural offspring of a union between spirits of earth and fire.

In melee they fight with their clawed hands (1—6 hit points of damage each) and a surprisingly powerful bite for 2—12 hit points of damage.

They are peculiarly 'immune' to metal. Metal simply does not exist for lava children. Thus any metal object can pass through them without harming them and they can move through metal without hindrance. Any metal worn by a victim of their attack is ignored for the purposes of computing armour class.

Most lava children have 4 hit dice and are of the fighter class, but some are exceptional. In any group of 3—7, there will be one higher-level fighter — a 'warrior' with 5 hit dice — which hits at +1. A group of 8—10 will contain one warrior and one magic-user, also of 5 hit dice. A group of 11—14 will include one warrior, one magic-user and one cleric, each with 5 hit dice, while a group of 15—18 will include all the above plus one double-classed warrior/magic-user of 6 hit dice.

Magic-users have the use of the following spells, once each per day: *affect normal fires, burning hands, feather fall, light, fools gold, pyrotechnics, fireball* and *slow.* They cast these spells at the 6th level of magic-use.

Clerics have the use of the following spells: *cure light wounds, light, remove fear, find traps* (x2), *slow poison, continual light, dispel magic.*

Lava children are completely immune to fire and earth magic but vulnerable to air and water magic, taking one extra hit point of damage from the latter per level of the caster.

Lava children live underground or in volcanic regions. It is said that their highest leaders are triple-classed warrior/magic-user/clerics of 7 hit dice.

They speak their own sibilant tongue and the common tongue.

LIZARD KING

FREQUENCY: *Very rare*
NO. APPEARING: *1*
ARMOUR CLASS: *3*
MOVE: *15"//12"*
HIT DICE: *8*
% IN LAIR: *20%*
TREASURE TYPE: *E*
NO. OF ATTACKS: *1*
DAMAGE/ATTACK: *5—20*
SPECIAL ATTACKS:
 Skewering — see below
SPECIAL DEFENCES: *Nil*
MAGIC RESISTANCE: *20%*
INTELLIGENCE: *Average*
ALIGNMENT: *Chaotic evil*
SIZE: *L (about 8' tall)*
PSIONIC ABILITY: *Nil*
 Attack/Defence Modes: *Nil*
LEVEL/X.P. VALUE:
 VI/550 + 10 per hit point

The lizard king is a variety of the lizard man (see **ADVANCED DUNGEONS & DRAGONS MONSTER MANUAL**) — taller, more intelligent and more human-like than a normal lizard man. It dwells in damp areas, usually near an underground river or lake. It will have 10—100 lizard men followers/guards from which it demands two human sacrifices each week. These followers will always make every effort to meet the demands of their master since the king, if it lacks human sacrifices to eat, will substitute two of its followers for each human not available.

The trident of the lizard king is a fearsome weapon which can inflict 5—20 hit points of damage on a victim. If the 'to hit' die roll is 5 or more greater than the score needed to hit, the trident will skewer the victim, doing double normal damage and a minimum of 15 hit points. However, the trident's special properties only function when used by lizard kings; sages have pondered this singular weapon behaviour for many years but have so far come to no conclusions — certainly the trident behaves, in the hands of a human, just like a normal trident.

With the exceptions noted, the lizard king has all the characteristics of the normal lizard man.

MAGNESIUM SPIRIT — MANTARI — MEAZEL — MEENLOCK — MEPHIT — MEZZODAEMON — MITE

MAGNESIUM SPIRIT

FREQUENCY: *Very rare*
NO. APPEARING: *1*
ARMOUR CLASS: *0*
MOVE: *36"*
HIT DICE: *6+1*
% IN LAIR: *Nil*
TREASURE TYPE: *Nil*
NO. OF ATTACKS: *1*
DAMAGE/ATTACK: *3—12*
SPECIAL ATTACKS: *Energy and strength drain — see below*
SPECIAL DEFENCES: *Can only be hit by silver and magical weapons; and see below*
MAGIC RESISTANCE: *50% and see below*
INTELLIGENCE: *Very*
ALIGNMENT: *Lawful evil*
SIZE: *M*
PSIONIC ABILITY: *Nil*
    Attack/Defence Modes: *Nil*
LEVEL/X.P. VALUE: *VII/1,300 + 8 per hit point*

It is believed that only three or four of these creatures exist, having been summoned originally to the *Prime Material Plane*, and stranded there, by an evil magic-user of high experience level who died as a result of the strain of the summoning. Their actual plane of origin is a matter of conjecture. Their behaviour is completely dominated by their need to inhabit the body of a character of 5th or higher level in order to perform the complex spell-casting ritual which will return them to their place of origin. Only a human body will give them the necessary psychic frame of reference, so they attack only humans.

In appearance the magnesium spirit resembles a cylinder of white flame, 5' tall and 3' diameter, with a wispy tail 5' long. However they do not give off any discernable heat.

Moving at extraordinary speed, the spirit will approach a party containing humans and quickly reach a position within 10' of its selected victim (chosen at random from the humans present), in which position it will pause and flare up in a split-second blinding flash of white light. All who are within 20' and who are observing the spirit (including non-humans) must make a saving throw versus petrification to escape blindness for 12 turns (two full hours). Treat the effects as the *blindness* spell of the illusionist.

The spirit will then attack, automatically gaining initiative each round even against *hasted* opponents. If it scores a hit it drains one energy level and two points of strength from the victim (the latter recoverable at the rate of 1 point per hour, the energy level drain being permanent); it also inflicts 3—12 hit points of damage. Once it has hit it is locked onto its victim's body and will merge gradually into that body, draining energy and strength and causing 3—12 hit points of damage per round as it does so. After two melee rounds of this merging process, the only way to hit the spirit without harming its victim is with holy water which will cause 2—7 hit points of damage to the spirit per vial-full and also force it to abandon the merging process (though it may attack the same victim or another human victim in the next round). During the merging process, the spirit causes damage automatically, requiring no 'to hit' roll.

If the spirit has achieved three rounds of the merging process without being forced to abandon its victim (i.e. two rounds during which it is vulnerable to normal attack and one round during which it is vulnerable only to holy water) it will have taken over its victim and the human persona will have been negated. If the victim has five or more

energy levels (hit dice) at that time (since he will have lost four, one from the initial attack and three from three rounds of the merging process, he must have been at least 9th level before the attack) the spirit will use the body to shriek out its spell, which takes 5 segments, and then body and spirit will vanish in a flash of light. The spirit has gone back to its plane of origin, never to return.

If the victim has fewer than five energy levels remaining (i.e. was at most 8th level before the spirit's first attack), the spirit will abandon the body and seek another, turning to another nearby human (if one is available) and commencing the attack process all over again on him. The body of the first victim, now a mindless husk, will collapse and will resist all resurrection attempts (though a powerful spell such as a *wish* will bring back the victim if used properly).

The magnesium spirit can only be harmed by silver or magical weapons. It has 50% magic resistance as well as immunity to *sleep*, *charm*, *hold*, *paralysation* and *fear* spells. It is vulnerable to holy water at all times, whether during the merging process or otherwise, taking 2—7 hit points of damage per vial-full thrown onto it.

MANTARI

FREQUENCY: *Very rare*
NO. APPEARING: *1—3*
ARMOUR CLASS: *9*
MOVE: *18"*
HIT DICE: *1+1*
% IN LAIR: *Nil*
TREASURE TYPE: *Nil*
NO. OF ATTACKS: *1*
DAMAGE/ATTACK: *Special — see below*
SPECIAL ATTACKS: *Nil*
SPECIAL DEFENCES: *Nil*
MAGIC RESISTANCE: *Standard*
INTELLIGENCE: *Animal*
ALIGNMENT: *Neutral evil*
SIZE: *S*
PSIONIC ABILITY: *Nil*
    Attack/Defence Modes: *Nil*
LEVEL/X.P. VALUE: *III/65 + 2 per hit point*

This flying creature bears a close resemblance to the marine ray, with a flat body about 3' long (and nearly as wide) and a 4' long thin whip-like tail. The mantari (singular and plural) usually preys on giant rats and the like for food, but it is normally (85%) aggressive when encountering other creatures and humans. It flies with its tail held vertically downwards, but when attacking — diving onto its victim from a height of 10'—12' above ground — the tail assumes a forward-pointing acute angle with the body.

It strikes solely by whipping a victim with its tail. The sting in the tip of the tail is not poisonous, but acts on the victim's nervous system. The number of hit points of damage inflicted by a hit is equal to the difference between 19 and the victim's constitution (so a victim with constitution 12 would take 7 hit points of damage). No saving throw is permitted against the effects of the sting.

Furthermore, if the same victim is hit in two successive melee rounds, the damage inflicted by the second hit is four times normal. There is no additional damage bonus for the third or subsequent successive hit on the same victim — each counts as four times normal.

The mantari is found in most types of locale, though its preferred haunts are dirty dungeon chambers where its prey abounds. For purposes of aerial combat it is manoeuvrability class C.

MEAZEL

FREQUENCY: *Uncommon*
NO. APPEARING: *1*
ARMOUR CLASS: *8*
MOVE: *12"*
HIT DICE: *4*
% IN LAIR: *95%*
TREASURE TYPE: *B*
NO. OF ATTACKS: *2*
DAMAGE/ATTACK: *1—4/1—4*
SPECIAL ATTACKS: *Nil*
SPECIAL DEFENCES:
　See below
MAGIC RESISTANCE:
　Standard
INTELLIGENCE: *Low*
ALIGNMENT: *Chaotic evil*
SIZE: *M*
PSIONIC ABILITY: *Nil*
　Attack/Defence Modes: *Nil*
LEVEL/X.P. VALUE:
　III/85 + 4 per hit point

Solitary bipeds just less than man-sized, meazels are rarely encountered outside their lairs — either marshes or small, dank caverns underground. They have natural thieving abilities at the 4th level of
experience and will rarely attack openly, preferring to hide and,
moving quietly and swiftly, attempt to strangle stragglers from behind
or to pick pockets in search of the gold they love. The meazel is a
traditional enemy of orcs and kobolds.

Meazels rarely venture far from their lairs and take all corpses there to
be eaten in safety. Piles of sacks full of bones are often to be found
near a meazel lair (any gems the creature has found in treasure will be
in these sacks, since it does not recognise the value of precious and
semi-precious stones). For the same reason, there will be no gems in
the lair.

Most creatures of the underworld will attack meazels, for they have a
nasty reputation even among dungeon denizens.

In combat they attack with their two claws, each inflicting 1—4 hit
points of damage. Alternatively, they use a piece of tough, thin cord
to strangle their victims; a 'hit' indicates that the cord has been
wrapped round the victim's neck and he will die from strangulation
within two melee rounds unless he breaks free, or the meazel dies or
is forced to release its hold (for example to defend against attack
from another quarter). However the creature can only execute this
kind of attack against a victim which is man-sized or smaller and only
if it can approach the victim from the rear undetected, achieving
surprise.

Description: The meazel has skin which varies from light grey to dark
green; irregular patches of an angry red colour will occur on most
(35%) individuals due to a skin disease — neither harmful to the
creature beyond its disfiguring effect, nor contagious — prevalent in
the species, these patches giving the meazel almost a leprous appearance. The eyes are jet black and the feet partially webbed.

MEENLOCK

FREQUENCY: *Very rare*
NO. APPEARING: *3—5*
ARMOUR CLASS: *7 (but*
　see below)
MOVE: *9"*
HIT DICE: *4*
% IN LAIR: *100%*
TREASURE TYPE: *Nil*
NO. OF ATTACKS: *2*
DAMAGE/ATTACK: *1—4/1—4*
SPECIAL ATTACKS:
　Paralysation
SPECIAL DEFENCES:
　Dimension door
MAGIC RESISTANCE: *Standard*
INTELLIGENCE: *Very*
ALIGNMENT: *Lawful evil*
SIZE: *S (2' tall)*
PSIONIC ABILITY: *Nil*
　Attack/Defence Modes: *Nil*
LEVEL/X.P. VALUE:
　IV/240 + 4 per hit point

Meenlocks are small bipedal creatures about 2' tall and covered in
black, shaggy fur. Their heads are white, cut with dark ridges. In total
they present a horrid appearance and will cause *fear* in any person
with four or fewer hit dice who sees them, this causing the victim to
fall inert to the ground for 5—8 melee rounds (the number of rounds
is halved if the victim makes his saving throw).

The meenlocks have their lair in dark, sealed, vertical shafts underground. If the seal is removed, the bottom of the shaft cannot be seen
and anything dropped in will land noiselessly on a thick moss 'carpet'
which lines the walls and floor of the shaft. The shaft will be dark and
a smell of rotting corpses will drift upwards. Characters other than the
most insensitive will also detect a strong emanation of evil even
without the use of a *detect evil* spell. After descending vertically for
20' or so, the shaft twists and curves, so it is impossible to see the
bottom even with a *light* spell, which will only reveal detail of the
upper parts.

If brave adventurers penetrate the shaft they will eventually find the
meenlock lair — a large space like a small cave at the very foot of the
shaft. The creatures will always attack (exception — bright light will
cause them to flee if they are able) and will use their two claws, each
of which inflicts 1—4 hit points of damage. The touch of the
meenlock causes *paralysation* (saving throw applicable). At close
quarters such as in their lair, however, the meenlocks' telepathic
powers are virtually useless — this is their reason for the artificial
smell of rotting corpses which they deliberately create in order to
deter entrance to the lair.

The creatures will use considerable ingenuity to extinquish sources
of light — torches, lanterns and so forth. They have a limited
dimension door ability over a distance of 6' every other melee round
— when using this ability, attacks on them are at —4 on the 'to hit'
roll. However they cannot use this power when carrying a victim —
three meenlocks are required for such a task.

It is if adventurers remove the seal from the top of the shaft but subsequently fail to penetrate the meenlocks' lair that the creatures will
take fullest advantage. When the adventurers depart, they will be followed at a safe distance by the nasty little beasts, which can climb
quickly and noiselessly up the shaft by using the deadening qualities
of the moss carpet. One of the adventurers will be 'marked' by the
meenlocks — selected at random, though if a paladin is present he will
be given priority — and the meenlocks will concentrate their subsequent attacks on him alone, being highly evil and greatly desirous of
wreaking vengeance on humankind. The victim selected will always be
human if one is present, but if not the creatures will choose an elf,
dwarf or any other near-human.

From the time of his 'marking' onwards, the chosen victim will
receive disturbing telepathic messages; the meenlocks can communicate telepathically over a 300' range. The messages will vary in
content but the threat will be the same — that the meenlocks are

pursuing the victim relentlessly and intend to make him one of them. The victim will also be conscious of stealthy movement in the shadows and of rustling, scratching noises (these will also be illusory and induced telepathically). Companions of the victim will hear and detect nothing and may conclude that their colleague is mentally aberrant.

The meenlocks will not attack until the party beds down to rest. However, until that time the victim will become increasingly preoccupied with his predicament and will be able to concentrate less and less upon his adventure. His efficiency will thus be reduced, though the extent and effect of this will vary and is to be determined by the referee. As a guide, for every hour the victim is harassed by meenlocks, his strength, dexterity, intelligence and wisdom will be reduced temporarily by 1 point each, in addition he will attack at −1 on the 'to hit' roll in melee and (if he is a spell-caster) victims of his spells will receive a +2 bonus on their saving throw. All these effects are cumulative but will disappear as soon as the meenlock threat has somehow been averted (if for example the party moves into an area which is brightly illuminated and which the meenlocks will not be able to enter).

When the party including the victim has bedded down to rest, the meenlocks will attack, moving very silently (80% chance of obtaining surprise even against a watchful guard — 100% against a sleeper). They will attempt to silence any guards and drag their victim away (they will not attack the victim with their claws unless absolutely necessary, but they show no similar mercy to others). If they succeed in doing so, they will take the victim to their shaft, sealing it after entry. After a short but gruesome treatment, the victim himself becomes a meenlock.

MEPHIT

	Fire	Lava	Smoke	Steam
FREQUENCY:	Very rare	Very rare	Very rare	Very rare
NO. APPEARING:	1	1	1	1
ARMOUR CLASS:	5	6	4	7
MOVE:	12″/24″	12″/24″	12″/24″	12″/24″
HIT DICE:	3+1	3	3	3+3
% IN LAIR:	Nil	Nil	Nil	Nil
TREASURE TYPE:	2—12	1—10	1—10	3—18
		platinum pieces each		
NO. OF ATTACKS:	2	2	2	2
DAMAGE/ATTACK:	1—3/1—3	See below	1—2/1—2	1—4/1—4
SPECIAL ATTACKS:	Breath Weapon	Breath Weapon	Breath Weapon	Breath Weapon
SPECIAL DEFENCES:	See below	See below	See below	See below
MAGIC RESISTANCE:	Standard	Standard	Standard	Standard
INTELLIGENCE:	Average	Average	Average	Average
ALIGNMENT:		Variable but always evil		
SIZE:	M (5' tall)	M (5' tall)	M (5' tall)	M (5' tall)
PSIONIC ABILITY:	Nil	Nil	Nil	Nil
Attack/Defence Modes:	Nil	Nil	Nil	Nil
LEVEL/X.P. VALUE:	III/150+4 per hit point	III/105+3 per hit point	III/105+3 per hit point	IV/175+4 per hit point

The various mephits are the evil messengers and errand-runners of the powerful creatures of the *Lower Planes*. They are common inhabitants of all these locales, from the *Nine Hells* to the *Abyss*. Their alignment varies, depending on their plane of origin, but they are always evil.

When mephits appear on the *Prime Material Plane*, they always have some demoniac or diabolic mission to perform (or a similar mission from another such evil personage). This can vary from a rigorous task (for example seeking out a particular victim and capturing him for transportation to *Hades*) to a more general mission (such as indiscriminate looting and killing).

Mephits are connoisseurs of the vulgar and tasteless; they share an extraordinarily twisted sense of humour (to a mephit, the sight of a creature writhing in agony is excruciatingly funny). They delight particularly in tormenting the helpless. If they can obtain them (and it is usual that they do) they will wear clothes of the most garish design and colour possible. They are often seen puffing upon smoking rolls of exceedingly foul-smelling dried vegetation. They adopt a strut-

ting gait and have shrill voices (they all speak a common mephit tongue and their alignment language).

All mephits are about 5' tall, with functional wings and fangs. Other forms of mephit are thought to exist though there is as yet no positive identification of type.

So far as can be ascertained, no particular type of mephit is more or less common on any of the *Lower Planes* — the types appear to be distributed in an indiscriminate fashion.

For purposes of aerial combat, all mephits are manoeuvrability class B.

Fire Mephit: These mischievous creatures are dull red in colour, with thin streaks of black. Their bodies are surrounded with wisps of flame — touching them with bare hands will cause 1 hit point of damage.

They attack with two claws (1—3 hit points of damage each plus 1 point of heat damage for a total of 2—4) and a breath weapon. This i either a jet of flame 15' long and 1' in diameter which automaticall hits a designated target in range and delivers 2—9 hit points of dama (damage halved if a saving throw is made) or a blanket of flame 5 square immediately in front of the mephit (4 hit points of damage t each victim — no saving throw permitted). The mephit is able to var the form of its breath weapon according to the circumstances. It ca breathe three times per day.

The fire mephit can *heat metal* and use *magic missile* (2 missiles) on each per day. Once every hour they may attempt to *gate* in anothe mephit — 25% chance of the attempt succeeding. The new arriv will be a fire, lava, smoke or steam mephit (equal probability eac type).

Lava Mephit: These mephits are dull red in colour and constantly oo molten lava from their bodies in small drops, just as though it we very heavy perspiration. The heat from their bodies can be sensed 3 away and anyone touching a lava mephit with bare flesh receiv 1—8 hit points of damage.

They attack using their claws (1 hit point of damage each plus 1— hit points of heat damage, for 2—9 points total) and a breath weapo

The latter consists of a molten blob of lava which automatically hits any single designated target within a 10' range (1—6 hit points of damage — no saving throw permitted). If the encounter takes place in a volcanic region where molten lava is available, these mephits can *regenerate* 2 hit points per round simply by keeping in contact with the lava (though this power *ceases* when the mephit is killed). The lava mephit can use its breath weapon once every three rounds, but unless in contact with molten lava the maximum number of lava blobs which can be projected is 8, and when this 'supply' is exhausted the mephit will no longer be able to breathe that day unless it subsequently 're-charges' by getting in contact with molten lava.

The smoke mephit is black in colour and has smoke oozing from its body. It will inhabit smoky and dark areas while on the *Prime Material Plane* and will never emerge into bright light unless forced to do so.

The touch of the lava mephit automatically dissolves materials dissolving wood slowly at but one inch thickness per hour and metals quickly — destroying plate armour in 3 melee rounds) and all lava mephits may *shape change* at will into a pool of molten lava (this action will not re-charge the breath weapon). Once per hour they may attempt to *gate* in 1—2 other mephits (equal probability each type; if two appear they will be of the same type) with a 25% chance of success.

Smoke Mephit: Like the fire mephits, these creatures attack with two claws (1—2 hit points of damage each) and a breath weapon. The latter consists of the discharge of a sooty ball of smoke which does 1—4 hit points of damage to a victim — no saving throw permitted. The ball of smoke will automatically hit any single designated victim within a 20' range. The victim, in addition to receiving damage, is blinded for 1—2 melee rounds. The smoke mephit can use its breath weapon every other melee round; there is no limitation on the total number of times it may breathe.

The smoke mephit can use *invisibility* and *dancing lights* once each per day and can, once every hour, attempt to *gate* in 1—2 other mephits (equal probability each type; if two appear they will be of the same type) with a 20% chance of success.

When a smoke mephit dies, it coughs up 1 hit point of flame damage to everyone within 10' (no saving throw permitted).

Steam Mephits: These mephits are grey in colour and constantly ooze hot water, leaving a trail of water behind them when they move. Touching a steam mephit with bare flesh will deliver 1 hit point of damage to the victim, together with a 50% chance of his being stunned for one melee round.

In addition to attacking with their two claws (each of which inflicts 1—4 hit points of damage) they can direct a jet of scalding water at any single designated victim within 20' — this will hit the victim automatically. The jet of water inflicts 1—3 hit points of damage (no saving throw permitted) and there is a 50% chance that the victim will also be stunned for one melee round. The mephit can use this breath weapon a limitless number of times at a frequency of once every two melee rounds.

Once per day the steam mephit can perform a 'rainstorm' of boiling water — treat as *ice storm* with 2—12 hit points of damage for all victims (no saving throws permitted). Once per hour it can *contaminate water* (as the reversal of *purify water*). Once per hour it may also attempt to *gate* in 1—2 other mephits (equal probability each type; if two appear they will be of the same type) with a 30% chance of success.

MEZZODAEMON

FREQUENCY: *Uncommon*
NO. APPEARING:
   1 (rarely 1—3)
ARMOUR CLASS: *—3*
MOVE: *15''*
HIT DICE: *10+40 points*
% IN LAIR: *Nil*
TREASURE TYPE:
   Individuals Q(x5), X
NO. OF ATTACKS: *2 or 1 weapon*
DAMAGE/ATTACK: *7—12/7—12*
   or by weapon +6
SPECIAL ATTACKS: *See below*
SPECIAL DEFENCES: *See below*
MAGIC RESISTANCE: *Special*
INTELLIGENCE: *High -*
   exceptional
ALIGNMENT: *Evil (neutral)*
SIZE: *M (about 7' tall)*
PSIONIC ABILITY: *Nil*
   Attack/Defence Modes: *Nil*
LEVEL/X.P. VALUE:
   VII/2.700 + 14 per hit point (RUSS)

Mezzodaemons inhabit the *Lower Planes* between the *Abyssal Layers and the Hells* — i.e. *Tarterus, Hades, Gehenna*. There they will be found in numbers. They freely associate with night hags and demons, (see **ADVANCED DUNGEONS & DRAGONS MONSTER MANUAL**), and are not averse to devils though they find the devils' strict regulations very tiresome. Mezzodaemons roam the *Astral* and *Ethereal Planes* at times and it is not too difficult to summon them to the *Prime Material Plane*, as they enjoy wreaking havoc here and they are willing to associate with evil humans and the like if the price is right and their 'superior' position is generally recognised.

A mezzodaemon can use its 18(00) strength to great advantage when attacking physically. Its horny hands and talons can be used to strike blows (each of which will inflict 7—12 hit points of damage) but one will often use some form of magical weapon (battle-axe, flail or sword — bastard or two-handed). A magic shield is usually used with a weapon. They have a +3 'to hit' bonus when so armed.

Mezzodaemons are able to employ virtually any magical item not restricted by alignment or affecting only a specific class, viz. *books, librams, tomes* and so on of magical nature affecting the reader. However, their innate magic resistance gives such items varying probabilities of failure, so they are likely to be shunned unless of great power.

The following powers can be used by mezzodaemons: *dimension door* (twice per day), become *ethereal* once per day, *magic jar* once per day, *passwall* four times per day, *repulsion* once per day, *wind walk* once

per day and *word of recall* once per day. They can use at will any one of the following powers during a melee round: *comprehend languages, detect invisibility, detect magic, ESP, invisibility, levitate, polymorph self* and *read magic*.

All mezzodaemons are unaffected by non-magical weapons (including iron and silver), paralysis and poisons of any sort. Acid, cold and fire cause them only half normal damage.

Magic resistance varies according to the level of the spell. They are 95% resistant to first level spells, 90% to second level, 85% to third level and so on to 55% resistant to ninth level spells. This is based on an 11th level of ability of the caster so will vary upwards or downwards according to whether the caster is of lower or higher level than 11th. A mezzodaemon can never be *charmed* and a *suggestion* spell will never affect it.

Mezzodaemons can see into both the infrared and ultraviolet spectra. They have a limited form of telepathy which allows communication with any creature of *low* or better intelligence.

Each mezzodaemon has his or her own name. They keep these names very secret, of course, to avoid being commanded by nycadaemons, demon lords, arch devils and like creatures, and to avoid entrapment by a *summoning* spell.

MITE

FREQUENCY: *Rare*
NO. APPEARING: *6—24*
ARMOUR CLASS: *8*
MOVE: *3''*
HIT DICE: *1—1*
% IN LAIR: *10%*
TREASURE TYPE: *C*
NO. OF ATTACKS: *1*
DAMAGE/ATTACK: *1—3*
SPECIAL ATTACKS: *Nil*
SPECIAL DEFENCES: *Nil*
MAGIC RESISTANCE: *Standard*
INTELLIGENCE: *Low*
ALIGNMENT: *Lawful evil*
SIZE: *S (2' tall)*
PSIONIC ABILITY: *Nil*
   Attack/Defence Modes: *Nil*
LEVEL/X.P. VALUE:
   I/5 + 1 per hit point

Mites are a mere 2' in height, humanoid with large heads and evil faces. Their skin varies in colour from light grey to violet. They inhabit networks of narrow tunnels above and below main dungeon corridors; their scurrying feet and high-pitched twittering voices can often be heard by roving groups of adventurers. However they are rarely seen and never openly attack.

They will attempt to ensnare the lone adventurer or unwary straggler using trapdoors, nets, tripwires and other such means, bundling their captive off before help arrives. Those captured by mites are robbed, stripped, bound and beaten. Then, somewhat later, they are returned helpless to the main corridor at the mercy of wandering monsters.

In melee they attack with a nasty bite which can inflict 1—3 hit points of damage. They have borrowed from their cousins the jermlaine the latter's technique of beating captives with loaded clubs attempting to stun them, and a victim trapped by their methods will almost certainly (90%) be dealt with in this manner by his mite captors.

The entrances to their tunnels are hidden and can only be detected as if they were secret doors. The tunnels are small and difficult of access to those of human build.

Mites are related to jermlaine and snyads. So far as can be detected they have no language as such — their vocal twittering does not appear to convey more than very rudimentary information.

NECROPHIDIUS – NEEDLEMAN – NILBOG – NONAFEL – NORKER – NYCADAEMON

NECROPHIDIUS (Death Worm)

FREQUENCY: *Very rare*
NO. APPEARING: *1*
ARMOUR CLASS: *2*
MOVE: *9"*
HIT DICE: *2*
% IN LAIR: *10%*
TREASURE TYPE: *Nil*
NO. OF ATTACKS: *1*
DAMAGE/ATTACK: *1–8*
SPECIAL ATTACKS: *Paralysation (and see below)*
SPECIAL DEFENCES: *Immune to poison (and see below)*
MAGIC RESISTANCE: *See below*
INTELLIGENCE: *Average*
ALIGNMENT: *Neutral*
SIZE: *L*
PSIONIC ABILITY: *Nil*
    Attack/Defence Modes: *Nil*
LEVEL/X.P. VALUE:
    III/118 + 2 per hit point

This creature appears to be the skeleton of a giant snake with a fanged human skull as a head. It is totally silent, immune to *sleep, charm* and mind-affecting spells, immune to poison and will never need to check morale. Its bite (1–8 hit points of damage) causes paralysation unless the victim makes his saving throw (against magic – this is not a venom). The paralysation lasts 1–4 turns.

The necrophidius achieves surprise 50% of the time (1–3 on d6) and if it is not itself surprised it will execute the *Dance of Death* – a hypnotic, semi-magical swaying which rivets the attention of any victim observing the worm who fails to make his saving throw against magic. Failure means inability to act; treat as *hypnotism*. This allows the worm to advance and attack without opposition.

A necrophidius is created for one specific purpose and is therefore generally met in the role of assassin or guard – never as a wandering monster.

There are three ways of creating a necrophidius. The first is by means of a special magical *tome*, similar to a *Manual of Golems.* The second method is for a high-level magic-user to employ a *limited wish,* a *geas* and a *charm person.* The third method is for a high-level cleric to employ *quest, neutralise poison, prayer, silence* and *snake charm.* The materials include the complete articulated skeleton of a giant snake (poisonous or constrictor) and the skull of a cold-blooded murderer killed within the previous 24 hours. The cost is 500 gold pieces per hit point of the creature and it requires 10 days construction time.

Despite a number of characteristics to the contrary, the necrophidius is not a member of the undead class and cannot, for example, be turned by a cleric.

NEEDLEMAN

FREQUENCY: *Very rare*
NO. APPEARING: *5–50*
ARMOUR CLASS: *6*
MOVE: *9"*
HIT DICE: *3+4*
% IN LAIR: *25%*
TREASURE TYPE: *G*
NO. OF ATTACKS: *1–6*
DAMAGE/ATTACK: *1–2*
SPECIAL ATTACKS: *Surprise*
SPECIAL DEFENCES:
    See below
MAGIC RESISTANCE:
    Sub-standard – see below
INTELLIGENCE: *Low*
ALIGNMENT: *Neutral*
SIZE: *M*
PSIONIC ABILITY: *Nil*
    Attack/Defence Modes: *Nil*
LEVEL/X.P. VALUE:
    III/85 + 3 per hit point

This wood-dwelling, intelligent form of plant life looks like a zombie but in fact is neither animal nor of the undead class. Embedded in its 'flesh' all over its body are masses of small sharp needles, like pine needles. Each round it may 'fire' 1–6 of these needles, each of which inflicts 1–2 hit points of damage on a victim, up to a range of 20' with the accuracy of a short-range arrow. For practical purposes, its supply of needles is infinite.

The creature is particularly vulnerable to magic. Attacks on it by magical means will inflict triple normal damage on it, though it has a saving throw as normal. Other spells of a non-offensive nature (such as *charm plants*) will be triply effective against it, as appropriate. Of course, the fact that it is a plant makes it immune to certain spells.

Needlemen appear to hate elves and will attack them on sight.

When amidst conifers or heavy undergrowth, needlemen are nearly (75%) undetectable and will achieve surprise 75% of the time. It is very rare to encounter the creature outside this sort of natural habitat.

NILBOG

FREQUENCY: *Very rare (at best)*
NO. APPEARING: *4–40*
ARMOUR CLASS: *6*
MOVE: *6"*
HIT DICE: *1-1*
% IN LAIR: *40%*
TREASURE TYPE: *Individuals K; in lair C*
NO. OF ATTACKS: *1*
DAMAGE/ATTACK: *1–6 or by weapon type*
SPECIAL ATTACKS: *Nil*
SPECIAL DEFENCES: *See below*
MAGIC RESISTANCE: *Standard*
INTELLIGENCE: *Average*
ALIGNMENT: *Lawful evil*
SIZE: *S (4' tall)*
PSIONIC ABILITY: *Nil*
    Attack/Defence Modes: *Nil*
LEVEL/X.P. VALUE: *III/53 +1 per hit point*

This creature looks exactly like a normal goblin and has all the characteristics of that race (see ADVANCED DUNGEONS & DRAGONS MONSTER MANUAL — Goblin) with one important exception — it suffers from a curious spatio-temporal reversal. It remains a mystery why only goblins are susceptible to this strange disorder. Nilbogism (the name given to the disorder) appears to occur when overly heavy use of magic strains the fabric of the space-time continuum, and leads to some very strange localised events. The coincidence of conditions which lead to nilbogism is extremely rare and is only imperfectly understood. Although the creature itself does not in any sense transmit the disorder to those around it, some of the effects are transmitted.

Many and varied accounts have been received about the nature of the space-time disturbances which take place in the presence of nilbogs. Only one factor appears to be common — the adventurers will have no control over their own actions and will generally pursue courses of action contrary to their normal intent; for example they may feel an overwhelming compulsion to load all their treasure into an empty treasure chest in the nilbog lair and leave empty-handed. There are no saving throws against these effects, nor is there any known defence (though a powerful spell such as a *wish*, will, if used properly, have a good chance of rendering local immunity against the effects).

Another curious feature of nilbog power is that the creature gains hit points when it is struck, the addition being equal to the intended damage rolled. It can only lose hit points by such means as casting *cure wounds* spells on it, forcibly feeding it *healing* potions and so on.

For obvious reasons, encounters with these strange creatures are dreaded and, as a result, normal goblins tend to be treated with extreme caution lest they turn out ot be nilbogs. There appears to be no way of distinguishing between the two apart from the use of such spells as *commune* or by trial and error.

So far as is known, no other creature has been afflicted with nilbogism.

NONAFEL (Cat O' Nine Tails)

FREQUENCY: *Very rare*
NO. APPEARING: *1*
ARMOUR CLASS: *Parent 5,
   'children' 6*
MOVE: *Parent 9'', 'children' 12''*
HIT DICE: *9*
% IN LAIR: *40%*
TREASURE TYPE: *Nil*
NO. OF ATTACKS: *1*
DAMAGE/ATTACK:
   2—20 or 1—8
SPECIAL ATTACKS: *Nil*
SPECIAL DEFENCES:
   See below
MAGIC RESISTANCE: *Standard*
INTELLIGENCE: *Low*
ALIGNMENT: *Chaotic evil*
SIZE: *L*
PSIONIC ABILITY: *Nil*
   Attack/Defence Modes: *Nil*
LEVEL/X.P. VALUE:
   VII/1,400 + 12 per hit point

On first sight this creature appears to be a large black panther with yellow, bloodshot eyes. It is usually found in caves in warm zones of the underworld. It is carnivorous and its skin has been known to fetch as much as 1,500 gold pieces.

The creature displays a most unusual dissociative power which enables it to divide into nine individual black panthers. This transormation takes place in one segment of time and appears to be instinctive, requiring no concentration on the part of the 'parent' beast. The creature will always attack a party of adventurers or any other monster it encounters, usually (90%) transforming itself as soon as its enemies are sighted and then attempting to surround the party, all nine 'children' acting in co-operative fashion as though there exists some telepathic bond between them which gives them the effective power of a corporate brain. There is only a small chance (10%) that

the creature will remain in parent form before attacking, and even if this is the case the dissociation will take place after 1—2 melee rounds of combat.

If one or more of the 'children' are damaged during melee there is a 25% chance (check each melee round, but the chance is not cumulative) that the children will be re-associated to form the parent. This takes place by means of a *blink* operation and all the children can be re-associated so long as they are within a 50' radius (the re-association will not take place if all children are not within a 50' radius); the children can still engage in combat during the round of their re-association.

When re-associated, the parent can *regenerate* 9 hit points each round, one for each of the offspring (if one or more of the offspring were unharmed before re-association, the hit points due to them from the *regeneration* are lost and cannot be transferred to one of their damaged brethren). Once one round of *regeneration* has taken place, the parent will again dissociate into nine (or perhaps fewer, if one has been killed) offspring; again the parent can partake in combat during the melee round of dissociation. If an offspring is killed, the body will *blink* to the parent-body when re-association takes place, but the *regeneration* has no effect on that particular individual beast, and when dissociation next takes place, there will be one fewer offspring.

After the second dissociation, the whole process begins again, with a 25% chance each round that the parent will re-form if one or more of the children have been damaged.

The parent beast has 9 hit dice, each child 1 die. When the creature dissociates, the parent's hits will be divided as equally as possible between the children (so a parent of 49 hits will divide into five children with 5 hits each and four with 6 hits each).

The parent attacks as a 9HD monster using its flail-like tail to hit for 2—20 hit points of damage. The tail is swung over the head in a manner similar to the tail attack of a wyvern.

Each child fights as a 2HD monster, using its tail in a similar manner to inflict 1—8 hit points of damage.

NORKER

FREQUENCY: *Rare*
NO. APPEARING: *3—30*
ARMOUR CLASS: *3*
MOVE: *9''*
HIT DICE: *1+2*
% IN LAIR: *20%*
TREASURE TYPE: *E*
NO. OF ATTACKS: *2*
DAMAGE/ATTACK:
   1—3/1—6
SPECIAL ATTACKS: *Nil*
SPECIAL DEFENCES: *Nil*
MAGIC RESISTANCE:
   Standard
INTELLIGENCE: *Average*
ALIGNMENT:
   Chaotic evil
SIZE: *S (4' tall)*
PSIONIC ABILITY: *Nil*
   Attack/Defence Modes: *Nil*
LEVEL/X.P. VALUE:
   I/20 + 2 per hit point

Far-distant relatives of hobgoblins, norkers are similar in appearance to their hobgoblin cousins but have developed 3'' fangs which they use in melee to inflict 1—3 hit points of damage. In the same round they can also attack the same opponent with a club for 1—6 points of damage, but if they are disarmed they have no effective claw attack.

The norker also has a very tough skin — a form of exoskeleton — which gives it armour class 3.

In all other respects they are similar to hobgoblins (see ADVANCED DUNGEONS & DRAGONS MONSTER MANUAL).

NYCADAEMON

FREQUENCY: *Very rare*
NO. APPEARING: *1 (very
    rarely, 1—2)*
ARMOUR CLASS: *—4*
MOVE: *12"/36"*
HIT DICE: *12+36 points*
% IN LAIR: *Nil*
TREASURE TYPE: *Q(x10), X*
NO. OF ATTACKS: *2 or 1 weapon*
DAMAGE/ATTACK: *9—16/9—16
    or by weapon +8*
SPECIAL ATTACKS: *See below*
SPECIAL DEFENCES: *See below*
MAGIC RESISTANCE: *Special*
INTELLIGENCE:
    Exceptional — genius
ALIGNMENT: *Evil (neutral)*
SIZE: *L (about 8' tall and
    broad)*
PSIONIC ABILITY: *Nil*
    Attack/Defence Modes: *Nil*
LEVEL/X.P. VALUE:
    IX/6,800 + 16 per hit point

The race of nycadaemons are among the most powerful of the creatures native to the *Middle Lower Planes.* Like their cousins the mezzodaemons, nycadaemons are common to the planes of *Tarterus, Hades* and *Gehenna.* Unlike their related creatures, they are also able to enter the *666 Layers of the Abyss* and the *9 Hells* as they will. Nycadaemons are avoided by all lesser creatures — night hags, mezzodaemons, lesser and greater devils, and most demons (see **ADVANCED DUNGEONS & DRAGONS MONSTER MANUAL**) — for the race is totally wicked and domineering, caring not who or what they enslave or exploit, but always acting in an intelligent and carefully calculated manner aimed at maximising personal power and safety. Thus, these creatures will co-operate with other evil beings and races whenever mutual actions are likely to prove beneficial to themselves.

Nycadaemons are very strong (comparable in strength to stone giants — see **ADVANCED DUNGEONS & DRAGONS, MONSTER MANUAL**) and gain +8 on damage, so blows from their huge horny fists inflict terrible punishment (9—16 hit points of damage each). However, nycadaemons will employ suitably large magic weapons in conjunction with a shield (c.f. mezzodaemon) whenever such weapons are available. When using a weapon, these creatures have a +4 'to hit' bonus due to their strength.

As nycadaemons are clever and capable, they can use all sorts of magic items appropriate to their size and nature. These creatures have a graduated magic resistance which prevents low level magic from functioning except rarely, and even higher level spell devices are likely to malfunction with distressing regularity, so nycadaemons typically shun all but the most powerful dweomered objects, — some few miscellaneous objects, artifacts, relics and the like — and enchanted weapons which have no magical projections to be affected by their multi-planed structure.

The following powers can be used by nycadaemons: *command* three times per day, *dispel magic* twice per day, *dimension door* three times per day, *gaseous form* once per day, *mirror image* (4 images) twice per day, *reverse gravity* twice per day, *wind walk* three times per day and *word of recall* once per day. They may also employ any one of the following powers once per round: *comprehend languages, detect invisibility, detect magic, enlarge* (and reverse), *fear* (by touch), *invisibility* (up to 10' radius), *polymorph self, project image, read magic, telepathy.*

Only weapons of +2 or greater enchantment will cause damage to nycadaemons. Iron weapons and silver weapons do not harm these creatures, unless the weapons are enchanted as noted. Paralysis and poisons (including all gases) have no effect on them, and acids, cold and fire cause them only half normal damage. They *regenerate* 3 hit points of damage per *turn* (i.e. 0.3 hit points per melee round).

Nycadaemons are 100% resistant to magic of the first level, and this resistance decreases in 5% increments (c.f. mezzodaemon) to 60% at ninth level. This is based upon 11th level of ability; it decreases in 5% steps if the spell-caster is of 12th or greater level and increases by the same amount if the spell-caster is 10th level or lower. *Beguiling, charm* and *suggestion* never affect the nycadaemon.

Examples: If a nycadaemon faces a 5th level spell from a 13th level magic-user, its resistance is 80%—10% or 70%. If a 10th level magic-user casts a a 4th level spell at a nycadaemon, its resistance is 85%+5% = 90%.

The entire spectrum of radiation can be seen by nycadaemons (i.e. infrared, ultra-violet, X-rays, gamma rays etc.) The telepathic ability of these creatures allows them to communicate on the telepathic level with creatures of intelligence *low* or better.

Each nycadaemon has a personal name which they guard most carefully to avoid entrapment or servitude to some demon lord, arch devil or the like.

OGRILLON — OSQUIP

OGRILLON

FREQUENCY: *Rare*
NO. APPEARING:
    1—4 (5—30 in lair)
ARMOUR CLASS: *6*
MOVE: *12"*
HIT DICE: *2*
% IN LAIR: *20%*
TREASURE TYPE: *Individuals*
    M; in lair B, S
NO. OF ATTACKS: *2*
DAMAGE/ATTACK: *2—7/2—7*
SPECIAL ATTACKS: *Nil*
SPECIAL DEFENCES: *Nil*
MAGIC RESISTANCE: *Standard*
INTELLIGENCE: *Low*
ALIGNMENT: *Chaotic evil*
SIZE: *M*
PSIONIC ABILITY: *Nil*
    Attack/Defence Modes: *Nil*
LEVEL/X.P. VALUE:
    II/28 + 2 per hit point

The ogrillon is a smaller species of the ogre, being an orc-ogre cross-breed and displays the same general behaviour as its larger cousin (see **ADVANCED DUNGEONS & DRAGONS MONSTER MANUAL — Ogre**) with one exception — it never wields a weapon and fights with its horny fists. Because of the creature's strength of 18(01) each fist delivers 2—7 hit points of damage if it hits.

In appearance these creatures usually resemble orcs and will often associate with them for short periods. It is 90% unlikely that an ogrillon can be distinguished from an orc, even when the two types of creature are in the same group. However, some (10%) are ogrish in appearance though smaller. These also associate with orcs though they are easily distinguishable.

Ogrillons speak the ogrish tongue and their alignment language only.

OSQUIP

FREQUENCY: *Uncommon*
NO. APPEARING: *2—24*
ARMOUR CLASS: *7*
MOVE: *12" (½")*
HIT DICE: *3+1*
% IN LAIR: *80%*
TREASURE TYPE: *D*
NO. OF ATTACKS: *1*
DAMAGE/ATTACK: *2—12*
SPECIAL ATTACKS: *Nil*
SPECIAL DEFENCES: *Nil*
MAGIC RESISTANCE: *Standard*
INTELLIGENCE: *Animal*
ALIGNMENT: *Neutral*
SIZE: *S (2' high at shoulder)*
PSIONIC ABILITY: *Nil*
    Attack/Defence Modes: *Nil*
LEVEL/X.P. VALUE:
    III/60 + 4 per hit point

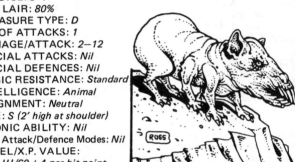

The osquip is a multi-legged hairless rodent-like creature the size of a small dog. Most specimens have 6 legs but some (25%) have eight and there are a few rare creatures (5%) with ten legs. The creature's hide is a very light yellow — almost colourless — and resembles very pliable leather. The eyes are small and set close together, each being heavily protected by surrounding ridges of hide-covered bone. The jaws are unusually large, the entire bony structure projecting several inches forward of the flesh; in each jaw there are large spade like teeth.

The creature will have its lair in the midst of a complex of tunnels beneath the basements of buildings in a town, or in a dungeon. The tunnel system will be quite extensive and the entrances to it, which are too small to permit the comfortable passage of a human or other man-sized creature, will be carefully hidden (the chance of finding them is the same as the chance of finding a secret door).

The creature feeds on rats, mice and other small vermin, though it is a ferocious beast and will always attack without fear, sometimes emerging to surprise a victim from one of the hidden entrances to its tunnel-system. It attacks with its powerful jaws and these can inflict a nasty bite for 2—12 hit points of damage. It has high dexterity (its natural armour class is 9).

By using its powerful jaws, it can burrow through rock at ½ movement rate. Its behaviour regarding other tunnel-dwelling creatures, such as jermlaine, mites and snyads, is unpredictable. Sometimes it will be encountered acting in co-operation with one or more of these types of creature; at other times the osquip will invade jermlaine, mite or snyad tunnel-systems on predatory missions.

PĔNANGGALAN – PERNICON – PHANTOM STALKER – POLTERGEIST – PROTEIN POLYMORPH

PĔNANGGALAN

FREQUENCY: *Rare*
NO. APPEARING: *1*
ARMOUR CLASS: *Normal 10;*
    head and gut when detached 8
MOVE: *As normal woman; head*
    and gut when detached 12"
HIT DICE: *Body variable; head*
    and gut when detached 4
% IN LAIR: *See below*
TREASURE TYPE: *Nil*
NO. OF ATTACKS: *1*
DAMAGE/ATTACK: *1–6*
    or by weapon type
SPECIAL ATTACKS: *Blood drain*
SPECIAL DEFENCES: *See below*
MAGIC RESISTANCE: *See below*
INTELLIGENCE: *Average*
ALIGNMENT: *Lawful evil*
SIZE: *M*
PSIONIC ABILITY: *Nil*
    Attack/Defence Modes: *Nil*
LEVEL/X.P. VALUE:
    Variable, but at minimum
    V/290 + 5 per hit point

A female vampire-type undead of fearsome power and nauseating appearance, this vile creature appears during the day as an attractive human female who may be of any character class. This is the female human which the pĕnanggalan was before death. She will fight with the same combat abilities as she had when alive, will have spell-use if formerly a spell-caster, thieving abilities if formerly a thief and so on. She will use the weapon (or at least the weapon-type) favoured by her in life. Her body will take the same amount of damage as it could before death (when fully rested) and will fight as though of that experience level. The head, however, will take 4HD of damage and a separate account of hits needs to be kept in case the head itself is struck in this form.

Exception: if the pĕnanggalan was a cleric before death, of whatever alignment, she will be unable to use 'good' spells in her new form and must restrict her spells to those of baneful effect.

A *know alignment* spell cast on the creature in this form will reveal the alignment the pĕnanggalan pursued while alive; as undead, however, the creature will act in accordance with the lawful evil alignment.

In this form the pĕnanggalan is impervious to *holy/unholy symbols* and cannot be turned or dispelled. It is also immune (in either form) to all spells which attempt to control the mind or body, like other undead.

In such a guise, the pĕnanggalan will seek to befriend any unwary party of travellers and attempt to join with them. It will prove extremely useful — over its years of undeath it will have acquired an extensive knowledge of the dungeon which it now roams; it will be able to guide parties to treasure and to warn them of possible dangers. Naturally, it will find some plausible reason for this knowledge and may sometimes make 'deliberate mistakes' or feign ignorance of areas of which it has knowledge, in order not to arouse the suspicion of the party (whose members would naturally become suspicious if their new companion displayed near-omniscience). Having joined a party of adventurers, the pĕnanggalan will remain with that party, even to accompanying them out of the dungeon. It will never, however, encamp for the night with the party in the dungeon, nor will it accompany them to spend the night in the supposed safety of the upper world, making some excuse for being elsewhere.

At night, the pĕnanggalan assumes its real undead form. Its head and internal organs detach themselves from the body, rising vertically from the abdomen, and fly in search of human prey, to feast on their living blood. For this reason, it will always return to one of its secret lairs before nightfall (a single pĕnanggalan may have as many as six identical lairs hidden in various parts of the dungeon). It is particularly fond of the blood of young children or of pregnant females, but lacking such a victim it will select the party member who appears to be most susceptible to hypnosis, preferring a female to a male. It will always attack humans and will ignore even near-humans.

Any unfortunate witness of the scene when the pĕnanggalan head and gut detach from the body must make his saving throw against magic or die immediately. If he makes the saving throw, he is treated as if the *feeblemind* spell had been cast on him.

The head and gut will 'fly' in search of a victim and, when one is discovered, the head will attempt to hypnotise the victim who must save against magic at −3 or fall completely under the control of the creature for as long as it takes to feed. It will make two small lacerations in the victim's throat and feast on the blood throughout the night. For each night's feeding, the victim will lose 1–6 hit points and 1 point each of strength and constitution. The pĕnanggalan will select the same victim each night, if possible, and will continue to visit and feed night after night until the victim is dead.

If the victim survives the night, he will remember none of the events except in snatches, as if from a faintly-remembered dream. If for some reason he avoids the subsequent attentions of the pĕnanggalan, he will continue to lose hit points at the rate of 1 hit point per night either until dead or until *dispel evil* is cast on him. Note that hit points drained by the penanggalan cannot be restored by magical means such as *cure wound* spells — in effect, the victim's maximum hits are being drained. Such spells will only take effect in respect of the lost points after *dispel evil* has been cast, and even powerful spells such as *restoration* will have no effect. Similarly the victim's lost strength and constitution points cannot be recovered until after *dispel evil* has been cast. Once *dispel evil* has been cast, however, the hit points are restored at the rate of 1 point per day and the strength and constitution points at the rate of 1 point of each per week.

If the victim succumbs on the first occasion to the pĕnanggalan, the creature must again hypnotise him the next night before feeding is possible. However the victim's saving throw is progressively more difficult; the throw is made at −4 on the second occasion, −5 on the third and so on. A break in the sequence of one or more nights will halt this progression; the saving throw will again be at −3 if a renewed attempt is made by a pĕnanggalan after a break of one or more nights.

If an intended victim makes his save against the creature's attempt at hypnosis, the pĕnanggalan will be able to exert no further influence over him and will flee from him in fear before searching for another prey. Furthermore, that person will be immune to further attempts by that pĕnanggalan and will be able to recognise one — any one — for what it is, no matter in what guise it appears. He will still, however, be losing hit points at the rate of 1 point per night, as described above, if the creature has fed at least once on his blood.

Note that the victim is 'asleep' throughout the visitations of the pĕnanggalan. He will never actually see the creature, even if he makes his saving throw against hypnosis. The creature will never attack a victim who is awake. If any person happens to see the head and gut when detached from the body (for example if the intended victim awakens before the creature has had time to commence hypnosis) he must save against *fear* or flee in abject terror. When in this form, however, the creature can be turned or dispelled by a cleric; treat as a wraith on the cleric/undead matrix. If the head and gut are thus turned, they must return to the lair and not venture forth again that night; if they are dispelled (a D result on the matrix) they are destroyed and the body will decay (see below). The head and gut will recoil before a strongly-presented *holy symbol* though it will not be harmed.

Should a pĕnanggalan kill a male victim, he remains lifeless, and if an attempt is made to *raise* him, his chances of surviving the *system shock* will be half normal. If the attempt fails, no further attempts can possibly succeed. If it kills a female victim, she will rise from the grave after three days as a pĕnanggalan (not under the control of the original creature). If an attempt is made to *raise* her during that three-day period, her chances of surviving the *system shock* are half normal, and failure of that attempt means that no further attempt can possibly succeed — the process by which she becomes a pĕnanggalan is then inexorable.

If an attempt to *raise* any victim succeeds, however, the victim will return to normal (all hit points restored, strength and constitution back to normal) after two months of rest and recuperation; further-more that victim will be immune to further attacks by a pĕnanggalan and will recognise one for what it is.

After the pĕnanggalan head and gut have left the body in the lair, the internal organs swell up, whether feeding takes place or not, and cannot return to the abdomen until they have been soaked in vinegar for an hour, during which time they return to normal size. For this reason, the creature will always keep a large vessel filled with vinegar concealed in each of its lairs, and a pĕnanggalan lair may often be detected by the distinctive odour of vinegar which permeates it.

If a ray of sunlight strikes the creature's head and gut when they are detached from the body, the head will be paralysed and will fall help-less to the ground until nightfall. Thus, the creature will always attempt to reunite head and body before cock-crow. In any event, if the head and body are not reunited within seven hours after initial separation, both will start to decay and the evil life-force which animates the creature will be forced to return to *Hell*. Thus, to destroy the body or the head is a sure way of destroying the creature itself.

When separated from the body, the head takes 4HD of damage.

In either form, the creature takes normal damage from all weapons. If it is weaponless and in human form, it can bite for 1—6 hit points of damage, but it will try to avoid using this mode of attack for fear of revealing its true nature.

When detached from the body, the internal organs constantly drip a highly volatile and foul mixture of blood and digestive juices which cause 1—4 hit points of damage on bare flesh (which breaks out in sores and boils in a painful eruption). This horrid liquid evaporates after one round in contact with air.

For purposes of aerial combat, the pĕnanggalan is manoeuvrability class D.

PERNICON

FREQUENCY: *Rare*
NO. APPEARING: *4—40*
   (in lair 300—3,000)
ARMOUR CLASS: *3*
MOVE: *12"*
HIT DICE: *1—4 hit points*
% IN LAIR: *20%*
TREASURE TYPE: *1—4 gems*
   and 25% chance of 100—
   600 gold pieces
NO. OF ATTACKS: *1*
DAMAGE/ATTACK: *1—3*
SPECIAL ATTACKS:
   Constitution drain
SPECIAL DEFENCES: *Nil*
MAGIC RESISTANCE: *Standard*
INTELLIGENCE: *Semi-*
ALIGNMENT: *Neutral*
SIZE: *S (2" long)*
PSIONIC ABILITY: *Nil*
   Attack/Defence Modes: *Nil*
LEVEL/X.P. VALUE:
   I/7 + 1 per hit point

A brightly-coloured insect rather like a grasshopper about 2" long — red, yellow, ochre and light blue — the pernicon inhabits the outer regions of deserts and is much prized by the nomads of these regions because the antennae on its head are water-diviners, vibrating and giving off a low hum when within 120' of a large quantity of water.

The pernicon is usually inoffensive but will attack in large numbers if disturbed, accidentally or otherwise. It leaps on its victim and grips exposed flesh with the pincers at the rear of its abdomen. If it hits, the pernicon will inflict 1—3 hit points of damage and will also drain water and other body fluids from the victim, causing the loss of 1 point of constitution. Each round thereafter this process will continue automatically, without the need of a 'to hit' roll.

Even when the pernicon is killed its pincers continue to grip fast, and removing it from the victim's body will inflict a further 1—4 hit points of damage. If a victim's constitution falls below 3 he collapses unconscious. If it drops below zero he dies. If a victim is not killed he will recover lost constitution points at the same rate as lost hit points. However, if he is killed, a *raise dead* will only restore half of his original constitution, a *raise dead fully* only 75% of it.

PHANTOM STALKER

FREQUENCY: *Very rare*
NO. APPEARING: *1—2*
ARMOUR CLASS: *3*
MOVE: *12"/24"*
HIT DICE: *6*
% IN LAIR: *Nil*
TREASURE TYPE: *Nil*
NO. OF ATTACKS: *2*
DAMAGE/ATTACK: *1—4/1—4*
SPECIAL ATTACKS: *See below*
SPECIAL DEFENCES:
   Impervious to fire
MAGIC RESISTANCE: *Standard*
INTELLIGENCE: *Semi-*
ALIGNMENT: *Neutral*
SIZE: *Variable — usually L*
PSIONIC ABILITY: *Nil*
   Attack/Defence Modes: *Nil*
LEVEL/X.P. VALUE:
   V/375 + 6 per hit point

Phantom stalkers are creatures from the *Elemental Plane of Fire,* and are usually found on the *Prime Material Plane* only in the capacity of servitors to high-level magic-users. They are conjured by the use of a spell similar to the one for summoning an invisible stalker (see **ADVANCED DUNGEONS & DRAGONS MONSTER MANUAL**). Phantom stalkers serve as body-guards, fighting to protect their masters. A wizard must exercise great care in instructing one, for it will follow the orders to the letter, perverting the intent if possible, anxious for release back to its native plane.

There is one explicit instruction inherent in their conjuration. If the summoner is killed, his phantom stalker(s) will instantly vanish, re-appearing 1—4 hours later, intent on vengeance, having unerringly tracked the summoner's slayer from the *Ethereal Plane* Phantom stalkers only gain this ethereal tracking ability upon the expiration of their masters, and it disappears as soon as the summoner's slayer has been tracked.

Phantom stalkers have the ability to *polymorph* themselves and have been known to appear in various forms, but the most common is that of a reddish, 8' tall humanoid with huge fiery eyes. They can *fly*, and this ability is apparently unimpaired by whatever shape they assume (though their manoeuvrability class will vary according to the shape).

Phantom stalkers normally attack with their sharp claws, each of which can inflict 1—4 hit points of damage. They are invulnerable to damage from fire, and magical *fire* attacks actually heal them 1 hit point for each attack die. However, they save against *cold* at —2 and such attacks add 1 hit point of damage for each die. If a melee is going against a phantom stalker and its death is imminent, it can cast forth its life essence in one 6-dice *fireball*, after which it de-materialises and dies. They will sometimes simply explode the *fireball* on themselves in order to harm as many foes as possible. This is only done as a last resort and is never done if it would harm the phantom stalker's summoner, unless the summoner is directly and immediately responsible for the phantom stalker's demise (for example having ordered it to engage in a hopelessly futile and suicidal battle).

POLTERGEIST

FREQUENCY: *Rare*
NO. APPEARING: *1—8*
ARMOUR CLASS: *10*
MOVE: *6"*
HIT DICE: *1—4 hit points*
% IN LAIR: *95%*
TREASURE TYPE: *Nil*
NO. OF ATTACKS: *Nil*
DAMAGE/ATTACK: *Nil*
SPECIAL ATTACKS: *Fear*
SPECIAL DEFENCES:
   *Invisibility; silver or magic
   weapons to hit*
MAGIC RESISTANCE: *Standard*
INTELLIGENCE: *Low*
ALIGNMENT: *Lawful evil*
SIZE: *M*
PSIONIC ABILITY: *Nil*
   Attack/Defence Modes: *Nil*
LEVEL/X.P. VALUE:
   II/34 + 1 per hit point

Though a wandering poltergeist is infrequently encountered (in which case it can be turned or destroyed by a cleric as if it were a skeleton) this undead creature usually remains in the room or corridor in which it was originally 'killed' (and such is the strong bond between the poltergeist and its surroundings that it is in this case treated as a ghoul in the cleric/undead matrix).

The poltergeist is invisible (—4 to hit unless the attacker can *see invisible*) and non-corporeal; only silver and magical weapons can harm it.

The poltergeist attacks physically by throwing an object — any nearby object light enough to be thrown by a man will suffice — with a chance of hitting its target equal to that of a 5HD monster. If the victim is struck he takes no damage but must save against *fear*

(spells) or flee the area and run in random directions for 2—24 melee rounds before recovering.

There is a 50% chance that the victim will drop whatever he is holding during his flight, but not necessarily at the beginning (roll to determine for how many rounds he must flee, roll again to determine whether he drops whatever he is holding, and if so roll a third time to determine in which of the melee rounds of flight he does so).

Once a person has made his saving throw, he is immune to further *fear* effects from the poltergeist while in that area.

Sprinkled holy water or a strongly-presented *holy symbol* drives back the poltergeist but does not harm it.

PROTEIN POLYMORPH

FREQUENCY: *Rare*
NO. APPEARING: *1*
ARMOUR CLASS: *2*
MOVE: *9"*
HIT DICE: *6—8*
% IN LAIR: *50%*
TREASURE TYPE: *D*
NO. OF ATTACKS: *Variable*
DAMAGE/ATTACK:
   6—36 or by weapon type
SPECIAL ATTACKS: *See below*
SPECIAL DEFENCES: *Nil*
MAGIC RESISTANCE: *Standard*
INTELLIGENCE: *Average*
ALIGNMENT: *Chaotic neutral*
SIZE: *L*
PSIONIC ABILITY: *Nil*
   Attack/Defence Modes: *Nil*
LEVEL/X.P. VALUE:
   6HD: V/400 + 6 per hit point
   7HD: VI/575 + 8 per hit point
   8HD: VI/925 + 10 per hit point

Protein polymorphs are intelligent cellular colonies with the ability to assume any form they choose. They may take the form of inanimate objects or animate creatures of 8 or fewer hit dice (depending on the size of the protein polymorph — 6, 7 or 8 hit dice). The form assumed may actually be that of several forms connected by a near-invisible (10% chance of detection) cord or film of protoplasm. The cells of the protein polymorph may specialise or de-specialise at will, taking on different textures and colours, changing completely in only one round.

These 'creatures' are extremely versatile. They may imitate anything from a pile of treasure to a small-sized room, to a party of half a dozen humans or a dozen kobolds. They will, in general, assume any form likely to draw prey, for they feed on humans and animals with little regard for type and size. They may even mix inanimate objects within their structure to add authenticity — a room or a corridor may, for instance, be part-stone and part protein polymorph. Imitated creatures may wear real clothing and wield real weapons (often acquired from previous victims).

There are limits to the protein polymorph's degree of cellular control — it cannot accurately copy facial expressions, nor can it effectively duplicate the sound of speech. These limitations may lead to the exposure of the imposture as animate creatures. Similarly, if a protein polymorph disguises itself as an inanimate object, there is a base chance of detecting the imposture from a distance of 10' away, but upon touch the animate nature of the cells is instantly revealed.

The normal attack of a protein polymorph is to bludgeon its prey and then enfold and crush it, inflicting 6—36 hit points of damage per round. When in the form of weapon-wielding creatures, multiple or single, it will attack as the creatures themselves would normally attack, doing damage by weapon-type as appropriate.

Protein polymorphs possess the normal strengths of imitated creatures but not those creatures' special abilities.

QUAGGOTH – QUIPPER – QULLAN

QUAGGOTH

FREQUENCY: *Rare*
NO. APPEARING: *2–24*
ARMOUR CLASS: *6*
MOVE: *12″*
HIT DICE: *1+2*
% IN LAIR: *50%*
TREASURE TYPE: *A*
NO. OF ATTACKS: *2 or 1*
DAMAGE/ATTACK: *1–4/1–4*
   or by weapon type
SPECIAL ATTACKS: *See below*

SPECIAL DEFENCES:
   Immune to poison
MAGIC RESISTANCE: *Standard*
INTELLIGENCE: *Low*
ALIGNMENT: *Neutral*
SIZE: *L (7′+ tall)*
PSIONIC ABILITY: *Nil*
   Attack/Defence Modes: *Nil*
LEVEL/X.P. VALUE:
   Warrior II/28 + 2 per hit point
   Leader II/50 + 3 per hit point

Little is known of these great white shaggy bipeds. Some say they once formed a warlike cannibal race — their aggressiveness is unquestionable. Any fleeing or threatening party invites certain attack, and even a party which remains motionless within the quaggoths' field of view is 75% likely to be attacked by the creatures.

Quaggoths are usually (70%) unarmed, in which case they fight with two claws for 1–4 hit points of damage each. 30% of quaggoth groups encountered will be armed with either battle-axes or two-handed swords. A particular quaggoth group will always either be unarmed, except for the leader-type, or armed — there will never be a mixture of unarmed and armed creatures in the same group.

With every 12 quaggoths encountered there will be one leader-type with 15 hit points, 3HD and armour class 4. The leader-type will always be armed with a battle-axe or two-handed sword.

Quaggoths are totally immune to poison.

If a quaggoth is reduced to a number of hit points between zero and –5, it will continue to fight in a berserk fashion at +2 hit probability and +2 damage. When it reaches –6 hit points it dies.

Quaggoths have a particular hatred of surface-dwelling elves and have been known to become slaves of the drow in order to assist the latter in their warfare against elves. They speak a halting, primitive form of the common tongue and can only grasp very simple concepts.

QUIPPER

FREQUENCY: *Very rare*
NO. APPEARING: *5–50 (5% chance of 10–100)*
ARMOUR CLASS: *8*
MOVE: *9″*
HIT DICE: *1–4 hit points*
% IN LAIR: *Nil*
TREASURE TYPE: *Nil*
NO. OF ATTACKS: *1*
DAMAGE/ATTACK: *1–2*
SPECIAL ATTACKS: *Nil*
SPECIAL DEFENCES: *Nil*
MAGIC RESISTANCE: *Standard*
INTELLIGENCE: *Non-*
ALIGNMENT: *Neutral*
SIZE: *S (3′–6″ long)*
PSIONIC ABILITY: *Nil*
   Attack/Defence Modes: *Nil*
LEVEL/X.P. VALUE: *1/5+1 per hit point*

Quippers are small, vicious fish which usually swim in large shoals. They are dark green in colour and inhabit fresh-water lakes and streams.

The quipper is a rare species of cold-water piranha. If anyone is swimming or wading near a shoal the quippers may (25%) not attack. However if they do attack and score a hit, drawing blood with their sharp teeth and inflicting 1–2 hit points of damage, the entire shoal will go berserk and will inflict double the normal number of attacks per round.

Up to 20 quippers can attack a human-sized victim simultaneously. When determining initial attack, roll first to determine whether or not the attack is made. Then roll percentage dice again, if there is to be an attack, to determine the percentage of the shoal which actually attempts to hit in the first round. Roll attacks for that number of quippers, and if at least one hits, all the shoal will attack in the next round (no more than 20 can actually attempt to hit). If all the quippers attacking in the first round fail to hit, it is only 40% likely that they will pursue their attack the next round.

QULLAN

FREQUENCY: *Rare*
NO. APPEARING: *1–6*
ARMOUR CLASS: *10*
MOVE: *12″*
HIT DICE: *2*
% IN LAIR: *10%*
TREASURE TYPE: *most types in lair but in small quantity (10% of A at most)*
NO. OF ATTACKS: *1*
DAMAGE/ATTACK: *5–11*
SPECIAL ATTACKS: *See below*
SPECIAL DEFENCES: *See below*
MAGIC RESISTANCE: *Standard*
INTELLIGENCE: *Low*
ALIGNMENT: *Chaotic evil*
SIZE: *L (8′ + tall)*
PSIONIC ABILITY: *Nil*
   Attack/Defence Modes: *Nil*
LEVEL/X.P. VALUE:
   III/73 + 2 per hit point

Qullans are strong, large, seemingly insane humanoids which wear warpaint in a wild variety of clashing colours and sport their battle-scars proudly, often emphasising them with cosmetic paint. They never wear armour, either wandering naked or clad in tiger-skins.

They attack with broadswords which they have honed to an incredible sharpness — a technique so far not emulated by man. These swords hit at +3 hit probability and have a +3 damage bonus (so they inflict 5—11 damage). However, the swords blunt easily — there is a cumulative 20% chance per hit that the sword will be blunted and will revert to normal broadsword properties. They wield these broadswords two-handed (though this confers no advantage).

All members of the qullan race continually radiate *confusion* in a 5' radius. Anyone in melee with them must make a saving throw or be confused, either standing still, attacking the nearest qullan without regard for personal safety or attacking the nearest friend — equal probability. (Roll d6 for effect; 1—2 means stand still; 3—4 means attack qullan; 5—6 means attack friend. Repeat this roll to determine action each round until the victim saves). A victim of *confusion* may attempt to save each melee round he is within the radius of

effect, and the effect disappears if he moves outside that radius of effect.

Qullans have never been befriended by human or near-human races; without exception, every encounter has seen the qullans attacking, irrespective of the alignment or size of the party.

Qullans are so totally chaotic that any attempt to force one to do anything it would not normally do causes its inherent powers of *confusion* to 'feed back', resulting in the instant death of the creature (this same reaction occurs whenever a qullan fails to save against any *charm* or *control* type of spell). Thus, no-one has ever been able to learn the methods they use to forge the sharp edges on their swords, nor has anyone been able to induce a qullan to restore the edge to one of their fine broadswords for a non-qullan.

A human or near-human may use a qullan sword in melee, since the swords are not in any way magical. However, the sword has the normal chance of blunting if it scores a hit, and a captured sword will thus only display its exceptional qualities for 5 hits at most.

RETRIEVER — REVENANT — ROTHÉ

RETRIEVER

FREQUENCY: *Very rare*
NO. APPEARING: *1*
ARMOUR CLASS: *—2*
MOVE: *18"*
HIT DICE: *10*
% IN LAIR: *10%*
TREASURE TYPE: *Z*
NO. OF ATTACKS: *4*
DAMAGE/ATTACK:
  3—18/3—18/3—18/3—18
SPECIAL ATTACKS: *Eye rays*
SPECIAL DEFENCES: *Nil*
MAGIC RESISTANCE: *Standard*
INTELLIGENCE: *Low*
ALIGNMENT: *Chaotic evil*
SIZE: *L (12' tall)*
PSIONIC ABILITY: *Nil*
  Attack/Defence Modes: *Nil*
LEVEL/X.P. VALUE:
  VII/4,950 + 14 per hit point

Retrievers are constructed by Demogorgon (see **ADVANCED DUNGEONS & DRAGONS, MONSTER MANUAL** — *Demon, Demogorgon*) in his laboratories in the *Abyss*; in doing so, Demogorgon deliberately constructs the creatures so as to strike maximum terror into their victims. They will rarely be found on the *Prime Material Plane* except when engaged on a specific mission to retrieve (usually dead or alive) one who has offended Demogorgon or one of the more powerful denizens of the *Abyss*.

Retrievers are giant spider-like creatures whose front four limbs end in huge cleavers. Though they are large — approximately the size of a mammoth — they are very fast and nimble in the open, where they have room to manoeuvre. They each have six eyes, two for vision and four which project rays (up to 2 of the latter may function each round — determine which at random). These rays are, respectively, *fire, cold, lightning* and *transmutation*. Once used, a particular eye cannot be used again for 6 rounds, at which time it will have re-charged. These rays can only hit one target within a range of 60'.

The rays of *fire, cold* and *lightning* each do damage equal to the current hit points of the retriever, a save (against dragon breath) indicating half damage. Magic items must also save against these attacks if their owner fails to save. The *transmutation* ray transmutes the victim into mud, stone, gold or lead (determine which of the

four at random). A successful save against petrifaction indicates no effect. A *stone to flesh* spell will restore a petrified character to normal but only a *philosopher's stone* can restore a lead or gold figure. Characters turned to mud can only be revived by the use of *mud to rock* followed by *stone to flesh*, both spells being cast within one turn of the transmutation.

Retrievers can attack with all four cleavers simultaneously on the same victim, each inflicting 3—18 hit points of damage. However they cannot use the eye rays when attacking with their cleavers. Generally speaking, they will use their eye rays first then, when the eyes are recharging, use the cleavers.

Demons sometimes mount howdahs on the back of a retriever and ride on the creature to the hunt.

Creatures of lower order will flee in panic on sight of a retriever, and even an adventurer of 5th experience level or lower (or a monster of less than 6 hit dice) will do so unless he saves against magic when a retriever comes within 30' of him.

REVENANT

FREQUENCY: *Very rare*
NO. APPEARING: *1*
ARMOUR CLASS: *10*
MOVE: *9"*
HIT DICE: *8*
% IN LAIR: *Nil*
TREASURE TYPE: *Nil*
NO. OF ATTACKS: *1*
DAMAGE/ATTACK: *2—16*
SPECIAL ATTACKS: *Paralysation*
SPECIAL DEFENCES: *See below*
MAGIC RESISTANCE: *See below*
INTELLIGENCE: *See below*
ALIGNMENT: *Neutral*
SIZE: *M*
PSIONIC ABILITY: *Nil*
  Attack/Defence Modes: *Nil*
LEVEL/X.P. VALUE:
  VII/1,275+10 per hit point

Under exceptional circumstances, those who have died a violent death may return from beyond the grave to wreak vengeance on their killer — as a revenant. There are few who can make this journey — to do so, a dead character must have wisdom or intelligence greater than 16 and

a constitution of 18: all their characteristics must sum to 90 or more: and if both these criteria are met, the chance of the character becoming a revenant after death is 5%.

Although undead, the revenant is motivated by sheer self-will. Therefore, as it is not inherently evil, it cannot be turned or destroyed by clerics, nor are *holy/unholy symbols,* holy water or other religious paraphernalia able to affect it. Weapons — normal and magical alike — do not affect the creature, and the surest way to kill it is to reduce it to ashes. Like other undead it is immune to all spells attempting to control or influence its mind or body.

Even if a revenant is dismembered, its limbs will continue to function independently, as though guided by the same mind. Like a troll (see **ADVANCED DUNGEONS & DRAGONS MONSTER MANUAL**), it has *regenerative* properties which cause the limbs to slither together, re-unite and re-create the revenant. It can also *regenerate* 3 hit points of damage per round even after 'death', except by burning. It is immune to acid and to gas.

The process of decay of the corpse which now houses the revenant has only slightly been attenuated, after 3-6 months of rebirth, the corpse will decompose rapidly and the spirit of the revenant will be forced to return to the plane from whence it came.

The sole purpose of the revenant's existence is to wreak vengeance on its killer, together with any person or persons who aided his killer in the act. Though it will never attack any one else, except in self-defence, it will stop at nothing to achieve its purpose, being able to locate its intended prime victim wherever he may be. (Those who aided the killer will also be tracked if they happen still to be in the company of the killer, but if they are elsewhere they will be ignored by the revenant which will concentrate on the killer only.)

Its mode of attack is to lock its claw-like hands around its victim's throat and then to strangle him, doing 2—16 hit points of damage each round and not releasing its grip until the victim or the revenant is dead. If necessary it will adopt other means to try to kill its victim,

using extreme cunning and guile, but it will never, under any circumstances, resort to the use of weapons.

The revenant can also stare into his killer's eyes and that person must make his saving throw against magic or be paralysed with terror for 2-8 rounds. This power works against none but the revenant's killer.

The revenant will retain all the abilities it had before death, though it will be a creature with 8 hit dice, whatever experience level was previously attained, and will always be of neutral alignment, no matter what alignment it followed in life. It can converse fluently in the neutral and common tongues, though stiffness of its vocal chords deters it from using speech except under extreme circumstances (e.g. to cast a spell. if it was formerly a spell-caster, on its killer). Note that a revenant may never cast a spell at a person other than its killer, whatever the spell-type.

If the associates of the killer are with him in a party, they will be dealt with after the killer has been destroyed, and in that respect they, too, will be regarded as 'killers'. They cannot escape, for if they attempt to do so while the revenant is occupied with the killer, the revenant will track all of them down subsequently.

Immunity to certain spells apart (see above) the revenant has the same resistance to magic as it had before death as a character.

The creature presents a pale, corpse-like appearance, with pallid skin drawn tightly over hollow cheekbones; its flesh is unusually cold and clammy. Its eyes — sunken in the face — are at times dull and heavy-lidded but, particularly when nearing its intended victim, they will blaze up with unnatural intensity. Animals will shy away from it, and about the revenant hangs an unmistakable aura of tragic anger, sadness and determination.

If the character who became the revenant died a particularly violent death, it may be unable to re-occupy its former body when it becomes a revenant. In such a case, the spirit will occupy any available, freshly-dead corpse. The revenant's new body may even be of opposite sex to the original character. However its killer and his active associates, if present, will always 'see' the revenant in its former body, while others around him will see it as it is, if they had not been involved in the killing.

When the revenant has completed its mission by killing all its intended victims, it will immediately disintegrate and will never return again. Its spirit rests in peace.

ROTHÉ

FREQUENCY: *Uncommon*
NO. APPEARING: *2—20*
ARMOUR CLASS: *7*
MOVE: *9"*
HIT DICE: *2*
% IN LAIR: *40%*
TREASURE TYPE: *Nil*
NO. OF ATTACKS: *3*
DAMAGE/ATTACK: *1—3/1—3/ 1—8*
SPECIAL ATTACKS: *Nil*
SPECIAL DEFENCES: *Nil*
MAGIC RESISTANCE: *Standard*
INTELLIGENCE: *Animal*
ALIGNMENT: *Neutral*
SIZE: *M (4' high)*
PSIONIC ABILITY: *Nil*
  Attack/Defence Modes: *Nil*
LEVEL/X.P. VALUE:
  1/20 + 2 per hit point

Rothe are small ox-like creatures with a mass of long black hair. They attack with two horns (1—3 hit points of damage each) and a bite (1— hit points of damage).

They are shy creatures with an aversion to bright light; they wi generally make their lairs underground, near a lake or river wher there is a good supply of lichen and moss to eat.

SANDMAN – SCARECROW – SCREAMING DEVILKIN – SHADOW DEMON – SHEET GHOUL – SHEET PHANTOM – SHOCKER – SKELETON WARRIOR – SKULK – SLAAD – SNYAD – SON OF KYUSS – STUNJELLY – SUSSURUS – SVIRFNEBLIN – SYMBIOTIC JELLY

SANDMAN

FREQUENCY: *Rare*
NO. APPEARING: *1–6*
ARMOUR CLASS: *3*
MOVE: *9"*
HIT DICE: *4*
% IN LAIR: *20%*
TREASURE TYPE:
　　100-2,000 gold pieces
NO. OF ATTACKS: *Nil*
DAMAGE/ATTACK: *Nil*
SPECIAL ATTACKS: *Sleep*
SPECIAL DEFENCES: *See below*
MAGIC RESISTANCE: *20%*
INTELLIGENCE: *Average*
ALIGNMENT: *Neutral (with*
　　evil tendencies)
SIZE: *M*
PSIONIC ABILITY: *Nil*
　　Attack/Defence Modes: *Nil*
LEVEL/X.P. VALUE:
　　IV/215 + 4 per hit point

The sandman's name describes it exactly — a man-like biped made entirely of sand, held together by some form of magical cohesion. Clearly, these are creatures from another plane, but what their purposes are on the *Prime Material Plane*, none can say.

Any character or monster coming within 20' of the sandman must save against magic or go to *sleep*, irrespective of experience level. Those who manage to stay awake must attempt to save again each time they touch the sandman or are touched by it (a hit on the sandman with a weapon does not constitute a 'touch').

Once the sandman has put a victim to sleep it will take no further action against him, leaving him to doze, though if the encounter took place in its lair it will eject the sleeper first.

Sandmen automatically attack humans and need never check morale.

Sleepers will remain asleep for 3 full turns whatever happens. Thereafter, there is a cumulative 10% chance per turn of a sleeper waking of his own accord, and a 95% chance per round of him waking if violently disturbed.

Sandmen have the natural ability of *protection from normal missiles*.

SCARECROW

FREQUENCY: *Very rare*
NO. APPEARING: *1–6*
ARMOUR CLASS: *6*
MOVE: *6"*
HIT DICE: *5*
% IN LAIR: *Nil*
TREASURE TYPE: *Nil*
NO. OF ATTACKS: *1*
DAMAGE/ATTACK: *1–6 plus*
　　special
SPECIAL ATTACKS: *Charm*
SPECIAL DEFENCES: *Nil*
MAGIC RESISTANCE: *Standard*
INTELLIGENCE: *Non-*
ALIGNMENT: *Evil (lawful,*
　　neutral or chaotic)
SIZE: *M*
PSIONIC ABILITY: *Nil*
　　Attack/Defence Modes: *Nil*
LEVEL/X.P. VALUE:
　　IV/165+5 per hit point

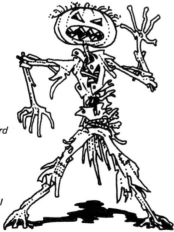

Enchanted versions of regular scarecrows, these creatures are created from a variety of materials — wooden bodies and limbs, turnip heads for instance — and will vary in appearance. They will always, however, appear evil and of malign intent. To create a scarecrow, either a special *manual* must be used or a high-level evil cleric must employ *animate object, quest, prayer* and *command*. Construction of a scarecrow requires 3 weeks but the cost of materials is only 1 gold piece per hit point. The scarecrow will obey its creator's simple instructions, following orders literally so long as they require no interpretation on its part.

Meeting the glance of the scarecrow causes any intelligent creature to become *charmed* unless they make their saving throw against magic. The touch of the scarecrow, which requires a successful 'to hit' roll and also does 1–6 hit points of damage, has the identical effect.

The effect of the *charm* is one of fascination, rather than the obeyance of instructions. The victim will stand and gape, rooted to the spot — as if under the influence of a *hold person* spell — allowing the monster to strike freely at him, again and again. If the scarecrow is killed, or leaves the area, all victims recover immediately from their *charm*.

SCREAMING DEVILKIN

FREQUENCY: *Rare*
NO. APPEARING: *1–4*
ARMOUR CLASS: *2*
MOVE: *12"*
HIT DICE: *3*
% IN LAIR: *20%*
TREASURE TYPE: *M*
NO. OF ATTACKS: *1*
DAMAGE/ATTACK: *1–6*
SPECIAL ATTACKS: *Scream*
SPECIAL DEFENCES: *Nil*
MAGIC RESISTANCE: *Standard*
INTELLIGENCE: *Low*
ALIGNMENT: *Lawful evil*
SIZE: *S (3' tall)*
PSIONIC ABILITY: *Nil*
　　Attack/Defence Modes: *Nil*
LEVEL/X.P. VALUE:
　　III/90+3 per hit point

This small creature resembles the mephits in physical appearance, though as far as is known it is solely a resident of the *Prime Material Plane* and has no allegiance to demons or (beyond its alignment) to devils. It is 3' tall — rather smaller than the mephits — and has a muscular barbed tail about 2½' long. Its leathery wings have a 5' span and provide its only means of movement, its legs and arms being disproportionately small and useless for movement or combat. For purposes of aerial combat, it is manoeuvrability class D.

It always attacks and never willingly breaks off a fight, striking with its tail, with its cruel barbs, for 1–6 hit points of damage. It also has a painful howling scream which it sets up continuously in the presence of other beings. Nothing can stop this screaming other than the slaying of the beast or magically-induced *silence*. Conversation — even shouting — is inaudible through it, and those who do not have their ears well plugged must attempt a saving throw each melee round they are within 60' of the creature. If the throw is not successful, the victim cannot attack or cast or control spells, though he may defend. Only one saving throw is required each round, no matter how many of these screaming devilkins are within range.

Note that, even if a person makes his save in one round, he must attempt it again in the next if he is to take any action.

If a magic-user or cleric or other spell-caster makes his save, he may cast a spell containing a verbal component in that round, even though the words may be inaudible because of the screaming.

SHADOW DEMON

FREQUENCY: *Very rare*
NO. APPEARING: *1*
ARMOUR CLASS:
    9, 5 or 1 (see below)
MOVE: *12" (but see below)*
HIT DICE: *7+3*
% IN LAIR: *Nil*
TREASURE TYPE: *Nil*
NO. OF ATTACKS: *3*
DAMAGE/ATTACK: *1–8/1–6/1–6*
SPECIAL ATTACKS: *See below*
SPECIAL DEFENCES: *See below*
MAGIC RESISTANCE: *See below*
INTELLIGENCE: *Very high*
ALIGNMENT: *Chaotic evil*
SIZE: *M*
PSIONIC ABILITY: *Nil*
    Attack/Defence Modes: *Nil*
LEVEL/X.P. VALUE:
    VI/825 + 10 per hit point

This foul creature of dark evil from the *Lower Planes* is the essence of a demon imprisoned in the form of a shadow, which it exactly resembles. Like the shadow, (see **ADVANCED DUNGEONS & DRAGONS MONSTER MANUAL**) the creature cannot be detected 90% of the time, since it appears as a vague shape and can easily be confused, in the guttering light conditions of a dungeon, with the shadows of dungeon features or of adventurers themselves. It is not, however, from the *Negative Material Plane* and so its attacks do not drain the strength of a victim, as do those of the shadow. Instead, it attacks normally with two claws (1–6 hit points of damage each) and a vicious bite for 1–8 hit points of damage.

The body structure of the creature is most peculiar and leads to the creature being more powerful in darkness and more vulnerable in conditions of bright light.

Thus, in daylight or its equivalent, the shadow demon is AC9 and sustains double damage from all attacks. In torchlight it is AC5 and suffers normal damage from attacks; in these conditions it attacks at +1 hit probability. In darkness or near-darkness it is AC1, attacks at +2 hit probability and suffers only half normal damage from attacks.

The creature is totally immune to fire, cold and lightning, of the ordinary or magical kinds. However if a *light* spell is cast upon it, the shadow demon is affected as if by a *fireball* (so a *light* spell cast by a 5th level magic-user would do 5–30 hit points of damage to it, whatever the illumination conditions at the time).

Though in normal circumstances (only 50% chance even if the creature is seen) they will not be discerned, the creature has small wings — too small to give it flying abilities, but large enough to boost the creature's leap in its initial attack to a distance up to 30'. Following this initial leap, it will attack with all four of its claws (for 1–6 hit points of damage each), though not with its bite. It will always leap to the attack if it has not been detected by its potential victims. The wings also give it the ability to half-fly, half-run, at 18" movement rate one melee round in every ten — it will usually use this manoeuvre as a prelude to escape if necessary.

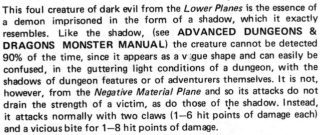

Once every day the shadow demon can cast *darkness 10' radius* and *fear* over a 30' radius. Once every week it may execute a *magic jar* attack on a victim, though if the victim makes his save against this attack, the shadow demon will be stunned for 1–3 rounds. A suitable receptacle must be at hand.

Shadow demons are treated as 'special' on the cleric/undead matrix. It is thought they are formed from manes (see **ADVANCED DUNGEONS & DRAGONS MONSTER MANUAL** — Demon, Manes (Sub-Demon)) though the high intelligence of the shadow demon, which is evident when it engages in conflict, seems to put this theory in doubt.

SHEET GHOUL

FREQUENCY: *Very rare*
NO. APPEARING: *1*
ARMOUR CLASS: *2*
MOVE: *9"*
HIT DICE: *4+2*
% IN LAIR: *Nil*
TREASURE TYPE: *Nil*
NO. OF ATTACKS: *3*
DAMAGE/ATTACK: *1–3/1–3/1–6*
SPECIAL ATTACKS: *Acid squirt*
SPECIAL DEFENCES: *See below*
MAGIC RESISTANCE: *Standard*
INTELLIGENCE: *Average*
ALIGNMENT: *Chaotic evil*
SIZE: *M*
PSIONIC ABILITY: *Nil*
    Attack/Defence Modes: *Nil*
LEVEL/X.P. VALUE: *IV/170 + 5 per hit point*

A sheet ghoul is created when a sheet phantom (see below) kills a victim. It is treated as a spectre on the cleric/undead matrix.

The sheet ghoul attacks with its two claws (1–3 hit points of damage each) and its filthy fangs (1–6 hit points of damage). Its touch does not cause the paralysation for which the ghoul is feared (see **ADVANCED DUNGEONS & DRAGONS MONSTER MANUAL**), but each round it can also attack by squirting a fine jet of corrosive acid from its nose (automatic hit on the opponent it is attacking within 10') which inflicts 2–7 hit points of damage.

These creatures are subject to all attack forms except *sleep, charm* and similar spells.

SHEET PHANTOM

FREQUENCY: *Very rare*
NO. APPEARING: *1*
ARMOUR CLASS: *3*
MOVE: *6"*
HIT DICE: *3*
% IN LAIR: *Nil*
TREASURE TYPE: *Nil*
NO. OF ATTACKS: *1*
DAMAGE/ATTACK: *1–4*
SPECIAL ATTACKS:
    Suffocation
SPECIAL DEFENCES: *Nil*
MAGIC RESISTANCE: *Standard*
INTELLIGENCE: *Average*
ALIGNMENT: *Chaotic evil*
SIZE: *See below*
PSIONIC ABILITY: *Nil*
    Attack/Defence Modes: *Nil*
LEVEL/X.P. VALUE:
    III/105 + 4 per hit point

This greatly-feared undead creature is a form of wraith, but is unusual as a member of the undead class in that it in no way resembles a human. It appears as a near-transparent rectangle with varying dimensions — 11' to 16' broad, 7' to 12' long and ¼" thick. It moves along ceilings and attacks by dropping on a potential victim; if it hits the intended target, it envelops him, causing suffocation for 1–4 hit points of damage each round subsequent to the initial attack (no damage even if the initial attack succeeds). A victim enveloped by a sheet phantom cannot move, and any damage inflicted on the sheet phantom while it is enveloping a captive will also accrue to that victim. Only one man-sized victim may be enveloped at a time, since the creature wraps its whole form around the victim in a tight cylinder, and he cannot fight back unless the weapon he uses is short (e.g. a dagger) and was actually in his hand when the creature fell on him.

If the victim of a sheet phantom's enveloping dies from suffocation (or as a result of damage inflicted, unwittingly, by his comrades), the sheet phantom merges with his body and the whole becomes a sheet ghoul (see *Sheet Ghoul* above).

There are sufficient similarities between this creature and the lurker above (see **ADVANCED DUNGEONS & DRAGONS MONSTER MANUAL**) to lend credence to the speculation that the one is some kind of undead form of the other.

These creatures are vulnerable to all attack forms except *sleep, charm* and other similar spells and are treated as wraiths on the cleric/undead matrix.

SHOCKER

FREQUENCY: *Rare*
NO. APPEARING: *6—24*
ARMOUR CLASS:
    0 or 10 (see below)
MOVE: *9″*
HIT DICE: *1+2*
% IN LAIR: *Nil*
TREASURE TYPE: *15% chance*
    of 1—4 gems each, see below
NO. OF ATTACKS: *11*
DAMAGE/ATTACK: *10 hit points*
SPECIAL ATTACKS: *See below*
SPECIAL DEFENCES: *See below*
MAGIC RESISTANCE: *See below*
INTELLIGENCE: *Semi-*
ALIGNMENT: *Neutral (chaotic)*
SIZE: *M*
PSIONIC ABILITY: *Nil*
    Attack/Defence Modes: *Nil*
LEVEL/X.P. VALUE:
    III/65+2 per hit point

Little is known of the origin and purpose of this unusual creature in form, when on the *Prime Material Plane*, it is approximately man-sized and bipedal; its body is clothed in faint, light blue sparks and even when it is some distance away, anyone with good hearing will hear a very faint crackling which increases in intensity as the shocker approaches. It is quite clear that this creature does not have its origin on the *Prime Material Plane*, though its purpose in visiting that plane has not been divined; some say it is from the *Negative Material Plane* while others postulate the existence of an *Electromagnetic Plane*, conterminous with all three *Material Planes* and the *Elemental Plane*. Whatever the case, its existence on the *Prime Material Plane* is rarely prolonged and this has led to speculation that its form while on the *Prime Material Plane* is merely a projection — that the shocker's actual body never leaves its plane of origin.

The shocker attacks by discharging 10 points of electrical damage on a successful hit (save against *death magic* indicates half damage). Metal armour is treated as AC10 against their attack (though appropriate magical and dexterity bonuses still apply) and shockers gain a bonus of +2 on the 'to hit' roll when attacking plate mail.

Only magical weapons affect a shocker and if it is struck by a hand-held metal weapon, the effect is as though the shocker had attacked, the discharge being conducted by the metal to the body of the attacker. The shocker has AC10 against such attacks, but against missile fire and non-metal weaponry it is treated as AC0. When a shocker discharges, it collapses to fine, inert dust — so a shocker only has one successful attack.

1—4 gems will sometimes (15% chance) be discovered in the body structure of each shocker and these will be revealed when the creature has discharged.

A shocker is immune to electrical attacks, to poison and to paralysation; it is not affected by spells (such as *sleep* and *charm*) which affect the mind. Against other magical attacks it has 50% resistance.

SKELETON WARRIOR

FREQUENCY: *Very rare*
NO. APPEARING: *1*
ARMOUR CLASS: *2*
MOVE: *6″*
HIT DICE: *9+2 to 9+12*
% IN LAIR: *90%*
TREASURE TYPE: *A*
NO. OF ATTACKS: *1*
DAMAGE/ATTACK: *By weapon type*
SPECIAL ATTACKS : *+3 hit probability*
    with weapons
SPECIAL DEFENCES: *See below*
MAGIC RESISTANCE: *90%*
INTELLIGENCE: *Exceptional*
ALIGNMENT: *Neutral (evil)*
SIZE: *M*
PSIONIC ABILITY: *See below*
    Attack/Defence Modes: *See below*
LEVEL/X.P. VALUE:
    10th-12th level :
    VII/2,550 + 14 per hitpoint
    13th-15th level :
    VIII/3,700 + 16 per hit point

These are undead lords of the 10th-15th level, formerly powerful fighters (and will have psionic abilities if possessed in life). They are only affected by magical weapons and have 90% magical resistance. Their appearance is similar to that of a lich (see **ADVANCED DUNGEONS & DRAGONS MONSTER MANUAL**) — skeletal creatures clad in the rich, but faded and rotting trappings of a powerful fighter.

It is said that the skeleton warriors were forced into their lich-like state ages ago by a powerful and evil demi-god who trapped each of their souls in a golden circlet. A skeleton warrior's sole reason for remaining on this plane is to search for and regain the circlet which contains its soul.

Anyone possessing one of these circlets may control the skeleton warrior whose soul is stored therein within a 240' range. The controller can see through the warrior's 'eyes' when controlling a warrior in this way, but he may not himself move nor may he cast spells — he is literally unable to do so. Thus, while in 'active control' the controller may cause the skeleton warrior to fight, to search for treasure and so forth. The controller may also control the creature in a 'passive mode'; the skeleton warrior will be inert while under passive control and the controller cannot see through its 'eyes', but the controller can move, fight and cast spells.

In either case, control is lost if the skeleton warrior moves more than 240' from the controller, or vice versa, or if the circlet is removed from the controller's head. If the circlet remains in his possession, the controller can resume control at a later time, but if it leaves his possession, whether by accident or deliberate act, the skeleton warrior will immediately stop what it is doing and proceed at double speed (12″ movement rate) to attack and destroy the former controller, never resting until this task is accomplished or control is re-established. If the circlet falls into the possession of the skeleton warrior, it will 'die' and vanish, never to reappear, and the circlet will turn to fine, valueless dust.

When a circlet first comes in to the possession of a character, particularly if he does not recognise its significance, he may be unaware that the skeleton warrior whose soul is imprisoned therein will be tracking him. To establish control, he must not only put the circlet on his head but must also be able to see the skeleton warrior and concentrate on the establishment of control over the creature. If he does not do this, the skeleton warrior will attack him in an attempt to destroy him and gain possession of the circlet. Once control has been established in the first instance, however, it will only be broken as indicated above. The circlet cannot be worn with any other head-gear to be effective; the wearing of a helm, for instance, will nullify its powers, though the skeleton warrior will still be aware of its presence.

The mere sight of a skeleton warrior will cause any creature below 5 hit dice to flee in panic. Clerics have no chance of turning them.

Skeleton warriors usually fight with two-handed swords, but other types of weapon have been known to be used. Whatever weapon is used, the skeleton warrior attacks with a +3 'to hit' bonus, though the weapon itself does not become magical.

SKULK

FREQUENCY: *Rare*
NO. APPEARING: *1–8*
ARMOUR CLASS: *7*
MOVE: *12"*
HIT DICE: *2*
% IN LAIR: *40%*
TREASURE TYPE: *A*
NO. OF ATTACKS: *1*
DAMAGE/ATTACK: *By*
weapon type
SPECIAL ATTACKS: *Nil*
SPECIAL DEFENCES:
Camouflage — see below
MAGIC RESISTANCE: *Standard*
INTELLIGENCE: *Average*
ALIGNMENT: *Chaotic evil*
SIZE: *M*
PSIONIC ABILITY: *Nil*
Attack/Defence Modes: *Nil*
LEVEL/X.P. VALUE:
II/36 + 2 per hit point

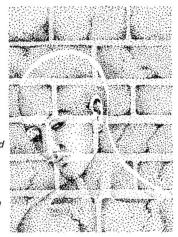

Skulks were once members of the human race with tendencies to extreme cowardice. As years passed and the race grew more and more resentful of 'normal' humans, they developed a progressively-improving ability of camouflage and now are able to blend into any background. There is only a 10% chance of sighting an immobile skulk.

Skulks live by theft and murder on the edges of civilisation. They keep to small bands, moving often and camping in deep dark forests or underground lairs. Their usual tactics of attacking unsuspecting victims from behind or murdering entire sleeping families make them universally despised, and if a skulk is captured it is usually the recipient of an unpleasant death at the hands of the community. However, they are rarely seen, and even more rarely captured, because of their camouflage ability, and their cunning is such that they are nearly impossible to track (one-fifth normal chance, even for a ranger, so if a skulk passes through a secret door, for instance, a ranger tracking it would only have a 5% chance of following the trail).

A skulk moves quickly and quietly, freezing into immobility and near-invisibility at the first hint of danger. Their favourite tactic is to attack from behind at +4 'to hit', doing triple damage if successful (as a 5th level thief). They will never openly attack a party which looks powerful, though they may set an ambush in an attempt to pick off a straggler or sentry, or (even better) attack when the party members are sleeping. They much prefer weak or helpless victims. Skulks still exhibit extreme cowardice and will flee at the slightest wounding or setback, taking whatever treasure they can.

They speak the common tongue and their alignment tongue. 20% of skulks will also speak another language — usually a near-human tongue such as elvish.

SLAAD

The slaadi are great frog-like beings, who dwell on the outer plane of *Limbo* where also dwell the githzerai (q.v.). Their form is of a large bipedal frog, though some of the more powerful slaadi have *polymorph self* and/or *shape change* abilities and will sometimes appear as men (see the individual descriptions below). In frog form their heads are huge and their claws extremely sharp and long.

The slaad hierarchy ascends from the comparatively weak red slaad to the dreaded *masters* — creatures of unequalled ferocity and malignity.

All slaadi have names and may be summoned by a form of the *cacodemon* spell (see **ADVANCED DUNGEONS & DRAGONS PLAYERS HANDBOOK**) which will affect the red, blue and green varieties as a demon type IV, V or VI. Slaadi masters have a 5% chance of manifesting themselves if their name is spoken. If a master does appear, it will immediately swallow the summoner and remove him to *Limbo*.

Occasionally the slaadi will be found roaming the *Prime Material Plane* on missions of woe.

All slaad speak a common slaad language — they are disdainful of the languages of others. However, they all have a special form of telepathy which allows them to understand and converse with any intelligent creature.

Slaadi Symbols: The symbols are magical symbols of rank in the form of a jewel encased in the creature's skull beneath the skin of the forehead. These are artificial devices which encase the slaad's life-force; they may be removed by certain spells. On threat of destruction of the gem, an intelligent being may force the monster to fulfil three 'requests', if they are within the beast's capacity. However, this can be a very risky business since the slaad, when released and the gem replaced, must be rewarded very well for its labour or it will turn on its would-be controller and kill him. Rewards will usually comprise human beings which the slaad takes back to *Limbo* as its slaves; very rich treasure would, however, suffice.

The symbols have no intrinsic value — their value lies in the power of the owner to control the slaad from which the symbol was taken. To remove a symbol from a slaad, the following spells are effective:

Hold word, power word: stun or *mind blank;* any of these spells will paralyse the slaad for 1–4 melee rounds and the symbol is caused to emerge from the creature's forehead.

Limited wish: the caster may use a *limited wish* to 'wish' the symbol from its position in the skull to the caster's hand; however, the creature gets a saving throw against the spell, and if the die roll is in the range of 01-65 the symbol will remain in place and the slaad will immediately attack the caster berserkly.

Wish or *trap the soul:* as *limited wish*, but the creature has no saving throw.

Alter reality: as *limited wish*, but the creature's saving throw is halved (i.e. the spell will succeed unless 01-32 is rolled).

Any slaad seeing a symbol being used by other than its slaad owner will react as does a slaad master to a summoning. Slaad symbols are unique and readily identifiable by another slaad.

Blue Slaad

FREQUENCY: *Rare*
NO. APPEARING: *2–12*
ARMOUR CLASS: *5*
MOVE: *7"*
HIT DICE: *8+4*
% IN LAIR: *35%*
TREASURE TYPE: *Z*
NO. OF ATTACKS: *5*
DAMAGE/ATTACK:
2–16/2–12/2–12/2–12/2–12
SPECIAL ATTACKS: *See below*
SPECIAL DEFENCES: *See below*
MAGIC RESISTANCE: *40%*
INTELLIGENCE: *Low*
ALIGNMENT: *Chaotic neutral*
SIZE: *L (10' high)*
PSIONIC ABILITY:
Defence strength 47
Attack/Defence Modes:
Nil/F,G
LEVEL/X.P. VALUE:
VII/2,000 + 12 per hit point

Though the blue variety is stronger than the red, the blue slaad is still a relatively weak member of the slaad race, more often used to run errands and carry out missions for the masters than for anything else. Its main colour is light electric blue, broken by streaks of grey.

There is a great sense of rivalry between blue and red slaadi, and neither type will help the other except in direst emergency.

On each of the blue slaad's claws are two scimitar-like blades. Thus the creature has, effectively, four claw attacks (2–12 points of damage each) as well as its bite (2–16 hit points of damage).

Blue slaadi have only defensive psionics. Their magical abilities (usable at will) are: *telekinese* 1,000 gold pieces weight, *passwall, hold* one person (normal saving throw). Four times per day they can attempt to *gate* in other slaadi. There is a 40% chance of the gate opening, and if it does the creature gated in will be a green slaad (35%), another blue slaad (50%) or a red slaad (15%).

Death Slaadi *(The Lesser Masters)*

FREQUENCY: *Very rare*
NO. APPEARING: *1–2*
ARMOUR CLASS: *-4*
MOVE: *12"*
HIT DICE: *15+7*
% IN LAIR: *50%*
TREASURE TYPE: *Z(x4)*
NO. OF ATTACKS: *3 or 2*
DAMAGE/ATTACK: *2–20/*
   3–18/3–18 or two sword
   attacks at 1–8 plus bonuses
SPECIAL ATTACKS: *See below*
SPECIAL DEFENCES: *+2 or*
   better weapon to hit; see
   below
MAGIC RESISTANCE: *75%*
INTELLIGENCE: *Genius*
ALIGNMENT: *Chaotic neutral*
SIZE: *M (6' high)*
PSIONIC ABILITY: *207*
   Attack/Defence Modes:
     All/all
LEVEL/X.P. VALUE:
   X/13,250 + 20 per hit point

Only four of these fearsome monsters are known to exist. They have rarely been seen in slaad form since they use human form exclusively on the *Prime Material Plane*, wearing no armour but using deadly swords of great magical power (such as *swords of sharpness*, for example).

In human form they attack with their sword twice in a single melee round. In slaad form they attack with two claws (3–18 hit points of damage each) and a bite for 2–20 hit points of damage; a successful bite drains 1–3 experience levels of the victim (saving throw permitted — if successful it negates the effect).

They may travel the planes at will and also have the following powers at will: *astral projection, ESP, fear, darkness* 15' radius, *detect invisibility, detect magic, invisibility, advanced illusion, cloudkill, wind walk, locate object, shape change* (slaad/man), *flame strike, weakness.* Once per round they may attempt to *gate* in another slaad with a 90% chance of the gate opening (equal chance of red, blue, green or grey slaad appearing). Once per day they can use any *symbol, power word; stun, unholy word,* generate an 8d6 *fireball,* create a *phantasmal killer.*

Green Slaad

FREQUENCY: *Rare or very rare*
NO. APPEARING: *1–6*
ARMOUR CLASS: *3*
MOVE: *9"*
HIT DICE: *9+3*
% IN LAIR: *50%*
TREASURE TYPE: *C, F, G*
NO. OF ATTACKS: *3*
DAMAGE/ATTACK: *2–16/3–8/3–8*
SPECIAL ATTACK: *See below*
SPECIAL DEFENCES: *+1 or*
   better weapon to hit;
   see below
MAGIC RESISTANCE: *50%*
INTELLIGENCE: *Average*
ALIGNMENT: *Chaotic neutral*
SIZE: *L (7'+ high)*
PSIONIC ABILITY: *76*
   Attack/Defence Modes: *B,D/nil*
LEVEL/X.P. VALUE.
   VIII/4,350 + 14 per hit point

This creature is pale green in colour with streaks of grey. Though it normally appears as a bipedal giant toad, it can change shape with its innate power of *polymorph self.*

A magical weapon with at least a +1 bonus is needed to damage this creature which attacks with its bite (2–16 hit points of damage) and its relatively small claws (3–8 hit points of damage each).

Its magical powers, which it can use at will, are: *telekinese* 1,250 gold pieces weight, *polymorph self, cause fear,* cause *continual darkness* 15' radius, *ESP, detect invisibility, detect magic, locate object, produce flame.* Once per day a green slaad can generate a 12d6 *delayed blast fireball.* Once per hour a green slaad may attempt to *gate* in other slaadi with a 50% chance of the gate opening. If successful, the slaad which appears will be red (35%), blue (35%) or green (30%). These creatures have 18(76) strength and may travel the planes at will.

If a green slaad has its mortal form destroyed but its symbol remains intact, it will reincarnate after 24 hours as a blue slaad, remaining in that form for a year and a day before turning green once again and resuming its former powers.

Grey Slaadi *(The Executioners)*

FREQUENCY: *Very rare*
NO. APPEARING: *1–2*
ARMOUR CLASS: *1*
MOVE: *12"*
HIT DICE: *10+6*
% IN LAIR: *20%*
TREASURE TYPE: *Special*
NO. OF ATTACKS: *3 or 2*
DAMAGE/ATTACK: *2–16/*
   4–10/4–10 or two sword
   attacks at 1–8 plus bonuses
SPECIAL ATTACKS: *See below*
SPECIAL DEFENCES: *+ 1 or better*
   weapon to hit; see below
MAGIC RESISTANCE:
   55% and see below
INTELLIGENCE: *High*
ALIGNMENT: *Chaotic neutral*
SIZE: *M (6' high)*
PSIONIC ABILITY: *160*
   Attack/Defence Modes:
     A,C,D/F,G,H
LEVEL/X.P. VALUE:
   IX/6,200 + 16 per hit point

These creatures are the most feared non-master slaadi, being the ones most often sent to the *Prime Material Plane* as Executioners of their masters' will. They appear in normal form as relatively small slaadi, a uniform light grey in colour. They will more normally visit the *Prime Material Plane,* however, as humans (with charisma at least 12). They have 18(00) strength.

When fighting in slaad form, the executioners use their two claws for 4–10 hit points of damage each and a bite for 2–16 hit points of damage. In human form they attack twice per round with a sword — usually (75%) a +2 magical sword but sometimes (25%) a more powerful magical weapon such as a *sword of sharpness.* When on the *Prime Material Plane,* the executioners usually wear no armour, preferring instead light clothing. They will usually carry treasure — one or two powerful magical items with a pouch of gold or platinum

Once per melee round they may use one of the following powers: cause *fear,* cause *darkness* (15' radius or less, at will), *know alignment, infravision* 60', create an *illusion, flame strike, wind walk, shape change* (slaad/man), *invisibility,* generate a ball of *lightning* (8d6+6 damage per ball). Once per day they can use a *symbol of pain* or *fear* and *power word: blind.* Given the time and the equipment, they can *enchant an item.* They may also, once per day, attempt to *gate* in 1–3 more grey slaad with a 60% chance of the gate opening.

Grey slaadi may travel the planes at will and are unaffected by *cold* or *disintegration* spells.

Red Slaad

FREQUENCY: *Rare*
NO. APPEARING: *3—18*
ARMOUR CLASS: *6*
MOVE: *6" (can hop at 9" rate for maximum of one turn in one hour)*
HIT DICE: *7*
% IN LAIR: *30%*
TREASURE TYPE: *F*
NO. OF ATTACKS: *3*
DAMAGE/ATTACK:
1—4/1—4/2—16
SPECIAL ATTACKS: *See below*
SPECIAL DEFENCES:
Regeneration — see below
MAGIC RESISTANCE: *35%*
INTELLIGENCE: *Low*
ALIGNMENT: *Chaotic neutral*
SIZE: *L (8' tall)*
PSIONIC ABILITY: *Nil*
Attack/Defence Modes: *Nil*
LEVEL/X.P. VALUE:
VI/875 + 8 per hit point

The commonest of the slaadi, the red slaad is regularly sent on missions by the masters to the *Prime Material Plane*, usually in search of human slaves. It has a dull red skin flecked with grey.

The red slaad attacks with its two claws (1—4 hit points of damage each) and its bite (2—16 hit points of damage). It may *regenerate* while still alive at the rate of 3 hit points per melee round. It may *gate* in 1—2 other red slaadi (35% chance of the gate opening) twice per day. Once per day it may use *power word: stun* which stuns all victims for 1—4 rounds.

Embedded in the skin under each of its claws there is a gland which produces small pellets. Each time it hits with a claw attack, there is a 40% chance that a pellet will be transferred into the flesh of its victim. A pellet thus lost is renewed immediately in the slaad's skin. If a victim has a pellet implanted, he must make his saving throw against poison; failure means death in 3-36 hours.

Once embedded, the pellet can only be affected by certain magical spells which must be cast in the period before death occurs. The pellet is neutralised by *alter reality, cure disease, slow poison, neutralise poison* or *barkskin*, while it can be removed from the victim by *limited wish* or *wish*. In the case of *limited wish* the pellet is removed in a neutral state and is useless. However if a full *wish* is used to extract the pellet from the victim, it can be incorporated into a charm against the slaad which secreted it, forcing it into obedience as would possession of its symbol but for double the number of tasks (six). However to create the charm requires *enchant an item, limited wish* and *spiritwrack*, costs 6,000 gold pieces and takes three months to prepare.

Ssendam — Lord of the Insane (Slaad Lord)

FREQUENCY: *Very rare*
NO. APPEARING: *1*
ARMOUR CLASS: *—6*
MOVE: *16"/19"*
HIT DICE: *197 hit points*
% IN LAIR: *30%*
TREASURE TYPE: *A(x4), F(x2)*
NO. OF ATTACKS: *3 or 1*
DAMAGE/ATTACK:
*2—16/2—16/2—16 plus
drain levels or special*
SPECIAL ATTACKS: *Spells*
SPECIAL DEFENCES:
*Regeneration, spells; +3
or better weapon to hit*
MAGIC RESISTANCE: *85%*
INTELLIGENCE: *Supra genius*
ALIGNMENT: *Chaotic neutral*
SIZE: *M*
PSIONIC ABILITY: *379*
Attack/Defence Modes:
All/all

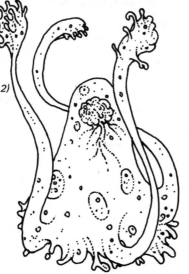

LEVEL/X.P. VALUE: *X/28, 695 **
**for destoring material form only — if actually killed, multiply
experience points figure shown by 10.*

This weird creature is claimed by some to be the most powerful of the slaadi. He either wanders the *Prime Material Plane* as a man. wearing no armour but using the *Black Sword* as a weapon (acts as a *power word : stun* on any victim struck), or as a golden amoeba with a man's brain in place of a nucleus. In either case he attacks as a monster of 16+ hit dice. In amoebic form he fights by extruding three corrosive pseudopoda each 10' long, each inflicting 2—16 hit points of damage on its victim and each draining 1—4 experience levels (saving throw permitted but a successful save merely halves the number of experience levels drained, with fractions rounded down).

He may *gate* in another slaad of any type (except Ygorl) at will, the gate opening automatically.

He may use the following powers at will: *fear, darkness 15' radius, blink, ESP, known alignment, dispel magic* (at 32nd level), *detect invisibility, detect magic, locate object, flame strike* (at double power), *ultravision 60', mass charm, astral projection, symbol of insanity, death.* Once per day he can use *unholy word* and any *power word.* Once per day he may also *fulfil another's wish*, though this takes a melee round during which he can do nothing else, so it is rarely used.

While alive, he *regenerates* 3 hit points per melee round. He may shape change at will and travel the planes instantaneously. He has 18(00) strength.

When encountered, Ssendam always gives his true name, though woe betide he who tries to use it.

Like gods and demi-gods, Ssendam always leaves his true form behind when he travels the planes. In *Limbo*, his form is that of a large, golden slaad.

Ssendam can only be damaged by a weapon with a +3 bonus or better.

Ygorl — Lord of Entropy (Slaad Lord)

FREQUENCY: *Very rare*
NO. APPEARING: *1*
ARMOUR CLASS: *—7*
MOVE: *18"*
HIT DICE: *210 hit points*
% IN LAIR: *75%*
TREASURE TYPE:
P(x4), Z(x2)
NO. OF ATTACKS: *2*
DAMAGE/ATTACK: *See below*
SPECIAL ATTACKS: *See below*
SPECIAL DEFENCES:
*+3 or better weapon
needed to hit, see below*
MAGIC RESISTANCE: *85%*
INTELLIGENCE: *Supra genius*
ALIGNMENT: *Chaotic neutral*
SIZE: *L*
PSIONIC ABILITY: *379*
Attack/Defence Modes:
All/all

LEVEL/X.P. VALUE: *X/28,950 **
**for destroying material form only — it Ygorl is actually killed
permanently, multiply the experience points figure by 10*

This fearsome slaad lord always appears as a skeletal, black, flightless, bat-winged man 12' tall wielding a sickle which measures 8' from tip to handle. He is always in shadow. The sickle is made of adamantite and has the word 'death' inscribed on its blade in the slaad tongue It has a magical bonus of +5 and on a strike its victim receives instant death unless he saves against poison, in which case the victim escapes with only 6—36 hit points of damage. Ygorl strikes twice each round with his sickle. Only the two slaadi lords, and others of similar status are immune to the effects of the sickle, the results on others being normal and permanent.

Ygorl may use the following abilities at will: *e.s.p.*, *darkness 15' radius*, *symbol* of *fear*, *detect magic*, *know alignment*, *detect invisibility*, *blink*, *sleep*, *phantasmal killer*, *advanced illusion*, *symbol of hopelessness*, *flame strike*. Once per round he may *gate* in another slaad (except Ssendam) at will, the gate opening automatically.

Once per day Ygorl may use *power word: kill*, any *symbol*, *unholy word*. He may travel by *astral projection* whenever he wishes.

Ygori does not appear to have the *shape change* power of other high-level slaadi; however it is clear that the form he assumes on the *Prime Material Plane* is not the same as his form in *Limbo*. Though no-one has seen him on his own plane, it is said that his form there is of a large slaad, 15' high and totally black.

When on the *Prime Material Plane*, Ygorl rides a neutral huge ancient brass dragon called Shkiv and can command undead as a 13th level cleric of the chaotic neutral alignment.

SNYAD (Pestie)

FREQUENCY: *Uncommon*
NO. APPEARING: *1–8*
ARMOUR CLASS: *–4*
MOVE: *21"*
HIT DICE: *1–1*
% IN LAIR: *95%*
TREASURE TYPE: *J*
NO. OF ATTACKS: *Nil*
DAMAGE/ATTACK: *Nil*
SPECIAL ATTACKS: *Nil*
SPECIAL DEFENCES: *See below*
MAGIC RESISTANCE: *Standard*
INTELLIGENCE: *Low*
ALIGNMENT: *Neutral*
SIZE: *S (2½' tall)*
PSIONIC ABILITY: *Nil*
   Attack/Defence Modes: *Nil*
LEVEL/X.P. VALUE: *1/7 + 1 per hit point*

Small bipeds, light brown in colour and with particularly high dexterity, pesties live in small passages adjoining dungeon corridors. The entrances to these tunnels are small and usually concealed behind piles of loose stone, making them difficult to detect even by elves (1 chance in 4 even if a search is being made, or 1 chance in 3 for an elf). They are totally silent and move with great speed, achieving surprise 90% of the time.

Their sole objective in leaving their tunnels and approaching a party of adventurers is to steal small items of treasure — gems, coins, pieces of jewellery, small weapons and the like. They will never attack and will avoid physical combat if they possible can. Their high dexterity gives them a +3 bonus on all saving throws against magical spells which can be dodged.

The snyad is a cousin of the mite and these two types of creatures will often act in co-operation, the mite's skill with traps complementing the high speed of the pestie.

They have no language, so far as can be ascertained, yet a group will work co-operatively together, and they and the mites appear to be able to gain speedy mutual understanding in their common task.

SON OF KYUSS

FREQUENCY: *Very rare*
NO. APPEARING: *1–3*
ARMOUR CLASS: *10*
MOVE: *9"*
HIT DICE: *4*
% IN LAIR: *Nil*
TREASURE TYPE: *Nil*
NO. OF ATTACKS: *1*
DAMAGE/ATTACK: *1–8*
SPECIAL ATTACKS: *See below*
SPECIAL DEFENCES:
   Regeneration and see below
MAGIC RESISTANCE: *Standard*
INTELLIGENCE: *Low*
ALIGNMENT: *Chaotic evil*
SIZE: *M*
PSIONIC ABILITY: *Nil*
   Attack/Defence Modes: *Nil*
LEVEL/X.P. VALUE:
   IV/215 + 4 per hit point

Truly horrible creatures in appearance, these ghastly undead appear as animated putrid corpses with fat green worms crawling in and out of all their skull orifices. Kyuss was an evil high priest, creating the first of these creatures under instruction from an evil deity. Since then the 'sons' have increased considerably in numbers.

Each son is surrounded by a spherical zone of *fear* 30' in diameter; a victim who fails to save against magic when entering this zone will flee in terror.

Each son *regenerates* 2 hit points per round; its limbs will *regenerate* even if severed, like those of a troll. Even after 'death' this process will continue, so the only way of destroying these creatures is by fire, lightning, acid or the application of holy water (or holy objects such as religious *symbols, holy swords* etc.) to their wounds.

The sons attack with a double-handed flailing of fists, causing 1—8 hit points of damage. Each successful hit has a 25% chance of inflicting advanced leprosy on the victim. This disease will be fatal in 1—6 months, and each month it progresses the diseased victim loses 2 points of charisma, permanently. It can be cured only by a magic spell, *cure disease*. The disease negates all *cure wound* spells. Infected creatures heal wounds at 10% of the normal rate.

In addition, one worm per melee round will jump from a son's head to an adjacent character in melee with a son. It needs the normal 'to hit' roll to land on the victim and will then burrow into him, taking one melee round to penetrate the skin, during which time if may be destroyed by the touch of cold steel, holy water or a blessed object. If it is not destroyed, the worm heads for the victim's brain, taking 1—4 melee rounds to reach it; during this time *remove curse* or *cure disease* will destroy it and *neutralise poison* or *dispel evil* will delay it by 1—6 full turns. If the worm reaches the brain, the victim becomes a son of Kyuss, the process of putrefaction setting in without further delay.

Sons of Kyuss are treated as mummies on the cleric/undead table. Like other undead, they are immune to mind-influencing spells.

STUNJELLY

FREQUENCY: *Rare*
NO. APPEARING: *1*
ARMOUR CLASS: *8*
MOVE: *3"*
HIT DICE: *4*
% IN LAIR: *Nil*
TREASURE TYPE: *See below*
NO. OF ATTACKS: *1*
DAMAGE/ATTACK: *2–8*
SPECIAL ATTACKS: *Paralysation*
SPECIAL DEFENCES: *Nil*
MAGIC RESISTANCE: *Standard*
INTELLIGENCE: *Animal*
ALIGNMENT: *Neutral*
SIZE: *L*
PSIONIC ABILITY: *Nil*
     Attack/Defence Modes:*Nil*
LEVEL/X.P. VALUE: *III/125+4 per hit point*

This relative of the gelatinous cube (see **ADVANCED DUNGEONS & DRAGONS MONSTER MANUAL**) looks just like a section of ordinary stone wall; it is usually 10' square and of thickness varying between 2½'–5'. Its attack has a paralysing effect — the victim must save versus paralysation or be paralysed for 5–20 melee rounds, during which the stunjelly will attempt to surround the victim and digest him. Like the gelatinous cube, it may have treasure of various types inside it.

The stunjelly does not have the transparency of the gelatinous cube; it is very slightly translucent, but any treasure inside it can only be seen in very rough outline in conditions of good illumination, while in normal torchlight the creature looks like solid wall without any inclusions.

SUSSURUS

FREQUENCY: *Very rare*
NO. APPEARING: *1*
ARMOUR CLASS: *4*
MOVE: *15"*
HIT DICE: *8*
% IN LAIR: *100%*
TREASURE TYPE: *Nil*
NO. OF ATTACKS: *2*
DAMAGE/ATTACK: *1–8/1–8*
SPECIAL ATTACKS: *Hug*

SPECIAL DEFENCES: *Nil*
MAGIC RESISTANCE: *See below*
INTELLIGENCE: *Low*
ALIGNMENT: *Neutral*
SIZE: *L*
PSIONIC ABILITY: *Not known*
     Attack/Defence Modes:
          Not known
LEVEL/X.P. VALUE:
     VI/550 + 10 per hit point

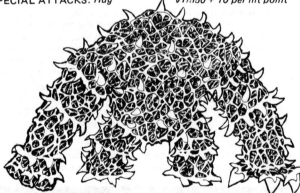

The size of a large gorilla, the sussurus appears at first sight like a headless ape which moves on all four limbs. In fact the 7' tall beast has no external organs, nor anything resembling a head. It 'sees' and 'hears' through vibrations and disturbances in the air and is therefore immune to all forms of magic which have their effects through such normal senses. It can thus detect the presence of invisible objects and beings.

The exoskeleton of the sussurus is honeycombed with small ducts and tiny passages through which the beast continually draws in the air on which it feeds. This constant inhalation causes the characteristic "dronesong" associated with the beast which only ceases when the beast dies. This weird sound is like a gentle wind blowing through trees; it can be heard up to ¼ of a mile away in still air through un-

obstructed airways, and one closed door in the path will not attenuate the sound sufficiently to render it inaudible at such distances. Underground, the sound reverberates around corridors and rooms, making location of its source difficult.

The dronesong has a curious effect on undead creatures, causing them to feel 'at peace' and to be rendered inert — an effect known as the 'sleep of the dead'. Any number may be slept by these means, but otherwise the dronesong acts as though it were an attempt by a second level cleric to turn away undead (so skeletons are affected on a roll of 7—20, zombies on a roll of 10—20, ghouls on a roll of 13—20, shadows on a roll of 16—20, wights on a roll of 19—20, ghasts on a roll of 20 and wraiths and more powerful undead are not affected). While 'asleep' the undead cannot be turned or destroyed, but if they are attacked physically they will awaken to defend themselves.

In windy locations it will often be immobile, taking in the air, and in such conditions it is 10% easier to surprise than normal (15% instead of the normal 5%). It is fast-moving, aggressive and dangerous when encountered, fighting with the claws on its two 'forepaws', each of which can inflict 1—8 hit points of damage. Additionally, if either claw hits on a roll of 18 or more (or a 20 in any event) the victim is crushed onto the exoskeletal spikes and suffers an additional 3—24 hit points of damage from this 'hug'.

The sussurus loathes fire and will immediately attack anyone carrying a torch or a lantern in an attempt to destroy the oxygen-consuming flames.

The sussurus is believed to have a life-span of over 1,000 years. Though it has no language as such, a sussurus communicates with others of its kind by slight and subtle variation in the dronesong; however it is only very rarely that two sussuri are close enough together to communicate in this way.

SVIRFNEBLIN *(Deep Gnome)*

FREQUENCY: *Very rare*
NO. APPEARING: *3–30*
ARMOUR CLASS: *2 and better*
MOVE: *9"*
HIT DICE: *3+6*
% IN LAIR: *Nil*
TREASURE TYPE: *Individuals K(x 2) and Q(x3)*
NO. OF ATTACKS: *1 or 2*
DAMAGE/ATTACK:
     By weapon type
SPECIAL ATTACKS: *See below*
SPECIAL DEFENCES: *See below*
MAGIC RESISTANCE: *20 %*
INTELLIGENCE: *Exceptional*
ALIGNMENT: *Neutral (good tendencies)*
SIZE: *S (about 3' tall)*
PSIONIC ABILITY: *Nil*
     Attack/Defence Modes: *Nil*
LEVEL/X.P. VALUE:
     3rd level: V/325 + 5 per hit point
     4th level: VI/575 + 6 per hit point
     5th level: VII/1,025 + 8 per hit point
     6th level: VII/ 1,800 + 10 per hit point

Far beneath the surface of the earth dwell the svirfnebli — the deep gnomes — a race related to the gnomes of the bright world. Small parties of these demi-humans roam here and there in the underworld mazes of small passageways, always in search of gem minerals. Their realm is in a region unknown, but thought to consist of a closely connected series of vast caverns in which thousands of these diminutive creatures labour for their king. Only males have ever been seen, and those only in very deep places beneath the ground.

All males of the race are doughty fighters. For every four svirfnebli encountered, there will be an additional leader-type with hit dice 4+7. If more than twenty normal deep gnomes are encountered there will be an additional 6th level fighter (hit dice 6+9) — a *burrow warden* with two 5th level assistants (hit dice 5+8). It is 25% probable that a 6th level deep gnome will have illusionist abilities of 5th, 6th or 7th level.

Note that a deep gnome of 6th level, if not an illusionist, is 50% likely to be able to summon an earth elemental. The type of earth elemental which can be summoned is found on this table:

Die roll	Elemental
1	24 hit dice earth elemental
2—6	16 hit dice earth elemental
7—10	12 hit dice earth elemental
11—15	8 hit dice earth elemental
16—18	xorn
19—20	summoning fails.

Elemental summoning can be attempted once per day by a deep gnome with the necessary power.

In addition to the abilities given above, all the svirfnebli have the following magical powers of illusionist nature: *blindness, blur, change self.* Each of these spell-like abilities can be used once per day by any deep gnome. All these creatures radiate *non-detection* identical to the spell of the same name.

The deep gnomes wear leathern jacks sewn with rings of mithral-steel alloy over fine chainmail shirts. They do not usually carry shields, as these devices would tend to hinder movement through the narrow corridors favoured by the svirfnebli. For every level above 3rd, a svirfneblin's armour class improves by 1 point — i.e. a 4th level deep gnome has AC1, 5th level AC0 and 6th level AC—1.

These gnomes are typically armed with a non-magical +1 dagger and a non-magical +1 pick (horseman's pick, for purposes of damage assessment). Each individual also carries a pouch of special darts, 7—10 hand-hurled missiles of about nine inches in length, with a 40' range and which inflict 1—3 hit points of damage. When one of these darts strikes it is constructed so as to compact and break a small glass bead containing a gas. Any creature struck on its front parts must save against poison; if it fails, the puff of gas has reached the creature's system and the creature will be *stunned* on the next round and *slowed* for the four rounds following that. Deep gnomes above 3rd level also carry 3—6 darts which contain an acid which eats a three-inch hole in armour protection in 1 round, or inflicts an additional 2—8 hit points of damage on non-protected targets (such as armour with holes, ring mail, chain mail etc.) A svirfneblin can hurl two darts in a single melee round.

Deep gnomes fight as fighters of the same level, but when hurling darts they add +2 to hit probability.

Despite their metal armour and arms, these small and fast-moving creatures are able to move very quietly. They are 60% likely to be unseen by any observer, even a kuo-toan, as deep gnomes are able to 'freeze' in place for long periods without any hint of movement. They are surprised only 1 in 12 due to their keen hearing and smelling abilities. They are likely to surprise opponents 90% of the time.

All deep gnomes are 20% magic resistant, gaining an extra 5% magic resistance for each level they attain above 3rd. No illusion, phantasm or hallucination is able to affect a svirfneblin's mind. Because of this and their high wisdom, speed and agility, they make all saving throws at +3 except against poison when their bonus is +2.

The svirfnebli communicate with each other by a form of racial empathy when outside their own domains. They have their own language, a dialect of gnomish which a normal gnome is 60% likely to understand. Most deep gnomes are also able to converse in the underworld cant (the trade language) and speak and understand a fair amount of kuo-toan and drow (tongues of their hated and feared enemies who, along with the mind-flayers, are the worst threat to any deep gnome gem-gathering expedition). All these small creatures can converse with speaking creatures from the *Elemental Plane of Earth* and it is 90% unlikely that any such creature will harm a svirfneblin, though the deep gnome might have to pay a heavy bribe in precious metal and gems so to escape.

Deep gnomes have infravision to 120' and can also see into the ultra-violet spectrum to a limited extent. They have normal gnomish

power with respect to determination of direction, distance beneath the surface, and detection of slopes and unsafe walls, ceilings or floors (see **ADVANCED DUNGEONS & DRAGONS PLAYERS HANDBOOK** — *Character Races*).

When being pursued by enemies, the svirfnebli will typically dash into a secret escape passage tunnelled to their size. Larger escape routes used by the deep gnomes will be filled with covered pit traps and rock deadfalls. A gnome leader is 75% likely to carry 3—12 small rock-like containers, and these will be strewn in the path of pursuing foes if no handy escape route is nearby. These crystals are crushed when stepped on by any creature weighing more than 100 pounds, and each releases a cloud of poison gas of about 10' diameter and 15' height. Any creature passing through such a gas cloud must save versus poison or lose consciousness for 1—12 turns. The gas cloud dissipates in 2 rounds.

Deep gnomes will usually aid any non-enemy for a fee, and they will certainly help in fighting drow, kuo-toans or mind flayers, providing there is a reasonable chance of defeating these mortal enemies. They love gems and will take great risks in order to gain them.

Description: A svirfneblin is gnarled and very muscular. Skin colour is medium brown to brownish gray. Deep gnomes have grey eyes and tend to be bald.

SYMBIOTIC JELLY

FREQUENCY: *Very rare*
NO. APPEARING: *1*
ARMOUR CLASS: *8*
MOVE: *1"*
HIT DICE: *2*
% IN LAIR: *100%*
TREASURE TYPE: *Nil*
NO. OF ATTACKS: *Nil*
DAMAGE/ATTACK: *Nil*
SPECIAL ATTACKS: *See below*
SPECIAL DEFENCES: *See below*
MAGIC RESISTANCE: *Standard*
INTELLIGENCE: *Very*
    (within the limitations
     of its existence)
ALIGNMENT: *Neutral*
SIZE: *S (2"—3" in diameter)*
PSIONIC ABILITY: *Nil*
    Attack/Defence Modes: *Nil*
LEVEL/X.P. VALUE:
    III/65 + 2 per hit point

This curious freak mutation takes the form of a globule of yellow jelly about 2½" in diameter. To obtain sustenance it must drain energy (which it can do remotely in a fashion whose means defy investigation) from a carnivorous creature — any monster which rends flesh except those which dwell on planes other than the *Prime Material* and those of the undead class — at the same time as the monster is itself eating. This peculiar requirement is the reason for the creature's unique behaviour.

It selects as its lair an unoccupied cave and sticks to the ceiling where it is virtually impossible to detect. When a monster — hopefully a powerful monster — ventures in, the jelly will use one of its magical powers — *charm monster* — to persuade the beast telepathically to remain in the cave and attack any creature or person entering. (The monster must be one which would normally, or at least occasionally, feed on flesh, otherwise the jelly will let it pass undisturbed). The jelly then uses its other magical power — an advanced form of *illusion* — to create two illusions. The first illusion makes the charmed monster appear to be a much weaker beast, the second creates illusory treasure in the cave. Those observing the illusions will fail to recognise them as such unless they save against magic at a penalty of —7.

If the intruder is killed by the creature the jelly has charmed, the jelly will drain power through the creature as it eats. If the charmed creature loses the battle, the jelly will attempt to *charm* the victor and persuade it to replace the former occupant.

TABAXI – TENTAMORT – TERITHRAN – THOQQUA – THORK – THROAT LEECH – TIGER FLY –
TIRAPHEG – TRILLOCH – TROLL – TWEEN

TABAXI *(Cat-man)*

FREQUENCY: *Rare*
NO. APPEARING: *2–8*
ARMOUR CLASS: *6*
MOVE: *15"*
HIT DICE: *2*
% IN LAIR: *15 %*
TREASURE TYPE: *Magical sword
   or miscellaneous weapon 5%*
NO. OF ATTACKS: *3 or by
   weapon type*
DAMAGE/ATTACK: *1–3/1–3/1–3
   or by weapon type*
SPECIAL ATTACKS: *Nil*
SPECIAL DEFENCES: *Nil*
MAGIC RESISTANCE: *Standard*
INTELLIGENCE: *Average (high
   cunning)*
ALIGNMENT: *Chaotic neutral*
SIZE: *M (6½' tall)*
PSIONIC ABILITY: *Nil*
   Attack/Defence Modes: *Nil*
LEVEL/X.P. VALUE: *II/20 + 2 per hit point*

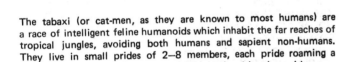

The tabaxi (or cat-men, as they are known to most humans) are
a race of intelligent feline humanoids which inhabit the far reaches of
tropical jungles, avoiding both humans and sapient non-humans.
They live in small prides of 2–8 members, each pride roaming a
large territory and rarely having anything to do with other prides.

The tabaxi are extraordinary hunters, taking their prey through
surprise and quick ambush. Two of them will often chase an animal
directly onto the claws of a third. They have learned how to avoid
detection by disguising their scent with aromatic herbs. This, combined with their natural camouflage and ability to move quickly and
silently, makes them deadly opponents in the tropical forest. Like
other cats, they will sometimes 'play' with their wounded prey until
it expires. They are also very adept at recognising a trap for what it is –
there is only a 10% chance of trapping a cat-man even if the trap is very
carefully hidden and cunningly constructed.

They are tool-users when they find it convenient to be so. Their tools
usually consist of bone or wooden weapons, with nothing more intricate than a bola or atlatl. However, tabaxi have an amazing aptitude
for weaponry, and can discover the use of a weapon, and become
adept in its use, in a remarkably short time so long as the weapon is
not a complex one.

Tabaxi will generally avoid human intruders in their forests, unless
they see an easy opportunity for the acquisition of weaponry.

The cat-men are tall and lithe and move with the smooth-easy grace
of cats. Their fine fur is tawny and striped with black, in a pattern
similar to that of a tiger. They wear no clothing. Their eyes are green-
yellow and slit-pupilled. They have retractable claws. A pride will
generally be 1–3 young (1 hit die, 50% chance of fighting if attacked,
50% chance of fleeing) 1–3 males and 1–3 females. The females are
at least the equal of the males in fighting ability.

Tabaxi speak a small amount of the common tongue in addition to
their own language. They will not engage in trade, as they consider it
demeaning.

Unless armed with a weapon, a cat-man will fight with its two foreclaws (1–3 hit points of damage each) and its bite (1–3 hit points of
damage).

TENTAMORT

FREQUENCY: *Rare*
NO. APPEARING: *1–10*
ARMOUR CLASS: *3 (tentacles);
   1 (head/body)*
MOVE: *1"*
HIT DICE: *2 per tentacle + 4 for
   the head/body for 8 total*
% IN LAIR: *95%*
TREASURE TYPE: *Nil*
NO. OF ATTACKS: *2*
DAMAGE/ATTACK: *1–6/1–6*
SPECIAL ATTACKS: *Constriction/
   paralysation/special*
SPECIAL DEFENCES: *Nil*
MAGIC RESISTANCE: *Standard*
INTELLIGENCE: *Non-*
ALIGNMENT: *Neutral*
SIZE: *S (but tentacles 10' long)*
PSIONIC ABILITY: *Nil*
   Attack/Defence Modes: *Nil*
LEVEL/X.P. VALUE:
   V/475 + 6 per hit point

There are a number of names by which this creature is known, but
'tentamort' is now in most common usage. The head/body of the
creature is quite small, in shape approximating to a sphere 2' in
diameter. From it grow a number of small tentacles, each of which
carries a row of suckers; using these, the creature can attach itself
firmly to almost any surface and can move slowly across that surface.
From the side of the body opposite the small tentacles grow two
longer (10' long) and thicker (up to 5" diameter) tentacles. Each of
these long tentacles has 2 hit dice and operates independently of the
other, attacking as a monster with 2 hit dice. The head/body has 4
hit dice but does not itself attack.

One of the long tentacles is a powerful constrictor. If it hits a victim it
will lash for 1–6 hit points of damage. A natural roll of 20, or a roll
2 or more greater than that required to hit, means that it has wrapped
itself round a victim, pinning his arms to his sides, and will automatically (no 'to hit' roll needed) constrict for 1–6 hit points of
damage each round thereafter until the tentacle or its victim is dead.

The other long tentacle has a hollow needle of bone, 6" long, at its
end. That tentacle will also flail a victim for 1–6 hit points of damage
and will also wrap itself round a victim on the required roll (20 or 2
or more greater than normal). This tentacle does not constrict; instead,
the melee round following the one in which the victim was trapped,
the needle will be inserted into the victim's flesh and he will be
paralysed instantly unless he makes a successful saving throw. Through
the needle, the creature will then inject a saliva-like fluid into the
victim, taking two melee rounds to inject a full dose if the victim is
man-sized. (This takes but one round if the victim is smaller than
man-sized, three or four rounds if larger than man-sized). When the
necessary dose has been administered, the victim's internal organs will
begin to soften and the creature will suck them out of the victim's
body through the needle. A man will die after two melee rounds of
this treatment (adjust this figure as above for creatures smaller or
larger than man-sized). If the tentacle is 'killed' during the time in
which the saliva is being injected, it will detach from the victim and
cure disease must be administered within an hour or the victim will
die. Once the dose of saliva has been administered, however, only more
powerful curative magic will save the victim from death within an hour
even if the tentacle is detached immediately. The *heal* spell will be
effective, as will *regenerate* followed by *cure wounds*.

If the head/body is killed both tentacles cease to function, but killing
one long tentacle does not affect the other.

If two victims are within reach, the tentacles will attack different targets, but if only one victim is available in range, both tentacles will concentrate on him.

The creature is a dark grey-green in colour; the needle is the colour of bone.

TERITHRAN

FREQUENCY: *Very rare*
NO. APPEARING: *1*
ARMOUR CLASS: *3 (6)*
MOVE: *15" (18")*
HIT DICE: *5+1*
% IN LAIR: *Nil (100%)*
TREASURE TYPE: *Various discharged magical items, mostly useless.*
NO OF ATTACKS: *2*
DAMAGE/ATTACK: *2–5/2–5*
SPECIAL ATTACKS: *See below*
SPECIAL DEFENCES: *Silver or magical weapons required to hit*
MAGIC RESISTANCE: *50%*
INTELLIGENCE: *Low average*
ALIGNMENT: *Neutral*
SIZE: *S (4' tall)*
PSIONIC ABILITY: *Nil*
 Attack/Defence Modes: *Nil*
LEVEL/X.P. VALUE: *VI/575 + 6 per hit point*

The Terithran is a creature of the *Ethereal Plane* — a short (4' tall) biped with long sinewy arms and an unusually large mis-shapen head. When on the *Prime Material Plane* it has a faint, shadowy appearance (though not so faint as a non-corporeal monster) which gives it AC3, though its actual AC is 6. Figures in parentheses above refer to characteristics on the *Ethereal Plane*.

In normal melee the creature fights with two claws for 2–5 hit points of damage each, but it will try to avoid this type of fighting if possible so as to make full use of its unique magical powers.

The terithran has come to dislike the swirls, eddies and warps which the use of large amounts of magic on the *Prime Material Plane* causes in the *Ethereal Plane,* its homeland (where it is never found out of its lair). If it notices such disturbances, it will materialise in the area of the magic-user responsible on the *Prime Material Plane* (1'–10' away from him) and attempt to drain his power and take him back to the *Ethereal Plane* for punishment. It will only appear when magic is being used, and then only if the magic is powerful enough. Clerical or druidic magic will not attract it, but magic cast by a magic-user or illusionist will (as could magic-user spells cast by a high level ranger).

Generally speaking, the use of a single spell will not attract the attention of a terithran unless the spell is of high level. Use of an 8th level magic-user spell has a 20% chance of attracting its attention, a 7th level spell 30% (a 6th level illusionist spell has a 10% chance, a 7th level spell 20%). Continual use of lower-level magic may attract it, however; if a total of 16 or more spell-levels of magic-user spells (or 13 of illusionist spells) have been used in successive melee rounds, even if no high-level spells have been involved, there is a 65% chance that a terithran has been attracted. Similarly, three consecutive uses of a magic item (such as a *wand of cold*) has the same chance of attracting it. Note that the spells need not have been cast by the same person; the requirement is fulfilled if all the spells have effect in the same 60'x60' area, though if more than one person has been involved in the magic-use, the terithran will appear half-way between them.

Note that spell-use by monsters will attract the terithran in the same way, and with the same chance, as spell-use by characters.

The terithran is 50% magic resistant on either *Plane* and also has a number of innate magical powers and one innate magical ability. The ability is *detect magic* and it has unlimited use of this. Its magical powers are:

Stunning blast: a charge of ethereal waves with the effect of a *power word: stun* on all creatures within a 10' radius; a saving throw against magic negates the effect.

Drain power: this power removes all magic ability from a magic-user (or illusionist or ranger) until an appropriate regenerative time has passed — treat as though the spell-caster had used up all his spells; a successful save as against breath weapons will negate this effect.

Cause serious wounds: as the clerical spell, activated by touch (a normal attack roll is required); there is no saving throw.

Transportation: this permits the terithran to transport itself and one other person (the offending spell-user) back to the *Ethereal Plane;* the victim must first be grasped (treat as a normal hit with two claws — if one or both score a 'hit' the victim has been grasped) but there is no saving throw.

While on the *Prime Material Plane* the terithran is limited to 6 power-uses per day. While in an encounter, therefore, it will have as its prime objective the grasping of the target spell-user and his transportation back to the *Ethereal Plane;* it will thus reserve one power-use for *transportation,* either with a victim or, if it fails to grasp and the melee is going against it, alone in escape. However it will use other powers (up to a maximum of 5 usages) to defend itself, to get to its intended victim and so forth.

Note that the touch of the terithran does not automatically *cause serious wounds;* this is only the case if the creature is using that particular power in that melee round (though if it is, the claw damage also applies).

If the creature is encountered (in its lair) on the *Ethereal Plane*, its claws do 2–9 hit points of damage each, it can have 16 power-uses per day and the power of *stunning blast* inflicts 2–7 8-sided dice of damage.

On the *Prime Material Plane* the terithran can only be hit by silver or magical weapons.

THOQQUA (Rockworm)

FREQUENCY: *Very rare*
NO. APPEARING: *1–2*
ARMOUR CLASS: *2*
MOVE: *12"(3")*
HIT DICE: *3*
% IN LAIR: *80%*
TREASURE TYPE: *10–60 gems (base 10 g.p)*
NO. OF ATTACKS: *1 and 1*
DAMAGE ATTACK: *4–32/2–12*
SPECIAL ATTACKS: *Heat*
SPECIAL DEFENCES: *Fire attacks heal*
MAGIC RESISTANCE: *Standard*
INTELLIGENCE: *Low*
ALIGNMENT: *Neutral*
SIZE: *S*
PSIONIC ABILITY: *Nil*
 Attack/Defence Modes: *Nil*
LEVEL/X.P. VALUE: *III/65 + 3 per hit point*

It is suspected that this beast is a larval form of some creature of the *Elemental Plane of Earth* or the *Elemental Plane of Fire,* though some postulate that its origin is an *Elemental Plane* so far undefined. It is shaped like a small purple worm 2' in diameter and 4'–5' long. In colour it is a reddish-silver. The creature lives on the *Prime Material Plane* in rock through which it can burrow at the rate of 30' per turn, creating a red-hot tunnel about 3' in diameter. The tunnel remains hot for two turns after construction; in the first turn the rock is a red colour and inflicts 4–14 hit points of damage on anyone touching it with bare skin, but in the second turn the rock returns to normal colour and a touch inflicts 2–7 hit points of damage. No saving throw is permitted in either case, though particularly in the first turn discernable heat will be radiated from the rock.

In melee the creature will initially charge at an opponent, being able to move at 48″ rate for this short burst over a distance no greater than 30′. If the charge hits a victim, he will suffer 4—32 hit points of damage from the heat and the momentum of the charge. Thereafter its mode of attack is simply to touch a victim for 2—12 hit points of heat damage, reverting to normal speed after the intial charge.

When a victim is struck by an attack by a thoqqua, whether as a result of a charge or normal attack, the prominent items he is wearing or carrying on the side of his body at which the attack is directed must save against normal fire or be rendered useless. If the attack is a charging attack, these saving throws are made at —4.

If a thoqqua is struck by a fire attack it temporarily (1—4 turns) adds the damage to its hit points. However cold attacks inflict double damage on the creature.

THORK

FREQUENCY: *Very rare*
NO. APPEARING: *1—6*
ARMOUR CLASS: *3*
MOVE: *6″//6″*
HIT DICE: *3*
% IN LAIR: *90%*
TREASURE TYPE: *1—20*
    platinum pieces
NO. OF ATTACKS: *1*
DAMAGE/ATTACK: *1—6*
SPECIAL ATTACKS:
    Breath weapon
SPECIAL DEFENCES: *Nil*
MAGIC RESISTANCE:
    Standard
INTELLIGENCE: *Animal*
ALIGNMENT: *Neutral*
SIZE: *L (9′ tall)*
PSIONIC ABILITY: *Nil*
    Attack/Defence Modes: *Nil*
LEVEL/X.P. VALUE:
    III/90 + 3 per hit point

These stork-like birds live exclusively in or near water. Although they are similar to the stork in appearance and shape, closer inspection will reveal that the feathers are metallic — they are in fact pure copper — and for this reason a bird is worth up to 200 gold pieces. An observer will also notice that wisps of steam will normally be seen rising from the bird's beak, though no discernable heat is radiated by the body.

The 'boiler bird' is a benign creature and will only attack in self-defence — if an obviously hostile party approaches within 30′, for example.

To attack, the thork squirts a jet of boiling water at its opponent. The jet takes the form of a cone with a 10′ base diameter at the extreme range of 40′. If a victim is struck by the water jet, he will suffer 4—32 hit points of damage (a successful saving throw halves the damage). All opponents are treated as AC10 for the purposes of this attack.

The bird is capable of sucking in the necessary quantity of water and heating it in one melee round, so its breath weapon attack will take place one round after the creature decides on this course of action. However it is capable of delivering only three such attacks each day, after which it will attempt to elude its enemies by swimming away (or, if it cannot escape, it will defend itself by striking with its beak for 1—6 hit points of damage).

The thork collects only platinum pieces or other small objects made of that metal; it normally conceals them under a boulder or in a chink in a rock face near the water's edge.

THROAT LEECH

FREQUENCY: *Common*
NO. APPEARING: *1—6*
ARMOUR CLASS: *10*
MOVE: *1″//1″*
HIT DICE: *1 hit point*
% IN LAIR: *Nil*
TREASURE TYPE: *Nil*
NO. OF ATTACKS: *1*
DAMAGE/ATTACK: *1—3*
SPECIAL ATTACKS: *Choke*
SPECIAL DEFENCES: *Nil*
MAGIC RESISTANCE: *Standard*
INTELLIGENCE: *Non-*
ALIGNMENT: *Neutral*
SIZE: *S (1″ long)*
PSIONIC ABILITY: *Nil*
    Attack/Defence Modes: *Nil*
LEVEL/X.P. VALUE: *I/6*

This leech is about 1″ long and resembles an inconspicuous twig. It is always found in fresh water (streams, pools etc.)

Anyone drinking water containing a leech may (10% chance) take it into his mouth unless the water is carefully filtered before drinking. The leech will fasten itself onto the soft flesh at the back of the victim's throat, sucking blood at the rate of 1—3 hit points of damage each melee round, until it becomes completely distended; after ten melee rounds of sucking, the leech will be bloated and will not suck any more blood.

Each melee round the leech is in the victim's throat, there is a 50% chance that the victim will choke, causing an additional 1—4 hit points of damage. A victim who chokes in three successive rounds will die at the third choking.

Apart from magical means which may suggest themselves, the only way to kill a throat leech in a victim's throat is to place a thin, heated metal object such as a wire into the bloated leech; the hot metal will cause the leech to burst and no further damage is inflicted on the victim. However the person administering the 'cure' by this method runs a risk of burning the victim's throat for 1—4 hit points rather than the leech — the chance of a successful probe is 5% for each dexterity point of the person making the attempt.

TIGER FLY

FREQUENCY: *Rare*
NO. APPEARING: *3—18*
ARMOUR CLASS:
    4 (male and female);
    9 (larva)
MOVE: *6″/18″*
HIT DICE: *6 (male);*
    4 (female); 1—1 (larva)
% IN LAIR: *40%*
TREASURE TYPE: *B*
NO. OF ATTACKS:
    2 and 1 (male); 1 (female);
    1 (larva)
DAMAGE/ATTACK:
    1—8/1—8 and 4—24 (male):
    4—16 (female), 2—8 (larva)
SPECIAL ATTACKS:
    Poison (male);
    paralysation (female)
SPECIAL DEFENCES: *Nil*
MAGIC RESISTANCE: *Standard*
INTELLIGENCE: *Non-*
ALIGNMENT: *Neutral*
SIZE: *M (5′ tall)*
PSIONIC ABILITY: *Nil*
    Attack/Defence Modes: *Nil*
LEVEL/X.P. VALUE:
    Male: V/275 + 6 per hit point
    Female: III/125 + 4 per hit point
    Larva: I/10 + 1 per hit point

The adult tiger fly is a large — almost man-sized — wasp with a human head and four 'arms'. The female's colouration is the same as that of a wasp, while the male is a uniform dull red. Tiger flies are manoeuvrability class C for the purposes of aerial combat.

Male tiger flies attack with two sickle-like forelimbs with which they can strike at the same opponent, even when flying. Each such successful attack inflicts 1–8 hit points of damage on the victim. The creature may also attempt to grasp its victim with its other two 'arms' — a normal 'to hit' roll is required, though these attacks inflict no damage — and if both these arms achieve hits the sting (which does 4–24 hit points of damage plus poison) is administered in the next melee round, requiring no 'to hit' roll. Once it has grasped a victim, the male tiger fly will not release him until the victim is dead or the tiger fly itself dies. Victims are permitted a saving throw against poison. The male tiger fly can use its sting 8 times per day.

The female will always attempt to attack with its sting and all four 'arms' will attempt to grasp a victim. A normal 'to hit' roll is required for each 'arm' and if two or more hit, the victim is grasped. The sting is administered in the next melee round, requiring no 'to hit' roll, and can be used up to 6 times per day. The sting inflicts 4–16 hit points of damage and paralyses the victim (who is allowed a saving throw). Once the female tiger fly succeeds in paralysing a victim it will lay its eggs in the victim's body and the larvae (1–3 per victim) will hatch in 13–24 hours whether the victim is killed or not. During the period following the injection of the eggs and the hatching of the larvae, only a very powerful spell such as *heal* will destroy the eggs. The victim will die from a massive internal haemorrhage when the hatching takes place and the larvae burrow out of his body.

Tiger fly larvae are white grubs which grow quickly to a length of 3½'–4'; they have horned black heads and large mandibles. The larvae will attack anything which moves, including each other, their mandibles inflicting 2–8 hit points of damage. Each larva has 1–1 hit dice, AC9 and moves at 6" rate; it cannot fly until it later develops into an adult tiger fly.

TIRAPHEG

FREQUENCY: *Very rare*
NO. APPEARING: *1*
ARMOUR CLASS: *10*
MOVE: *3"*
HIT DICE: *2*
% IN LAIR: *20%*
TREASURE TYPE: *Nil*
NO. OF ATTACKS: *3*
DAMAGE/ATTACK: *1–4/1–4/1–4*
SPECIAL ATTACKS: *Strange*
SPECIAL DEFENCES: *Illusions*
MAGIC RESISTANCE: *Standard*
INTELLIGENCE: *Average*
ALIGNMENT: *Neutral*
SIZE: *M (7' tall)*
PSIONIC ABILITY: *Nil*
    Attack/Defence Modes: *Nil*
LEVEL/X.P. VALUE:
    III/73 + 2 per hit point

This tripedal hermaphrodite is 7' tall, naked and hairless. Its shape is human-like, but there are significant deviations from human form. The creature has three heads of which the outer two are featureless. The middle head has three large, deeply-inset eyes, two to the front, (above the nose as a human) and one to the rear; it has ear-like organs on each side, but no mouth.

From the body of the creature spring three arms; the two at the shoulders are jointed in such a way that they can attack to the rear with equal facility as to the front of the body — these are prehensile limbs with a 6" long spike at the end of each. The third arm, emerging centrally from the chest, is like a human arm except that the hand has three strong fingers. Of the creature's three legs, the outer two are stumps and the central one has three unusually long and strong toes.

The tirapheg's mouth is located in its belly below the central arm; this for the sole purpose of eating, the creature's favourite diet being

decayed flesh. Above the mouth are three 3" long tentacles which writhe continuously — the function of these organs is unknown.

When this curious creature attacks to its rear the spikes will strike a victim at –2 on the 'to hit' roll because the single eye gives poor depth of vision. A spike causes 1–4 hit points of damage if it hits.

When attacking to its front, the creature strikes with the spikes, though with no 'to hit' penalty; if both spikes hit a victim, the central arm will hit the same victim automatically, requiring no 'to hit' roll, grasping the victim's neck and strangling him for an additional 1–4 hit points of damage.

Normally the tirapheg will shy away from other creatures, but its behaviour can be unpredictable and it has been known for a tirapheg to attack a party of adventurers for no apparent reason.

If the creature is cornered in melee, with the fight going against it but a retreat impossible (it moves very slowly) it will project two *illusions* — replicas of itself — which it controls telepathically. These illusions will fight as the original creature and will take no damage themselves, though they will do damage to opponents if they are not recognised for what they are (treat as *phantasmal force* except that the illusions disappear only when the creature is killed or when its opponents retreat out of sight). At the instant the illusions are created by the creature, it has the ability to generate a split-second blinding flash of light (to cover the appearance of the illusions) which causes all creatures and persons within a 30' range to stand *confused* for one melee round. The tirapheg and its illusions can attack in the melee round in which the illusions are created.

TRILLOCH

FREQUENCY: *Very rare (at best)*
NO. APPEARING: *1*
ARMOUR CLASS: *Not applicable*
MOVE: *12"*
HIT DICE: *Not applicable*
% IN LAIR: *Nil*
TREASURE TYPE: *Nil*
NO. OF ATTACKS:
    Not applicable
DAMAGE/ATTACK: *Nil*
SPECIAL ATTACKS: *Nil*
SPECIAL DEFENCES:
    Normally undetectable
MAGIC RESISTANCE: *See below*
INTELLIGENCE: *Animal*
ALIGNMENT: *Neutral*
SIZE: *Not applicable*
PSIONIC ABILITY: *Unknown*
    Attack/Defence Modes:
      Unknown
LEVEL/X.P. VALUE:
    Not applicable

The trilloch is an energy being from the *Negative Material Plane* which lives on the waning life-force of dying creatures and uses its unique powers to accelerate the process which releases its 'food'. So far as is known, the creature has no fixed definite form. It cannot be detected by normal means, though a *detect magic* spell cast within 60' of the creature will reveal its distinctive aura and *dispel magic* within the same range will drive it away.

So far as is known, no other magic has any effect on a trilloch.

If melee occurs in the presence of a trilloch, detected or otherwise, all attacks will be at +1 hit probability and successful hits will inflict +1 damage. The creature can also influence the behaviour of unintelligent monsters, making them twice as likely to attack a party encountered.

A trilloch will often stay with a large, powerful monster, thriving on the huge amounts of life-force released by its victims. If this 'host' is killed, the trilloch will attach itself to the victor and stay with him either until driven off or until another, even more powerful creature, kills its new host, whereupon it will transfer to that creature.

Experience of trilloch behaviour is so limited that it may have yet other powers, as yet undetected. Certainly no means have yet been discovered whereby the creature can be harmed, so far as can be detected.

TROLL

Trolls (fully detailed in ADVANCED DUNGEONS & DRAGONS MONSTER MANUAL) are horrid carnivores found in nearly every clime. They are feared by most creatures. However, certain creatures have cross-bred with them to produce fearsome sub-species of the troll race.

All the sub-species have the troll's ability to direct their various attacks at different opponents if desired.

Trolls have the ability to *regenerate* as follows: 3 melee rounds after being damaged a troll will begin to *regenerate*. Regeneration repairs damage at 3 hit points per round; this regeneration includes the re-bonding of severed members. The loathsome members of a troll have the ability to fight on even if severed from the body; a hand can claw or strangle, the head bite, etc. Total dismemberment will not slay a troll, for its parts will slither and scuttle together, rejoin, and the troll will arise whole and ready to continue combat. To kill a troll, the monster must be burned or immersed in acid, any separate pieces being treated in the same fashion or they create a whole again in 3—18 melee rounds.

The sub-species detailed below have all inherited some of these regenerative powers as well as the troll's great strength. All have the troll traits of knowing no fear and attacking unceasingly.

Giant Troll

FREQUENCY: *Rare*
NO. APPEARING: *1—12*
ARMOUR CLASS: *4*
MOVE: *12"*
HIT DICE: *8*
% IN LAIR: *30%*
TREASURE TYPE: *C*
NO. OF ATTACKS: *1*
DAMAGE/ATTACK: *2—16*
SPECIAL ATTACKS: *Nil*
SPECIAL DEFENCES:
    Regeneration
MAGIC RESISTANCE: *Standard*
INTELLIGENCE: *Low*
ALIGNMENT: *Chaotic evil*
SIZE: *L (10' + tall)*
PSIONIC ABILITY: *Nil*
    Attack/Defence Modes: *Nil*
LEVEL/X.P. VALUE:
    VI/725 + 10 per hit point

Giant trolls are hideous hill giant/troll crossbreeds (resembling the latter in all but size). They are greatly feared. Their skin is red-brown and they have red rimmed eyes. (See ADVANCED DUNGEONS & DRAGONS MONSTER MANUAL for description of the hill giant).

Despite their pot-bellied appearance they are immensely strong and inflict terrible damage (2—16 hit points of damage) with their favourite weapon — a large spiked club. It is rare (10% chance) for a giant troll to be encountered without such a weapon, but if so it can fight with its two claws, each of which inflicts 2—7 hit points of damage and can be directed at different opponents.

They *regenerate* as trolls but at a rate of 2 hit points per melee round, but cannot re-bond severed limbs.

They are able to catch missiles 25% of the time, if in reach.

Before a giant troll can be killed, at least 10 hit points of damage must be inflicted on it by fire. If this condition is not met and the giant troll is reduced to a single hit point, any further damage on it has no effect save to negate *regeneration*.

Giant trolls are found in nearly every clime. They have a very acute sense of smell and 90' infravision.

Giant Two-Headed Troll

FREQUENCY: *Very rare*
NO. APPEARING: *1—3*
ARMOUR CLASS: *4*
MOVE: *12"*
HIT DICE: *10*
% IN LAIR: *40%*
TREASURE TYPE: *D, Q*
NO. OF ATTACKS: *4*
DAMAGE/ATTACK:
    1—6/1—6/1—10/1—10
SPECIAL ATTACKS: *Nil*
SPECIAL DEFENCES:
    Regeneration
MAGIC RESISTANCE:
    Standard
INTELLIGENCE: *Average*
ALIGNMENT: *Chaotic evil*
SIZE: *L (10' + tall)*
PSIONIC ABILITY: *Nil*
    Attack/Defence Modes: *Nil*
LEVEL/X.P. VALUE:
    VII/1,800 + 14 per hit point

These ferocious ettin/troll crossbreeds are two-headed and stand at least 10' tall. They regenerate as do trolls but at the rate of 1 hit point every melee round, though they cannot re-bond severed limbs.

They attack with two claws (1—6 hit points of damage each) and two bites (1—10 hit points of damage each). Both bites are directed at one opponent.

These creatures prefer darkness; they are basically nocturnal and usually dwell in underground caverns. Their infravision is normal.

Like the ettin, the giant two-headed troll can only be surprised 1 chance in 6. They have adopted the ettin mode of dress — moth-eaten and filthy animal skins. (See ADVANCED DUNGEONS & DRAGONS MONSTER MANUAL — Ettin).

Ice Troll

FREQUENCY: *Rare*
NO. APPEARING: *1—6*
ARMOUR CLASS: *8*
MOVE: *9"*
HIT DICE: *2*
% IN LAIR: *10%*
TREASURE TYPE: *D (no
    magical items)*
NO. OF ATTACKS: *2*
DAMAGE/ATTACK: *1—8/1—8*
SPECIAL ATTACKS: *Nil*
SPECIAL DEFENCES:
    *Regeneration;
    impervious to cold;
    magical weapons to hit*
MAGIC RESISTANCE: *Standard*
INTELLIGENCE: *Semi-*
ALIGNMENT: *Chaotic evil*
SIZE: *L (9' tall)*
PSIONIC ABILITY: *Nil*
    Attack/Defence Modes: *Nil*
LEVEL/X.P. VALUE:
    II/44 + 2 per hit point

This relative of the normal troll closely resembles its stronger cousin except that it has a very cold, semi-transparent body. These creatures dwell in moist areas of dungeons, usually near running water, and have the *regenerative* powers of a normal troll but at a rate of 2 hit points per melee round, so long as the regenerating members can immerse themselves in water. A severed limb can move a distance of 30' in search of water and will always move towards water if there is some in range.

The ice troll attacks with two claws for 1—8 hit points of damage each. They may be directed against different opponents.

Ice trolls are unaffected by cold and can only be hit by magical weapons or missiles. Fire inflicts double damage on them.

They have superior (90') infravision and an acute sense of smell.

TWEEN

FREQUENCY: *Very rare*
NO. APPEARING:
   1 (rarely 1—3 — 10%)
ARMOUR CLASS: *10*
MOVE: *Variable*
HIT DICE: *1*
% IN LAIR: *Nil*
TREASURE TYPE: *Nil*
NO. OF ATTACKS: *1*
DAMAGE/ATTACK:
   By weapon type

SPECIAL ATTACKS: *Nil*
SPECIAL DEFENCES:
   Etherealness
MAGIC RESISTANCE: *Standard*
INTELLIGENCE: *Very*
ALIGNMENT: *Neutral*
SIZE: *M*
PSIONIC ABILITY: *Nil*
   Attack/Defence Modes: *Nil*
LEVEL/X.P. VALUE:
   I/14 + 1 per hit point

Spirit Troll

FREQUENCY: *Very rare*
NO. APPEARING: *1—2*
ARMOUR CLASS: *2*
MOVE: *15"*
HIT DICE: *5+5*
% IN LAIR: *Nil*
TREASURE TYPE: *Nil*
NO. OF ATTACKS: *3*
DAMAGE/ATTACK:
   1—6/1—3/1—3
SPECIAL ATTACKS:
   Strength point drain
SPECIAL DEFENCES:
   Regeneration;
   invulnerable to cold;
   magical weapons to hit;
   invisibility
MAGIC RESISTANCE: *30%*
INTELLIGENCE: *Very*
ALIGNMENT: *Chaotic evil*
SIZE: *L (8'+ tall)*
PSIONIC ABILITY: *Nil*
   Attack/Defence Modes: *Nil*
LEVEL/X.P. VALUE:
   VI/575 + 6 per hit point

This odious creature is the product of perverted magical inter-breeding of trolls and invisible stalkers, though the secret of its creation is believed to be lost and only thirty or so of these creatures are known to exist. The spirit troll is invisible; characters able to *see invisible* will observe it to be very similar to a troll, slightly shorter and with diffused features.

The creature can only be hit by magical weapons. Fire inflicts full damage on it but it is invulnerable to cold. It *regenerates* as does a troll, and at the same rate (3 hit points per round).

It attacks with its fangs and two sharp claws, against 3 different opponents if it so desires. The damage inflicted by its fangs (1—6 hit points) is normal except that the spirit troll adds to its own hit points the number of hit points of damage inflicted on its victim. Damage inflicted by the creature's claws (1—3 hit points each) is taken not only from the hit points of the victim but also from his strength points. Strength points lost in this way are recovered in 2—8 turns. If a character's strength is reduced to zero, he dies, and if it is reduced to 1 or 2 points, he will be rendered comatose, only recovering when (and if) sufficient points are recovered to raise his strength to 3 points or more.

The spirit troll has an acute sense of smell and superior (120') infravision.

The tween is a being existing on the *Ethereal Plane* but visible to observers on the *Prime Material Plane* as a smoky, human-like outline. Commonly they assume a squat human shape, but have limited *shape change* ability.

They can be attacked only by a character with the power to enter the *Ethereal Plane* or by such means as using *oil of etherealness*. If such a melee is joined, the tween will fight with a weapon, usually a sword.

The tween's contact with humans on the *Prime Material Plane* is its adoption of a host — each tween will usually have a host, though occasionally one is without a host temporarily (after the death of its host, for instance). After several hours with a new host, a tween will gradually assume the general shape and characteristics of that host, who will appear to have a 'shadow' nearby. Once a host has been selected, a tween will remain permanently with him until he or the tween dies. In selecting a host, a tween will prefer an intelligent being, human or near-human, though they have no particular preference for player-characters. A tween will communicate telepathically with its host.

The tween has the ability to see a few seconds into the future and is able to increase its host's luck. It is also able to move material things short distances, reacting with such speed that it can affect the movement of a weapon in melee. For example, it can move a sword so that it hits rather than misses. As a result, any character or creature with a tween 'partner' has two die rolls instead of one, whenever a die roll is called for, and may select the more advantageous of these rolls. (This applies to 'to hit' rolls, saving throws and the like).

In contrast, while a tween has a beneficial effect on the actions of its host, it has the reverse effect on any other creature — friend or foe, human or otherwise, player-character or otherwise — within 50' of the host. Again, two die rolls are made in respect of the persons or creatures affected whenever a die roll is called for; however the less advantageous is. selected.

A character with a tween partner is therefore something of a mixed blessing to any companions.

UMPLEBY — URCHIN

UMPLEBY

FREQUENCY: *Very rare*
NO. APPEARING: *1*
ARMOUR CLASS: *4*
MOVE: *9"*
HIT DICE: *6*
% IN LAIR: *Nil*
TREASURE TYPE: *See below*
NO. OF ATTACKS: *1*
DAMAGE/ATTACK: *1—4*
SPECIAL ATTACKS:
    Electric shock
SPECIAL DEFENCES: *Immune
    to electrical-type attacks*
MAGIC RESISTANCE: *Standard*
INTELLIGENCE:
    Low (but see below)
ALIGNMENT: *Neutral*
SIZE: *L (8' tall)*
PSIONIC ABILITY: *Nil*
    Attack/Defence Modes: Nil
LEVEL/X.P. VALUE:
    V/350 + 6 per hit point

The umpleby is a biped, about 8' tall and weighing about 400 pounds. It is covered in wild, straggly hair of varying shades of brown.

It is apparently rather a stupid creature; on meeting a party of adventurers it will simply shamble along with them, neither helping their endeavours nor willing to be left behind, constantly getting in their way and being apparently incapable of moving in silence. It will fight if attacked but will not normally fight in aid of a party, or against them. If it must, it strikes for 1—4 hit points of damage with its hands.

Its appearance, however, is deceptive. It has a great love of treasure and can detect precious metal and gems (more than 1,000 coins and/or 50 gems) up to 100' away, even through solid rock. In its lair it keeps a huge treasure trove of these items but it will never reveal the location of its lair, even if threatened with death (though *charm monster* may overcome this reluctance).

The umpleby can speak the common tongue in a halting fashion but will rarely do so and is in general an uncommunicative creature. However an offer of food and water (it is incessantly hungry and thirsty) will cause it to assume instant and total loyalty to its benefactor; it will help and advise him (though not to the extent of telling him the location of its lair). This loyalty will only be broken if the benefactor does not reward the umpleby with a reasonable proportion of any coins or gems discovered as a result of its advice; if such an event occurs, the umpleby will leave the party and, if the party pursues the creature, will refuse to co-operate in any way with any members of it.

Within the creature's body it can generate and store large quantities of static electricity. Each day it can deliver a total of 50 hit points of damage by 'discharging' wholly or partially — it does this simply by touching its victim, and a normal 'to hit' roll is required unless the victim is unsuspecting. Any metal armour of whatever type is treated as AC10 with regard to this attack, though appropriate magical and dexterity bonuses still apply. It does not have to deliver all 50 hit points in one strike and can regulate the amount of damage it inflicts, usually selecting the range 9—16 hit points of damage. When it delivers the 50th hit point of damage the umpleby immediately goes to sleep for one hour during which it 'recharges' up to 50% of its full potential, if left undisturbed. It requires at least four hours of sleep to recharge 75% and fully 8 hours to return to a full charge (potential 50

hit points of damage). If awakened prior to having completed a single hour of sleep, the umpleby will have recharged 4—16 points, and similar partial charging will have occurred if the creature is awakened after one hour but before four hours sleep, or after four hours but before eight hours.

The umpleby often makes nets out of its own hair and stores them by wrapping them around its waist. It can throw such a net 30' with the accuracy of a short-range arrow. The hair is very tough and is 50% more difficult to cut, break or burn than a magical *web*, though there is no danger of suffocation (see **ADVANCED DUNGEONS & DRAGONS PLAYERS HANDBOOK** — *Spells*).

It will only use its nets and electrical attacks if threatened. The creature is immune to attacks of an electrical nature.

URCHIN

	Black	Green	Red	Silver	Yellow
FREQUENCY:	*Uncommon*	*Rare*	*Rare*	*Very rare*	*Very rare*
NO. APPEARING:	*1—6*	*1—4*	*1—4*	*1—2*	*1—3*
ARMOUR CLASS:	*4*	*3*	*2*	*0*	*1*
MOVE:	*9"//15"*	*9"//18"*	*9"//18"*	*12"//21"*	*12"//18"*
HIT DICE:	*1+1*	*2+1*	*3+1*	*5+3*	*4+2*
% IN LAIR:	*10%*	*10%*	*10%*	*10%*	*10%*
TREASURE TYPE:			*See below for each type of urchin*		
NO. OF ATTACKS:	*1*	*2*	*3*	*5*	*4*
DAMAGE/ATTACK:	*1—6*	*2—7/2—7*	*2—5/2—5/2—5*	*2—5/2—5/2—5*	*1—6/1—6*
				2—5/2—5	*1—6/1—6*
SPECIAL ATTACKS:	*Nil*	*Nil*	*Venom*	*Venom*	*Venom*
SPECIAL DEFENCES:	*Nil*	*Nil*	*Nil*	*Nil*	*Nil*
MAGIC RESISTANCE:	*Standard*	*Standard*	*Standard*	*Standard*	*Standard*
INTELLIGENCE:	*Semi-*	*Semi-*	*Semi-*	*Semi-*	*Semi-*
ALIGNMENT:	*Neutral*	*Neutral*	*Neutral*	*Neutral*	*Neutral*
SIZE:			*All urchins are S (3' diameter)*		
PSIONIC ABILITY:	*Nil*	*Nil*	*Nil*	*Nil*	*Nil*
Attack/Defence Modes:	*Nil*	*Nil*	*Nil*	*Nil*	*Nil*
LEVEL/X.P. VALUE:	*II/28 + 2*	*II/50 + 3*	*III/85 + 4*	*V/400 + 6*	*IV/205 + 5*
	per hit point	*per hit point*	*per hit point*	*per hit point*	*per hit point*

The urchins constitute a family of marine creatures resembling 3' diameter balls of various colours with thousands of radiating spines 3" long. The more hit dice the urchin, the more spines the creature can fire in a melee round. For practical purposes, urchins have an unlimited supply of spines to use as missiles.

When the creature attacks, the spines are fired with the accuracy and range of a light crossbow, with a hit probability bonus numerically the same as the number of attacks (thus an urchin which attacks twice per round would fire two spines each round with the accuracy of a +2 light crossbow). If a spine hits, it inflicts hit points of damage which vary by type of urchin; the victim may also suffer additional effects (see individual descriptions below).

Urchins have the innate power of *clairvoyance* and use this power in hunting victims, though they will not normally attack humans or near-humans unless they themselves are threatened or attacked.

A dead urchin can be broken up quite easily; inside its body will be found a gem, its value and colour varying according to the type of urchin.

Although urchins are usually found in salt-water habitats (90%) there is a 10% chance that an encounter with an urchin will take place on land, always within half a mile of salt water. It has a rolling loco-motion on land and is capable of moving at a surprisingly high speed by this means.

Black Urchin: The most common of the urchins, the black urchin is more dark grey in colour than black.

Each melee round the black urchin can fire 1 spine with the accuracy of a +1 light crossbow. A successful hit inflicts 1—6 hit points of damage on its victim.

The gem contained within the creature is worth 10—100 gold pieces.

92

Green Urchin: This urchin is a pale green colour and is very difficult to detect by sight in water (5% chance).

Each melee round the creature can fire two spines with the accuracy of a +2 light crossbow. If a spine hits, it inflicts 2—7 hit points of damage on the victim.

The gem contained within the creature is worth 40—400 gold pieces.

Red Urchin: This creature is a dull red colour though its spines have black tips.

Each melee round the red urchin can fire 3 spines with the accuracy of a +3 light crossbow. If a spine hits, it inflicts 2—5 hit points of damage on a victim; the tips of the spines also carry a venom which will put the victim to sleep for 1—4 melee rounds unless he makes a saving throw against poison.

The gem contained within the creature is worth 90—900 gold pieces.

Silver Urchin: This, the rarest of the urchins, is a dull silver in colour with black tips on the spines.

Each melee round the silver urchin can fire 5 spines with the accuracy of a +5 light crossbow. If a spine hits, it inflicts 2—5 hit points of damage on a victim; the tips of the spines carry a venom which acts on the victim's nervous system and puts him into a catatonic trance for 1—3 days unless he makes his saving throw against poison.

The gem contained within the creature is worth 250—2,500 gold pieces.

Yellow Urchin: This creature is coloured a very pale yellow and like the green urchin is very difficult to see when in water (5% chance). Its spines have light green tips.

Each melee round the yellow urchin can fire 4 spines with the accuracy of a +4 light crossbow. If a spine hits, it inflicts 1—6 hit points of damage on a victim; the tips of the spines carry a venom which will paralyse the victim for 1—4 turns unless he makes his saving throw against poison.

The gem contained within the creature is worth 160—1,600 gold pieces.

 VISION – VODYANOI – VOLT – VORTEX

VISION

FREQUENCY: *Very rare*
NO. APPEARING: *1*
ARMOUR CLASS: *0 (10)*
MOVE: *15"*
HIT DICE: *8*
% IN LAIR: *Nil*
TREASURE TYPE: *Nil*
NO. OF ATTACKS: *Nil*
DAMAGE/ATTACK: *Nil*
SPECIAL ATTACKS: *Ageing*
SPECIAL DEFENCES: *Semi-ethereal,*
    immune to normal weapons and missiles
MAGIC RESISTANCE: *75%*
INTELLIGENCE: *High*
ALIGNMENT: *Lawful evil*
SIZE: *M*
PSIONIC ABILITY: *Nil*
    Attack/Defence Modes: *Nil*
LEVEL/X.P. VALUE:
    VI/825 + 10 per hit point

Misguided research by a high-level illusionist (which led quickly to his death) created the visions — summoned beings which appear as shadows. The visions are unable to return to their own plane until their physical manifestations are destroyed on the *Ethereal/Prime Material Plane;* thus they roam the underworld in perpetual frustration and attack all they meet.

A vision exists partially on the *Prime Material Plane* and partially on the *Ethereal Plane;* if attacked from the material plane they are treated as AC0, but if attacked ethereally they are AC10.

A vision attacks by suggestion, not by physical means. Anyone seeing a vision within 30' must roll 3d6, add 3, and compare the result with his intelligence. If the character's intelligence is the greater, he has saved and can no longer be threatened by that particular vision. Any previous 'ageing' he has suffered is seen to have been unreal. A character failing to save will believe that he has aged ten years (the effects of ageing are covered in **ADVANCED DUNGEONS & DRAGONS DUNGEON MASTERS GUIDE**). Each character seeing a vision is 'attacked' in the same way and must attempt the special saving throw, repeating this process each round.

If a character kills a vision, he must make a normal saving throw against magic; if this is successful, the apparent ageing vanishes, but if not it is real and permanent.

A vision can only be attacked by magical or silver weapons on either plane of its existence. The clerical *bless* spell inflicts 3—18 hit points of damage on it, while *dispel illusion* cast on a vision causes 0—5 (d6 minus 1) hit points of damage on it per level of the caster (so a 7th level illusionist casting this spell on a vision would roll d6 seven times, subtracting 1 from each roll and adding the results).

VODYANOI

FREQUENCY: *Rare*
NO. APPEARING: *1—3*
ARMOUR CLASS: *2*
MOVE: *6"*
HIT DICE: *8*
% IN LAIR: *30%*
TREASURE TYPE: *G*
NO. OF ATTACKS: *3*
DAMAGE/ATTACK:
    3—12/3—12/1—10
SPECIAL ATTACKS: *Nil*
SPECIAL DEFENCES: *See below*
MAGIC RESISTANCE: *Standard*
INTELLIGENCE: *Average*
ALIGNMENT: *Chaotic evil*
SIZE: *L (8' tall, 5' wide)*
PSIONIC ABILITY: *Nil*
    Attack/Defence Modes: *Nil*
LEVEL/X.P. VALUE:
    VI/650 + 10 per hit point

RUSS

These predators are close aquatic relatives of the umber hulk (see **ADVANCED DUNGEONS & DRAGONS MONSTER MANUAL**) which live in deep bodies of fresh water. They are similar in appearance to their cousins but have only two eyes (and thus lack the *confusion* ability of the umber hulk); their skin is green and slimy and they have webbed claws. They prey on large fresh-water creatures but view humans as particular delicacies. They are extremely territorial creatures and will ferociously defend the area around their lairs.

Their powerful claws are capable of rending the hull of any passing boat, while their strength and bulk allow them to overturn smaller vessels.

In melee they attack with their two claws (3—12 hit points of damage each) and their mandibles (1—10 hit points of damage). Once per day a vodyanoi can summon (with a 50% chance of success) 1—20 electric eels to its aid.

It is believed that a salt-water species exists which is twice as large and much more ferocious than the vodyanoi or the umber hulk, but little firm information is available.

VOLT

FREQUENCY: *Uncommon*
NO. APPEARING: *2–24*
ARMOUR CLASS: *3*
MOVE: *6"*
HIT DICE: *2+1*
% IN LAIR: *10%*
TREASURE TYPE: *Nil*
NO. OF ATTACKS: *1 and 1*
DAMAGE/ATTACK: *1–4 and 2–12*
SPECIAL ATTACKS: *Nil*
SPECIAL DEFENCES: *Immune
　　to electrical type attacks*
MAGIC RESISTANCE: *Standard*
INTELLIGENCE: *Animal*
ALIGNMENT: *Neutral*
SIZE: *S (about 2' diameter)*
PSIONIC ABILITY: *Nil*
　　Attack/Defence Modes: *Nil*
LEVEL/X.P. VALUE:
　　II/50 + 3 per hit point

This curious but dangerous little creature appears as a near-spherical bundle of bristly grey hair with two bulbous eyes, two small curved horns and a 3' long tail. It floats as if by *levitation* with mobility added. With regard to aerial combat, it is manoeuvrability class D.

It first attacks by propelling itself towards its victim's neck and biting — 1–4 hit points of damage if the bite succeeds. A successful bite means that it has locked onto its victim's neck and cannot be detached until it (or its victim) is dead. During the time it is attached it will continue to drain blood from the victim's neck for 1–4 hit points of damage each round and will also lash the victim with its tail. The tail produces a jolt of electrical energy each time it strikes, for 2–12 additional hit points of damage per round. After the volt has attached itself to a victim's neck, it requires no 'to hit' roll either for its bite or for its tail attack.

These are bad-tempered creatures and will usually attack even if they are not themselves attacked or threatened.

VORTEX

FREQUENCY: *Very rare*
NO APPEARING: *1–8*
ARMOUR CLASS: *0*
MOVE: *15"*
HIT DICE: *2+2*
% IN LAIR: *Nil*
TREASURE TYPE: *Nil*
NO. OF ATTACKS: *1*
DAMAGE/ATTACK: *See below*
SPECIAL ATTACKS: *Nil*
SPECIAL DEFENCES: *Nil*
MAGIC RESISTANCE: *Standard*
INTELLIGENCE: *Non-*
ALIGNMENT: *Chaotic neutral*
SIZE: *Variable*
PSIONIC ABILITY: *Nil*
　　Attack/Defence Modes: *Nil*
LEVEL/X.P. VALUE:
　　II/50 + 3 per hit point

The vortex appears as a whirlwind — 4" high, 1" base diameter and 3" diameter top (though larger ones are believed to exist on the *Elemental Plane of Air*). It appears to be free willed and cannot be summoned. The physical form of the vortex is a small sphere about the size of a grapefruit which bobs and dodges about in the centre of the whirlwind. Its small size and its speed of movement make it difficult to hit; thus its high AC value.

If a character is 'hit' by the vortex, he suffers no immediate damage but is caught in the whirling cone of air and starts to spin. Thereafter he can only be released when the vortex is killed and he will take 1–3 hit points of damage per round as a result of the spin. Additionally there is a 5% cumulative chance per melee round of a spinning victim being killed by a particularly violent air-current.

A single vortex is only large enough to accommodate one victim of human size, though it could contain two smaller creatures simultaneously. A victim trapped inside the vortex cannot hit the being's sphere — only those who are not trapped may do so.

WHIPWEED — WITHERSTENCH — WITHERWEED

WHIPWEED

FREQUENCY: *Uncommon*
NO. APPEARING: *1–2*
ARMOUR CLASS: *Stalks 6; base 4*
MOVE: *3"*
HIT DICE: *Stalks 2+4; base 1+4*
% IN LAIR: *50%*
TREASURE TYPE: *Nil*
NO. OF ATTACKS: *2*
DAMAGE/ATTACK: *1–10/1–10*
SPECIAL ATTACKS: *See below*
SPECIAL DEFENCES: *Nil*
MAGIC RESISTANCE: *Standard*
INTELLIGENCE: *Semi-*
ALIGNMENT: *Neutral*
SIZE: *Variable*
PSIONIC ABILITY: *Nil*
　　Attack/Defence Modes: *Nil*
LEVEL/X.P. VALUE:
　　III/120 + 4 per hit point

This strange creature was originally named in the belief that it was a plant; though it displays behaviour which supports that theory, it also has many qualities which are not plant-like (though the druidic spells relating to plants affect it, curiously enough).

The whipweed has two stalks, thin and whip-like with a few appendages which look like small leaves. When fully grown, the stalks are up to 15' long, though smaller specimens are just as common. The stalks are connected to a spheroidal base or 'body' which contains a small brain and is equipped with eight small legs; the creature is thus capable of limited movement and can withdraw the root-like appendages below its body from the earth to permit locomotion. The whipweed hates sunlight so is usually found underground or in the heart of a deep forest. It draws its sustenance from the remains of its animal prey, though it has no mouth and its food appears to be absorbed by the stalks and transferred internally to the body.

Its need to embed its 'roots' into the earth is not fully understood; certainly the creature can survive apparently without limit in rocky areas containing virtually no soil, and a small crevice in a rock appears to be quite sufficient to cater for its need to root from time to time.

It attacks anything which moves within range of its stalks, each stalk hitting as a monster with 3 hit dice and capable of inflicting 1–10 hit points of damage. The stalks will attack different victims if two are in range. If a stalk is 'killed', the body is not affected, and to kill the creature the body must be destroyed. If the body is destroyed (reduced to zero hit points or below) the whipweed dies but the stalks go into a mad frenzy for one melee round before they become inert; during this time they attack three times each and each attack inflicts double the normal damage on the victim if successful.

If both stalks are destroyed the base/body will attempt to escape

WITHERSTENCH (Skunk Beast)

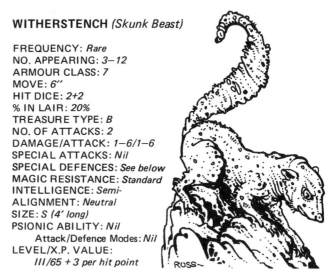

FREQUENCY: *Rare*
NO. APPEARING: *3—12*
ARMOUR CLASS: *7*
MOVE: *6''*
HIT DICE: *2+2*
% IN LAIR: *20%*
TREASURE TYPE: *B*
NO. OF ATTACKS: *2*
DAMAGE/ATTACK: *1—6/1—6*
SPECIAL ATTACKS: *Nil*
SPECIAL DEFENCES: *See below*
MAGIC RESISTANCE: *Standard*
INTELLIGENCE: *Semi-*
ALIGNMENT: *Neutral*
SIZE: *S (4' long)*
PSIONIC ABILITY: *Nil*
    Attack/Defence Modes: *Nil*
LEVEL/X.P. VALUE:
    III/65 + 3 per hit point

A bizarre relative of the skunk, this beast has little fur — and what little there is sprawls in dirty patches over the skin, which itself is blotchy yellow and covered in tiny purple spots. It lives mainly in dank and filthy areas where carrion — its food — can be found.

In melee it attacks with two claws for 1—6 hit points of damage each. Its spots constantly emit a powerful and nauseating odour. All within 30' of the creature must save against poison or be nauseated, retching uncontrollably. Victims who fail to make their saving throw will be helpless and unable to defend against the creature's attack. However the effects wear off after the skunk beast moves out of a 30' range.

WITHERWEED

FREQUENCY: *Uncommon*
NO. APPEARING: *1*
ARMOUR CLASS: *8*
MOVE: *Immobile*
HIT DICE: *3 (or more)*
% IN LAIR: *100%*
TREASURE TYPE: *See below*
NO. OF ATTACKS: *Variable*
DAMAGE/ATTACK: *See below*
SPECIAL ATTACKS: *See below*
SPECIAL DEFENCES: *Nil*

MAGIC RESISTANCE: *Standard*
INTELLIGENCE: *Non-*
ALIGNMENT: *Neutral*
SIZE: *Variable — see below*
PSIONIC ABILITY: *Nil*
    Attack/Defence Modes: *Nil*
LEVEL/X.P. VALUE:
    3HD: III/90 + 3 per hit point
    4HD: III/125 + 4 per hit point
    5HD: IV/165 + 5 per hit point
    6HD: V/275 + 6 per hit point

This weed is usually found amongst ruined masonry, across doors or smothering a long-forgotten treasure chest in the underworld. It is typically quite extensive; an average specimen will cover an area approximately 20' square, though weeds up to twice this size have been known and even larger ones are theoretically possible. The average specimen has 3 hit dice, but larger weeds have 4, 5 or even 6 hit dice.

The weed is dry and is therefore easily burned, but, when burning, it produces toxic smoke; anyone inhaling the smoke must save against poison or die instantly. The fire will burn and the smoke will stream forth for 1 round per square foot of vegetation. Only a strong wind will blow the heavy, oily smoke away — otherwise it forms a cloud of volume equal to 9 times the area of the witherweed and will take at least four hours to dissipate.

The weed attacks with its many, equally spaced fronds; an average specimen will have 13—24 so positioned that at least one frond can attack each person confronting it. A frond hit drains 1—4 dexterity points from its victim (a successful saving throw against poison will halve the number of points drained). If a victim has the maximum of 4 dexterity points drained from a single hit he also suffers a nervous seizure — total collapse for 2 melee rounds, followed by a further 5 melee rounds during which he attacks at —2 hit probability and moves at 75% of his normal rate; dexterity bonuses (if any) do not apply during this 7-round period.

A victim becomes incapacitated if his dexterity is reduced below 3, and dies if it is reduced to zero or below. Half the dexterity points lost are recovered by living victims naturally at the rate of 1 point per day, but the remainder can only be regained by the casting of *cure disease* on the victim.

XILL – XVART

XILL

FREQUENCY: *Very rare*
NO. APPEARING: *1–6*
ARMOUR CLASS: *0*
MOVE: *15''*
HIT DICE: *5*
% IN LAIR: *15%*
TREASURE TYPE: *C*
NO. OF ATTACKS: *4*
DAMAGE/ATTACK:
　　1–4/1–4/1–4/1–4
　　or by weapon type
SPECIAL ATTACKS: *See below*
SPECIAL DEFENCES:
　　See below
MAGIC RESISTANCE:
　　70% (but see below)
INTELLIGENCE: *Very*
ALIGNMENT: *Lawful evil*
SIZE: *M*
PSIONIC ABILITY: *Nil*
　　Attack/Defence Modes: *Nil*
LEVEL/X.P. VALUE: *V/325 + 5 per hit point*

Xill are bipedal, flame-red creatures, with short, powerful bodies and four arms, all of which can wield weapons simultaneously. If unarmed, they fight with four claws for 1 4 hit points of damage each. The high dexterity of the xill not only accounts for its low armour class (its natural AC is 4) but also gives the creature a hit probability bonus of +3 when attacking (+5 with missiles).

The xill has apparently only one aim in life – to produce young; the creatures are asexual and reproduce by producing eggs which must gain sustenance prior to hatching in the stomach of a living human or near-human. Thus they will try to snatch victims alive.

Xill have the innate power of *etherealness*. They may transfer from the *Ethereal* to the *Prime Material Plane* in one segment (6 seconds), but the reverse process takes two melee rounds. A xill will usually initiate an attack by emerging suddenly from the *Ethereal Plane* near to a chosen victim, achieving surprise 90% of the time. In attacking, it will use two of its arms in an attempt to grapple its victim, while using the other two (which might carry weapons) to subdue. The subduing attacks are resolved in the same way as attacks to subdue a dragon. Upon announcement of intent to *strike to subdue*, all hit points of damage scored by attacks on the victim (from the two subduing arms) are considered non-fatal battering/bruising damage. Each melee round the following fraction is calculated.

$$\frac{\text{Total number of 'subdual' hit points scored}}{\text{Total number of hit points of the victim}}$$

The result is converted into a percentage, and that is the percentage chance of the victim being subdued in that round. Percentile dice are rolled to determine the result and if the score is less than or equal to the percentage derived, the victim is subdued.

The grappling attacks are normal; both grappling arms must score a hit for the grapple to be successful, otherwise it is assumed that the victim has been able to avoid being grappled. However if the victim has previously been subdued, the grappling attack will always succeed in the next melee round. If the xill succeeds in grappling a victim, it will then inject a paralysing fluid into his bloodstream through its claws, (normal saving throw applicable) in the next melee round. Victims grappled thus have one melee round to break free before the fluid is injected, and they may attempt to do so by 'saving against strength'– a d20 is rolled, and if the result is lower than the victim's strength, he has escaped from the clutches of the xill.

In summary, the xill attempts to grapple and paralyse the victim, or to subdue and grapple him. Once either of these results has been achieved, it will attempt to become *Ethereal* (and its power to do so

will extend to its paralysed/subdued victim) and carry the victim to its lair on the *Ethereal Plane* to inject the eggs. During this two-melee-round transitory period when the xill and its victim are turning *ethereal,* the xill cannot move, it is vulnerable to magic (i.e. its magic resistance is reduced to zero) and can be hit by weapons at –3 hit probability. When the transition is complete, however, the creature can only be attacked ethereally and its normal magic resistance is restored.

If attacked in its lair on the *Ethereal Plane*, the first priority of the xill will be to save and protect its young and to remove any egg-bound prisoners to a safe place, only then attacking the invaders.

The xill eggs hatch after 1–4 days in the victim's stomach; for the next 2–8 days the larvae collectively inflict 11–20 hit points of damage on the victim per day as they mature, and they then emerge from the victim, killing him instantly, as 2–16 small xill which grow rapidly (1–4 hours) into full-sized creatures.

Protection from evil will always succeed, on either plane, in warding off a xill.

XVART

FREQUENCY: *Uncommon*
NO. APPEARING: *40–400*
ARMOUR CLASS: *7*
MOVE: *6''*
HIT DICE: *1–1*
% IN LAIR: *40%*
TREASURE TYPE: *K*
NO. OF ATTACKS: *1*
DAMAGE/ATTACK:
　　2–5 or by weapon type
SPECIAL ATTACKS: *Nil*
SPECIAL DEFENCES: *Nil*
MAGIC RESISTANCE: *Standard*
INTELLIGENCE: *Average*
ALIGNMENT: *Chaotic evil*
SIZE: *S (3' high)*
PSIONIC ABILITY: *Nil*
　　Attack/Defence Modes: *Nil*
LEVEL/X.P. VALUE:
　　1/5 + 1 per hit point
　　Leaders: 1/20+2 per hit point

These small humanoid creatures have bright blue skin and orange eyes. They usually wear loose cloth doublets.

Xvarts are mediary between goblins and kobolds and will generally attack the latter. They fear humans and will only attack a human party if the xvarts are greatly in the majority.

In every group of 20 xvarts there will be one carrying a net, used to entangle and hinder opponents in melee. If 100 xvarts are encountered, one will be a strong leader-type, from 3½' to 4½' tall with 8–11 hit points and attacking as a monster with 2 hit dice.

Ordinary xvarts fight with small swords for 2–5 hit points of damage; leaders use a hand axe, mace, flail or morning star with damage by weapon type. Though most xvarts are of the fighter class, a few (5% of a group encountered) will have magic use at 1st or 2nd experience level. One or more tribal shamans will be found in a xvart lair.

Xvarts speak their own language and are fluent in the goblin and kobold tongues. If encountered in their lair, there will always be a leader of 11 hit points and two lieutenants of 8 hit points each, 3–30 giant rats used as guardians and females and young equal to 120% and 200% of the number of males, respectively. Shamans and xvarts with magical abilities will be present in the appropriate proportions.

Xvarts delight in taking prisoners for torture or ransom (or both). They have been known to assist or be assisted by wererats in these endeavours. Their lair is usually in an underground cavern or deep in the heart of a forest.

YELLOW MUSK CREEPER

YELLOW MUSK CREEPER

FREQUENCY: *Rare*
NO. APPEARING: *1*
ARMOUR CLASS: *7*
MOVE: *Immobile*
HIT DICE: *3*
% IN LAIR: *100%*
TREASURE TYPE: *Any*
NO. OF ATTACKS: *2–12*
DAMAGE/ATTACK: *Special*
SPECIAL ATTACKS: *Nil*
SPECIAL DEFENCES: *Nil*
MAGIC RESISTANCE: *Standard*
INTELLIGENCE: *Non-*
ALIGNMENT: *Neutral*
SIZE: *L*
PSIONIC ABILITY: *Nil*
    Attack/Defence Modes: *Nil*
LEVEL/X.P. VALUE:
    III/65 + 3 per hit point

The yellow musk creeper is a large light green climbing plant with leaves like ivy, dark green buds, and flowers like those of an orchid, bright yellow in colour with splashes of purple. Each plant will have 2–12 flowers and 1–4 buds; it extends over an area up to 20' square. Typically, the plant is found in soily areas underground, though specimens have been identified in the heart of thick forests. The creeper can climb up trees and rock faces with equal facility. It is sometimes planted deliberately in locations where it will 'guard' treasure.

When approached within 10', the creeper will 'attack', the flowers swaying in a hypnotic way before the face of the victim. A successful 'hit' indicates that one of the flowers has puffed a dust, smelling of musk, into the victim's face. The victim must then make a saving throw against magic or be entranced and walk into the mass of the plant, resisting any attempt to restrain him and taking the remainder of the melee round to do so.

Once the victim is in the heart of the plant, aerial roots attach to his skull (no 'to hit' roll required) and his brain is devoured at the rate of 1–4 intelligence points per round.

Any hit on a root will cause it to release, but so many roots will be attached simultaneously that the intelligence drain cannot be prevented by such means. The only way to kill the creeper is to stab at its bulbous root which will be found buried in the earth 1' below the surface. The root will have various personal belongings of previous victims buried near it, since the creeper appears capable of scraping together enough soil from the area nearby to cover evidence of its previous 'successes'.

The effects of the intelligence drain varies. If the drain in a given round reduces the victim's intelligence to zero or below, the victim dies, a bud flowers and a new bud appears. If the victim's intelligence is reduced to one or two points, the victim immediately becomes a yellow musk zombie (see *Zombie, Yellow Musk* for details).

Each creeper will have one yellow musk zombie for every two flowers. Intelligence loss in those not killed or transformed into yellow musk zombies is temporary and will be regained at the rate of one point per day of rest. A *heal* spell cast on the victim will restore all lost intelligence points immediately.

ZOMBIE, YELLOW MUSK

ZOMBIE, *Yellow Musk*

FREQUENCY: *Rare*
NO. APPEARING: *1–2*
ARMOUR CLASS: *Variable*
MOVE: *As human*
HIT DICE: *2*
% IN LAIR: *Nil*
TREASURE TYPE: *Nil*
NO. OF ATTACKS: *1*
DAMAGE/ATTACK:
    By weapon type
SPECIAL ATTACKS: *Nil*
SPECIAL DEFENCES: *Nil*
MAGIC RESISTANCE: *See below*
INTELLIGENCE: *Non-*
ALIGNMENT: *Neutral evil*
SIZE: *M*
PSIONIC ABILITY: *Nil*
    Attack/Defence Modes: *Nil*
LEVEL/X.P. VALUE:
    II/28 + 2 per hit point

Yellow musk zombies are victims of the yellow musk creeper whose intelligence has been reduced to 1 or 2 points. When this takes place, the victim becomes mindless, his skin turns yellow and his eyes become fixed and glazed. The draining process stops and the plant

injects a seed into the victim's skull, where it is to germinate. The victim is now a yellow musk zombie under the control of the plant; the zombie will fight on the plant's behalf, attempting to find new victims for it and drag them or tempt them into its clutches. (See *Yellow Musk Creeper* for further details).

Yellow musk zombies retain the same hit points, armour, weapons and belongings as they had prior to their 'capture'; however in melee they attack as monsters with 2 hit dice. They will not be able to use any of the spells or psionic abilities they controlled when 'alive' and will receive no dexterity or wisdom bonuses, though strength bonuses and penalties still apply.

They serve the parent plant for two months before wandering off to drop lifeless in some quiet corner, unless they are killed beforehand. In either case, the implanted seedling sprouts from the decaying corpse, growing quickly (within an hour after 'death') into a new yellow musk creeper.

A yellow musk zombie is not true undead and thus cannot be turned or destroyed/controlled by a cleric. However, like undead, it is immune to the effects of all mind-influencing spells such as *charm, hold, illusion, sleep* and so forth.

A yellow musk zombie can be cured of its affliction by the death of its master plant and the use of *neutralise poison* and *heal* cast on the creature in either order, one spell immediately after the other. The victim will thus be restored to his former self, though he will need four weeks rest before his original characteristics are restored.

TREASURE TYPES

Treasure Type	1,000's of Copper	1,000's of Silver	1,000's of Electrum	1,000's of Gold	100's of Platinum	Gems	Jewelry	Maps or Magic
A	1-6 :25%	1-6 :30%	1-6 :35%	1-10:40%	1-4 :25%	4-40 :60%	3-30:50%	Any 3: 30%
B	1-8 :50%	1-6 :25%	1-4 :25%	1-3 :25%	nil	1-8 :30%	1-4 :20%	Sword, armor, or misc. weapon: 10%
C	1-12:20%	1-6 :30%	1-4 :10%	nil	nil	1-6 :25%	1-3 :20%	Any 2: 10%
D	1-8 :10%	1-12 :15%	1-8 :15%	1-6 :50%	nil	1-10 :30%	1-6 :25%	Any 2 plus 1 potion: 15%
E	1-10: 5%	1-12 :25%	1-6 :25%	1-8 :25%	nil	1-12 :15%	1-8 :10%	Any 3 plus 1 scroll: 25%
F	nil	1-20 :10%	1-12:15%	1-10:40%	1-8 :35%	3-30 :20%	1-10:10%	Any 3 except swords or misc. weapons, plus 1 potion & 1 scroll: 30%
G	nil	nil	nil	10-40:50%	1-20:50%	5-20 :30%	1-10:25%	Any 4 plus 1 scroll: 35%
H	5-30:25%	1-100:40%	10-40:40%	10-60:55%	5-50:25%	1-100:50%	10-40:50%	Any 4 plus 1 potion & 1 scroll: 15%
I	nil	nil	nil	nil	3-18:30%	2-20 :55%	1-12:50%	Any 1: 15%
J	3-24 pieces per individual	nil	nil	nil	nil	nil	nil	nil
K	nil	3-18 pieces per individual	nil	nil	nil	nil	nil	nil
L	nil	nil	2-12 pieces per individual	nil	nil	nil	nil	nil
M	nil	nil	nil	2-8 pieces per individual	nil	nil	nil	nil
N	nil	nil	nil	nil	1-6 pieces per individual	nil	nil	nil
O	1-4 :25%	1-3 :20%	nil	nil	nil	nil	nil	nil
P	nil	1-6 :30%	1-2 :25%	nil	nil	nil	nil	nil
Q	nil	nil	nil	nil	nil	1-4 :50%	nil	nil
R	nil	nil	nil	2-8 :40%	10-60:50%	4-32 :55%	1-12:45%	nil
S	nil	nil	nil	nil	nil	nil	nil	2-8 potions: 40%
T	nil	nil	nil	nil	nil	nil	nil	1-4 scrolls: 50%
U	nil	nil	nil	nil	nil	10-80 :90%	5-30:80%	1 of each magic excluding potions & scrolls: 70%
V	nil	nil	nil	nil	nil	nil	nil	2 of each magic excluding potions & scrolls: 85%
W	nil	nil	nil	5-30:60%	1-8 :15%	10-80 :60%	5-40:50%	1 map: 55%
X	nil	nil	nil	nil	nil	nil	nil	1 misc. magic plus 1 potion: 60%
Y	nil	nil	nil	2-12:70%	nil	nil	nil	nil
Z	1-3 :20%	1-4 :25%	1-4 :25%	1-4 :30%	1-6 :30%	10-60 :55%	5-30:50%	Any 3 magic: 50%

MONSTER TABLES

MONSTER LEVEL TABLES
All the creatures in the **FIEND FOLIO**™ Tome are listed in the *Monster Level Tables* according to their relative frequency and their level. Generally speaking, these tables should be used in the same way as the corresponding tables in **ADVANCED DUNGEONS & DRAGONS**™ **Dungeon Masters Guide** to determine the type of monster appearing in a random encounter. Those sections of the **Dungeon Masters Guide** which explain and amplify the tables therein will be relevant here, too, as will the *Dungeon Random Monster Level Determination Matrix*.

When using the *Monster Level Tables*, referees will have to use their judgment to determine whether the monster-type revealed by random use of the tables is appropriate to the setting of the encounter, since the tables take no account of this aspect and simply list all the monsters. For example, underground encounters with aarakocra will only occur in very special circumstances, if at all, and babblers will rarely be met outside the immediate area of their swamp habitat. In such cases, referees should use their judgment by selecting for the encounter a type of monster which is appropriate to the setting, if random use of the tables indicates one which is clearly "out of place". The *Encounter Listings* which follow the *Monster Level Tables* may be useful in this regard.

Certain special monster in the **FIEND FOLIO** Tome are not included in the *Monster Level Tables* since their appearance will either be confined to particular and exceptional circumstances (e.g. the aleax) or because, for individual reasons, these monsters have no "level" (e.g. the denzelian). The referee must judge the occasions on which such monsters appear. Monsters in this category are:

Aleax
Denzelian
Hound of ill omen
Terithran
Trilloch

Other monsters are included in more than one of the *Monster Lev Tables* since they, like humans and near-humans, have varying exp rience levels and hence varying hit dice and abilities; the level a nature of the encounter will determine the numbers and experien levels of such monsters when they are encountered, and guidelin which may be helpful in this respect are appended to each entr Similarly, there are monsters which, though they do not have experience "hierarchy", nevertheless have varying hit dice value these, too, will appear in more than one table and are appropriate marked.

The overall purpose of this section is to provide guidelines —, it is n the intention to dictate a hard-and-fast formula to which it is expect that referees will adhere. Random selection of monsters for encoun ters —even for random encounters — is no real substitute for creativ on the part of the referee; the tables are provided to assist rather th restrict. At all times, referees should evaluate their findings from t tables in the light of many factors — the level and environment of t encounter, the level of the dungeon (or, if outside a dungeon, t nature of the encounter area) and so forth. Remember that a conside able proportion of the creatures in this book (and in the **Monst Manual**) are not unintelligent; many monsters of the underworld (whatever the locale of the encounter) can be expected to act reason bly intelligently if threatened or if their territory is invaded.

DUNGEON RANDOM MONSTER TABLES

MONSTER LEVEL I

Dice Score	Creature Encountered	Numbers	AC	MV	HD	#AT	D
01	Al-mi'raj	1-4	6	18″	1	1	1-4
02-03	Ant, giant	1-4	3	18″	2	1	1-6
04-06	Bat, giant	1-6	8	3″/18″	½ or 1	1	1-2 or 1-4
07-13	Beetle, giant, fire	1-4	4	12″	1+2	1	2-8
14-15	Bullywug	3-18	6	3″//15″	1	3 or 1	BW or 1-2/1-2/2-‍
16-17	Carbuncle	1	2	3″	1	0	Nil
18-19	Cerebral parasite	1	n/a	n/a	n/a	0	Nil
20	Demon, manes	1-4	7	3″	1	3	1-2/1-2/1-4
21-22	Dire corby	2-5	6	12″	2	2	1-6/1-6
23	Dwarf	4-14 (2d6+2)	4	6″	1	1	BW or 1-8
24	Ear seeker	1	9	1″	1 hp	spec.	spec.
25	Elf	4-11 (1d8+3)	5	12″	1+1	1	BW or 1-10
26-28	Gibberling	6-17 (d12+5)	10	9″	1	1	1-8
29	Gnome	5-15 (2d6+3)	5	6″	1	1	BW or 1-6
30-33	Goblin	6-15 (d10+5)	6	6″	1-1	1	BW or 1-6
34	Halfling*	9-16 (d8+8)	7	9″	1d6	1	BW or 1-6
35-38	Hobgoblin	2-8	5	9″	1+1	1	BW or 1-8
39-46	Human — see *Human Subtable*						
47-50	Jermlaine	6-20 (2d8+4)	7	15″	½	1	1-2 or 1-4
51-54	Kobold	6-17 (d12+5)	7	6″	½	1	BW or 1-4
55-56	Mite	3-18	8	3″	1-1	1	1-3
57	Norker	2-8	3	9″	1+2	2	1-3/1-6
58-59	Ogrillon	1-4	6	12″	2	2	2-7/2-7
60-67	Orc	7-12 (d6+6)	6	9″	1	1	BW or 1-8
68-70	Piercer	1-4	3	1″	1 or 2	1	1-6 or 2-12
71-77	Rat, giant	5-20	2	12″//6″	½	1	1-3
78-79	Rot grub	1-3	9	1″	1 hp	0	Nil
80-84	Shrieker	1-2	7	1″	3	0	Nil
85-86	Skeleton	1-4	7	12″	1	1	1-6
87-90	Snayd	1-8	−4	21″	1-1	0	Nil
91-97	Tween	1	10	Var.	1	1	BW
98	Xvart	6-15 (d10+5)	7	6″	1-1	1	BW or 2-5
99-00	Zombie	1-3	8	6″	2	1	1-8

* Not encountered below the 4th level; treat as a roll of 71-77 (Rat, giant) thereafter.

Individual is 6th level — 60% chance: 3 items from Table I;
40% chance: 2 items from Table II.
Individual is 7th level — 70% chance: 3 items from Table I;
50% chance: 2 items from Table II;
10% chance: 1 item from Table III.
Individual is 8th level — 80% chance: 3 items from Table I;
60% chance: 2 items from Table II;
20% chance: 1 item from Table III.
Individual is 9th level — 90% chance: 3 items from Table I;
70% chance: 2 items from Table II;
30% chance: 1 item from Table III.
Individual is 10th level — 3 items from Table I;
80% chance: 2 items from Table II;
40% chance: 1 item from Table III.
Individual is 11th level — 3 items from Table I;
90% chance: 2 items from Table II;
50% chance: 1 item from Table III;
10% chance: 1 item from Table IV.
Individual is 12th level — 3 items from Table I;
2 items from Table II;
60% chance: 1 item from Table III;
20% chance: 1 item from Table IV.
Individual is 13th level — 3 items from Table I;
2 items from Table II;
1 item from Table III;
60% chance: 1 item from Table IV.

It is suggested that you personally select appropriate items, using random determination only when any item would be suitable to the particular individual. Note that some items are groups or multiples.

Magic Item Tables For Character Encounters

TABLE I

Die	Item (d20)
1	2 POTIONS: *climbing, flying*
2	2 POTIONS: *extra-healing, polymorph (self)*
3	2 POTIONS: *fire resistance, speed*
4	2 POTIONS: *healing, giant strength*
5	2 POTIONS: *heroism, invulnerability*
6	2 POTIONS: *human control, levitation*
7	2 POTIONS: *super-heroism, animal control*
8	1 SCROLL: 1 Spell, level 1-6
9	1 SCROLL: 2 Spells, level 1-4
10	1 SCROLL: *protection from magic*
11	1 RING: *mammal control*
12	1 RING: *protection +1*
13	1 ARMOR: leather +1
14	1 SHIELD: +1
15	1 SWORD: +1 (no special abilities)
6	10 ARROWS: +1
17	4 BOLTS: +2
18	1 DAGGER: +1 (or +2) *et al.*
19	1 JAVELIN +2
20	1 MACE +1

Monster Level I: Human Subtable

ce Score	Creature Encountered	Numbers
01-25	Bandit*	5-15
26-30	Berserker*	3-9
31-45	Brigand*	5-15
46-00	Character — see **Character Subtable** below	

pper level leaders and sub-leaders are not with groups numbering der 30, and at only 50% of normal level (rounded-up) for groups der 60. As a general rule, you may wish to exclude all of these counters on levels below whatever point you find them to be ikely.

aracter Subtable (Used For Encounters On All Dungeon Levels)

ce Score	Character Type	Maximum Number Per Party
01-17	CLERIC	3
18-20	Druid	2
21-60	FIGHTER	5
61-62	Paladin	2
63-65	Ranger	2
66-86	MAGIC-USER	3
87-88	Illusionist	1
89-98	THIEF	4
99	Assassin	2
00	MONK OR BARD	1 or 1

ty Magic Items: In order to simulate a party of adventurers, it is olutely necessary that characters and henchmen have and employ some ic devices. While it is possible to give such parties the whole gamut of s listed, it is suggested that you use the following lists and select rding to the following rule:

vidual is 1st level — 10% chance: 1 item from Table I.
vidual is 2nd level — 20% chance: 2 items from Table I.
vidual is 3rd level — 30% chance: 2 items from Table I;
10% chance: 1 item from Table II.
vidual is 4th level — 40% chance: 2 items from Table I;
20% chance: 1 item from Table II.
vidual is 5th level — 50% chance: 2 items from Table I;
30% chance: 1 item from Table II.

TABLE II

Die	Item (d8, d6)
1	1 SCROLL: 3 Spells, level 2-9 or 2-7
2	2 RINGS: *fire resistance, invisibility*
3	1 RING: *protection +3*
4	1 STAFF: *striking*
5	1 WAND: *illusion*
6	1 WAND: *negation*
7	1 *bracers of defense, armor class 4*
8	1 *brooch of shielding*
9	1 *cloak of elvenkind*
10	1 *dust of appearance*
11	1 FIGURINE OF WONDROUS POWER: *serpentine owl*
12	3 *javelins of lightning*
13	1 set: chainmail +1, shield +2
14	1 ARMOR: splint mail +4
15	1 SWORD: +3 (no special abilities)
16	2 WEAPONS: *crossbow of speed,* +2 hammer

TABLE III

Die	Item (d8, d6)
1	1 RING: *spell storing*
2	1 ROD: *cancellation*
3	1 STAFF: *serpent* — python or adder
4	1 *bag of tricks*
5	1 *boots of speed*
6	1 *boots of striding and leaping*
7	1 *cloak of displacement*
8	1 *gauntlets of ogre power*
9	1 *pipe of the sewers*
10	1 *robe of blending*
11	2 ROPES: *climbing, entanglement*
12	1 set: plate mail +3, shield +2
13	1 SHIELD: +5
14	1 SWORD: +4, *defender*
15	1 mace +3
16	1 spear +3

TABLE IV

Die	Item (d12)
1	1 RING: *djinni summoning*
2	1 RING: *spell turning*
3	1 ROD: *smiting*
4	1 WAND: *fire*
5	1 *cube of force*
6	1 *eyes of charming*
7	1 *horn of valhalla*
8	1 *robe of scintillating colors*
9	1 *talisman of either ultimate evil or pure good*
10	1 set: plate mail +4, shield +3
11	1 SWORD: *wounding*
12	1 *arrow of slaying* (select character type)

MONSTER LEVEL II

Dice Score	Creature Encountered	Numbers	AC	MV	HD	#AT	D
01-03	Anhkheg	1-3	2/4	12″ (6″)	3	1	3-18 (+ 1-4)
04-05	Assassin bug	2	5	6″/18″	1 + 1	1	1-4
06	Badger, giant*	1-4	4	6″ (3″)	3	3	1-3/1-3/1-6
07-14	Centipede, giant	3-13 (2d6 + 1)	9	15″	¼	1	Nil +S
15-24	Character — see *Character Subtable*						
25-26	Coffer corpse	1	8	6″	2	1	BW or 1-6
27-28	Crabman	2-8	4	9″//6″	3	2	1-4/1-4
29-30	Flind	2-8	5	12″	2 + 3	1	1-6 or 1-4 + S
31-33	Flump	2-8	0/8	6″	2	1	1-8 (+ 1-4)
34-37	Frog, giant	1-6	7	3″//9″	1 to 3	1	1-3 or 1-6 or 2-8
38	Frog, killer	2-7	8	6″//12″	1 + 4	3	1-2/1-2/2-5
39-40	Frog, poisonous	1-4	8	3″//9″	1	1	1 pt. +S
41	Galltrit	1-4	2	3″/18″	2 hp	1	1-2
42-43	Gas spore	1-2	9	3″	1 hp	1	S
44-48	Gnoll	4-10 (2d4 + 2)	5	9″	2	1	BW or 2-8
49-50	Goldbug	1-12	9	1″	1	1	1-4
51-54	Gorbel	1-8	3(10)	18″	2(5)	1	1-4 or 1-6
55-58	Grimlock	2-12	5	12″	2	1	BW or 1-6
59	Gryph	1-6	6	21″	2 to 4	1	2-12
60-61	Troll, ice	1-6	8	9″	2	2	1-8/1-8
62-65	Lizard man	4-10 (2d4 + 2)	5(4)	6″//12″	2 + 1	3	1-2/1-2/1-8
66	Nilbog	1-6	6	6″	1-1	1	BW or 1-6
67-70	Piercer	1-4	3	1″	3	1	3-18
71-73	Poltergeist	1-8	10	6″	½	0	Nil
74-75	Quaggoth	4-10 (2d4 + 2)	6	12″	1 + 2	2 or 1	1-4/1-4 or BW
76-78	Skulk	1-8	7	12″	2	1	BW
79-86	Toad, giant	1-4	6	6″ +6″ hop	2 + 4	1	2-8
87-94	Troglodyte	2-8	5	12″	2	3 or 1	1-3/1-3/2-5 or B
95-98	Volt	1-8	3	6″	2 + 1	2	1-4/and 2-12
99-00	Vortex	1-8	0	15″	2 + 2	1	1-3 +S

* Not encountered below the 3rd level; treat as a roll of 44-48 (Gnoll) thereafter.

Dice Score	Creature Encountered	Numbers	AC	MV	HD	#AT	D
01	Adherer	1-4	3	9″	4	1	1-3
02	Anhkheg	1-3	2/4	12″ (6″)	4 or 5	1	3-18 (+1-4)
03	Astral searcher	2-11	10	12″	2	1	1-6
04	Babbler	1-4	6	6″ or 12″	5	2	1-6/1-6/1-8
05-08	Beetle, giant, boring	1-3	3	6″	5	1	5-20
09	Berbalang	1	6	6″/24″	1+1	3	1-4/1-4/1-6
10	Blindheim	1-4	5	9″	4+2	1	1-8
11	Bonesnapper	1-3	4	6″	4	2	1-8/1-4
12-15	Bugbear	2-7	5	9″	3+1	1	BW or 2-8
16-21	Character — see *Character Subtable*						
22	Dark creeper	1	0	9″	1+1	1	1-4
23	Death dog	3-12	7	12″	2+1	2	1-10/1-10 +S
24-26	Devil, lemure	2-5	7	3″	3	1	1-3
27	Dragon — see *Dragon Subtable* below						
28	Elf, drow	2-7	4(+)	12″ or 15″	2(+)	1 or 2	BW
29	Enveloper	1	4	9″	Var.	2	1-8/1-8 +S
30	Firedrake	1-6	5	6″/18″	4	1	2-8
31	Firenewt	2-16	5	9″	2+2	1	BW
32-33	Fire snake	1-6	6	4″	2	1	1-4 +S
34	Forlarren	1	2	9″	3	2	1-4/1-4 +S
35	Frost man	1	5	12″	4	1	BW
36	Fungi, violet	1-3	7	1″	3	1-4	S
37	Gambado	1-4	6	12″	4	3	1-8/1-4/1-4
38	Garbug, violet	1-3	5	6″/9″	3+1	2	1-6/1-6 +S
39-41	Gelantinous cube	1	8	6″	4	1	2-8 +S
42-44	Ghoul	1-4	6	9″	2	3	1-3/1-3/1-6 +S
45	Huecuva	1-4	3	9″	2	1	1-6 +S
46	Imorph	1	5	6″	5	2	1-4/1-4
47	Iron cobra	1	0	12″	1	1	1-3 +S
48-50	Kenku	1-4	5	6″/18″	2-5	3 or 1	1-4/1-4/1-6 or BW
51-52	Leprechaun	1-4	8	15″	2-5 hp	0	Nil (S)
53-55	Lizard, giant	1-3	5	15″	3+1	1	1-8
56-58	Lycanthrope, wererat	2-5	6	12″	3+1	1	1-8
59	Mantari	1-3	8	18″	1+1	1	S
60	Meazle	1	8	12″	4	2	1-4/1-4
61-62	Mephit*	1	Var.	Var.	Var.	Var.	Var.
63	Necrophidius	1	2	9″	2	1	1-8 +S
64-66	Ochre jelly	1	8	3″	6	1	3-12
67-71	Ogre	1-3	5	9″	4+1	1	1-10 or BW
72-73	Piercer	1-4	3	1″	4	1	4-24
74	Qullan	1-6	10	12″	2	1	5-11 (2d4+3)
75	Screaming devilkin	1	2	12″	3	1	1-6
76	Sheet phantom	1	3	6″	3	1	1-4 +S
77	Shocker	1-3	0	9″	1+2	1	10 pts.
78-81	Spider, huge	1-3	6	18″	2+2	1	1-6 +S
82-85	Spider, large	2-5	8	6″*15″	1+1	1	1 +S
86-88	Stirge	5-15 (2d6+3)	8	3″/18″	1+1	1	1-3 +S
89	Stunjelly	1	8	3″	4	1	2-8 +S
90	Symbiotic jelly	1	8	1″	2	0	Nil
91	Thoqqua	1-2	2	12″ (3″)	3	2	4-32/2-12
92-93	Tick, giant	1-3	3	3″	2-4	1	1-4 +S
94	Tirapheg	1	4	3″	2	3	1-4 (x3)
95-96	Weasel, giant	1-4	6	15″	3+3	1	2-12
97-98	Whipweed	1-2	6/4	3″	(2+4)+(1+4)	2	1-10/1-10
99-00	Witherweed	1	8	Nil	3(+)	3-12(+)	S

*choose type, or determine randomly.

Dragon Subtable

Dice Score	Dragon Type	Age Category	(Hit Points/Die)
01-28	Black	very young	(1)
29-62	Brass	very young	(1)
63-00	White	very young	(1)

Determine the number of hit dice for a dragon as normal.

MONSTER LEVEL IV

Dice Score	Creature Encountered	Numbers	AC	MV	HD	#AT	D
01-02	Anhkheg	1-3	2/4	12" (6")	6	1	3-18 (+1-4) +S
03-06	Ape, carnivorous	1-3	6	12"	5	3	1-4/1-4/1-8 +S
07-08	Blink dog	2-5	5	12"	4	1	1-6 +S
09-10	Bloodworm, giant	1-3	4	6"	6	1	1-8 +S
11-12	Caterwaul	1	6(+)	18"-24"(+)	4+2	3	1-4/1-4/1-6 +S
13-21	Character — see *Character Subtable*						
22	Dark stalker	1	0/8	9"	2+1	1	1-6 +S
23	Denzelian	1-2	0	1"	6	Nil	Nil
24	Disenchanter	1	5	12"	5	1	S
25-26	Dragon — see *Dragon Subtable* below						
27-28	Ettercap	1-2	6	12"	5	3	1-3/1-3/1-8 +S
29	Eye killer	1	5	9"	4	1	1-6 +S
30-31	Firetoad	1-3	10	6"	4+1	1	S
32	Flail snail	1	4	3"	4-6	1(+)	1-8(+)
33-34	Garbug, black	1-3	5	6"/9"	2+2	1+6	1-4 +S
35-38	Gargoyle	1-2	5	9"/15"	4+4	4	1-3/1-3/1-6/1-4
39-40	Ghast	1-4	4	15"	4	3	1-4/1-4/1-8 +S
41-42	Gray ooze	1	8	1"	3+3	1	2-16 +S
43-44	Grell	1	4	12"	5	11	1-4 (x10)/1-6
45	Hell hound	1-2	4	12"	4-7	1	1-10 +S
46-47	Hook horror	2-5	3	9"	5	2	1-8/1-8
48	Hornet, giant	1	2/4	24"	5	1	1-4 +S
49-52	Hydra	1	5	9"	5	5	1-6 (x5) +S
53	Hydra, pyro-	1	5	9"	5	5	1-6 (x5) +S
54-55	Kamadan	1	4	18"	4+2	3(+)	1-3/1-3/1-6 + 1-4
56	Kuo-toa	2-12	4	9"//18"	2	1-2	BW or 2-5
57	Lava children	1-6	4	9"	4(+)	3	1-6/1-6/2-12 +S
58-65	Lycanthrope, werewolf	1-2	5	15"	4+3	1	2-8
66	Meenlock	2-5	7(S)	9"	4	2	1-4/1-4 +S
67-70	Mold, yellow	1	9	0"	Nil	1	1-8 +S
71-72	Owlbear	1	5	12"	5+2	3	1-6/1-6/2-12 +S
73-77	Rust monster	1	2	18"	5	2	S
78-79	Sandman	1-2	3	9"	4	1	S
80	Scarecrow	1-2	6	6"	5	1	1-6 +S
81	Shadow demon	1	9/5/1	12"(S)	7+3	3	1-8/1-6/1-6 +S
82-85	Snake, giant, constrictor	1	5	9"	6+1	2	1-4/2-8 +S
86	Son of Kyuss	1-2	10	9"	4	1	1-8 +S
87-90	Su-monster	1-2	6	9"	5+5	5	1-4 (x4)/2-8
91-92	Tiger fly	2	4	6"/18"	6 or 4	3 or 1	1-8/1-8/4-24 +S or 4-16 +S
93-94	Toad, ice	1	4	9"	5	1	3-12 +S
95-98	Toad, poisonous	1-3	7	6" +6" hop	2	1	2-5 +S
99-00	Yellow musk creeper	1*	7	Nil	3	2-12	S

* Plus number of yellow musk zombies equal to plant's flowers.

Dragon Subtable

Dice Score	Dragon Type	Age Category	(Hit Points/Dice)
01-09	Black	young/sub-adult	(2/3)
10-20	Blue	very young/young	(1/2)
21-30	Brass	young/sub-adult	(2/3)
31-36	Bronze	very young/young	(1/2)
37-49	Copper	very young/young	(1/2)
50-53	Gold	very young/young	(1/2)
54-69	Green	very young/young	(1/2)
70-74	Li lung	very young/young	(1/2)
75-82	Red	very young/young	(1/2)
83-88	Silver	very young/young	(1/2)
89-00	White	young/sub-adult	(2/3)

Determine the number of hit dice for a dragon as normal.

MONSTER LEVEL V

Dice Score	Creature Encountered	Numbers	AC	MV	HD	#AT	D
01-04	Anhkheg	1-3	2/4	12″ (6″)	7	1	3-18 (+1-4) +S
05-06	Cerebral parasite	1-3	Nil	Nil	Nil	0	S
07-19	Character — see *Character Subtable*						
20-25	Cockatrice	1-2	6	6″/18″	5	1	1-3 +S
26	Crypt thing	1	3	12″	6	1	1-8 +S
27-28	Displacer beast	1-2	4	15″	6	2	2-8/2-8
29-30	Doppleganger	1-3	5	9″	4	1	1-12 +S
31-32	Dragon — see *Dragon Subtable* below		4(+)	12″ or 15″	2(+)	1 or 2	BW
33	Elf, drow	3-12	4(+)	12″ or 15″	2(+)	1 or 2	BW
34	Githyanki	1-4	------------------------All Variable------------------------				BW
35	Githzerai	1-4	------------------------All Variable------------------------				BW +S
36-39	Hydra	1	5	9″	7	7	1-8 (x7) +S
40	Hydra, pyro-	1	5	9″	6	6	1-8 (x6) +S
41-42	Ice lizard	1-2	1	9″/15″	3+3	3	1-3/1-3/1-6 +S
43	Imp	1-2	2	6″/18″	2+2	1	1-4 +S
44	Khargra	1-2	−3	3″/15″	6	1	3-18 +S
45-47	Leucrotta	1-2	4	18″	6+1	1	3-18
48-55	Lizard, subterranean	1-3	5	12″	6	1	2-12
56-59	Lycanthrope, wereboar	1-3	4	12″	5+2	1	2-12
60-63	Minotaur	1-3	6	12″	6+3	2	2-8 or 1-4/BW
64-65	Phantom stalker	1	3	12″/24″	6	2	1-4/1-4 +S
66	Quasit	1	2	15″	3	3	1-2/1-2/1-4 +S
67-69	Shadow	1-3	7	12″	3+3	1	2-5 +S
70-71	Slithering tracker	1	5	12″	5	0	S
72-73	Snake, giant, amphisbaena	1	3	12″	6	2	1-3/1-3 +S
74-81	Snake, giant, poisonous	1	5	15″	4+2	1	1-3 +S
82-85	Snake, giant, spitting	1	5	12″	4+2	1	1-3 +S
86-93	Spider, giant	1-2	4	3″*12″	4+4	1	2-8 +S
94-95	Svirfneblin	2-5	2(+)	9″	3+6	1 or 2	BW +S
96-97	Tentamort	1-2	2/1	1″	2/4	2	1-6/1-6 +S
98	Trilloch	1	n/a	12″	n/a	n/a	S
99	Umpleby	1	4	9″	6	1	1-4 +S
00	Xill	1-2	0	15″	5	4	1-4 (x4) BW +S

Dragon Subtable

Dice Score	Dragon Type	Age Category	(Hit Points/Die)
01-09	Black	young adult/adult	(4/5)
10-20	Blue	sub adult/young adult	(3/4)
21-30	Brass	young adult/adult	(4/5)
31-36	Bronze	sub-adult/young adult	(3/4)
37-49	Copper	sub-adult/young adult	(3/4)
50-53	Gold	sub-adult/young adult	(3/4)
54-69	Green	sub-adult/young adult	(3/4)
70-74	Li lung	sub-adult/young adult	(3/4)
75-82	Red	sub-adult/young adult	(3/4)
83-88	Silver	sub-adult/young adult	(3/4)
89-00	White	young adult/adult	(4/5)

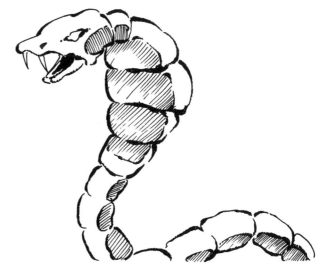

MONSTER LEVEL VI

Dice Score	Creature Encountered	Numbers	AC	MV	HD	#AT	D
01-02	Anhkheg	1-3	2/4	12″ (6″)	8	1	3-18 (+1-4) +S
03	Apparition	1	0	24″	8	1	S
04-07	Basilisk	1	4	6″	6+1	1	1-10 +S
08-11	Carrion crawler	1-2	3/7	12″	3+1	8	S
12-19	Character — see *Character Subtable*						
20	Devil, erinyes	1-2	2	6″/21″	6+6	1	2-8 +S
21	Djinni	1	4	9″/24″	7+3	1	2-16 +S
22-23	Dragon — see *Dragon Subtable* below						
24-26	Green slime	---	9	0″	2	0	S
27-29	Hellcat	1	6	12″	7+2	3	2-5/2-5/2-12
30-33	Hydra	1	5	9″	9	9	1-8 (x9) +S
34	Hydra, pyro	1	5	9″	7	7	1-8 (x7) +S
35-36	Jackalwere	1-2	4	12″	4	1	2-8 +S
37-38	Lammasu	1-3	6	12″/24″	7+7	2	1-6/1-6 +S
39	Lizard king	1	3	15″//12″	8	1	5-20 +S
40-41	Lycanthrope, werebear	1	2	9″	7+3	3	1-3/1-3/2-8 +S
42-43	Lycanthrope, weretiger	1-2	3	12″	6+2	3	1-4/1-4/1-12 +S
44-47	Manticore	1-2	4	12″/18″	6+3	3	1-3/1-3/1-8 +S
48-49	Medusa	1	5	9″	6	1	1-4 +S
50	Mold, yellow	---	9	0″	n/a	1	1-8 +S
51	Nightmare	1	−4	15″/36″	6+6	3	2-8/4-10/4-10
52-53	Ogre mage	1-2	4	9″/15″	5+2	1	1-12 +S
54-59	Otyugh	1	3	6″	6-8	3	1-8/1-8/2-5 +S
60-61	Penanggalan*	1	10/8	12″/9″	Var.	1	1-6 +S
62-63	Protein polymorph	1	2	9″	6-8	Var.	BW/6-36
64-65	Rakshasa	1	−4	15″	7	3	1-3/1-3/2-5 +S
66-67	Salamander	1-2	5/3	9″	7+7	2	BW/2-12
68-71	Scorpion, giant	1-3	3	15″	5+5	3	1-10/1-10/1-4 +
72	Slaad, red	1	6	6″ (9″)	7	3	1-4/1-4/2-16 +S
73-74	Spider, phase	1-3	7	6″*15″	5+5	1	1-6 +S
75	Spirit troll	1	2	15″	5+5	3	1-6/1-3/1-3 +S
76	Sussurus	1	4	15″	8	2	1-8/1-8
77	Terithran	1	3(6)	15″ (18″)	5-1	2	2-5/2-5 +S
78-83	Troll	1-3	4	12″	6+6	3	5-8/5-8/2-12
84-85	Troll, giant	1-2	4	12″	8	1	2-16
86	Vision	1	0(10)	15″	8	Nil	S
87-90	Wight	1-4	5	12″	4+3	1	1-4 +S
91-92	Wind walker	1	7	15″/30″	6+3	1	3-18
93-96	Wraith	1-2	4	12″/24″	5+3	1	1-6 +S
97-00	Wyvern	1	3	6″/24″	7+7	2	2-16/1-6 +S

Dragon Subtable

Dice Score	Dragon Type	Age Category	(Hit Points/
01-09	Black	old	(6)
10-20	Blue	adult	(5)
21-30	Brass	old	(6)
31-36	Bronze	adult	(5)
37-49	Copper	adult	(5)
50-53	Gold	adult	(5)
54-69	Green	adult	(5)
70-74	Li lung	adult	(5)
75-82	Red	adult	(5)
83-88	Silver	adult	(5)
89-00	White	old	(6)

Determine number of hit dice for a dragon as normal.

MONSTER LEVEL VII

Dice Score	Creature Encountered	Numbers	AC	MV	HD	#AT	D
01-04	Black pudding	1	6	6″	10	1	3-24 +S
05	Bulette	1	−2/4/6	14″ (3″)	9	3	4-48/3-18/3-18 +S
06-12	Character — see *Character Subtable*						
13-14	Chimera	1-2	6/5/2	9″/18″	9	6	1-3/1-3/1-4/1-4/2-8/3-12 +S
15-16	Cifal	1-2	6	6″	8(10)	1	1-12
17	Couatl	1	5	6″/18″	9	2	1-3/2-8 +S
18	Demon, succubus	1	0	12″/18″	6	2	1-3/1-3 +S
19	Demon, type I (vrock)	1	0	12″/18″	8	5	1-4/1-4/1-8/1-8/1-6 +S
20	Demon, type II (hezrou)	1	−2	6″//12″	9	3	1-3/1-3/4-16 +S
21	Demon, type III (glabrezu)	1	−4	9″	10	5	2-12/2-12/1-3/1-3/2-5 +S
22	Devil, barbed	1	0	12″	8	3	2-8/2-8/3-12 +S
23	Devil, bone	1	−1	15″	9	1	3-12 +S
24	Devil, horned	1	−5	9″/18″	5+5	4 or 1+1	1-4/1-4/2-5/1-3 or 1-3/BW
25	Devil, styx	1	−1	6″/15″	6+6	1	2-8
26-27	Dragon — see *Dragon Subtable* below						
28	Efreeti	1	2	9″/24″	10	1	3-24 +S
29-30	Elemental*						
	Air	1	2	36″	12	1	2-20 +S
	Earth	1	2	6″	12	1	4-32 +S
	Fire	1	2	12″	12	1	3-24 +S
	Water	1	2	6″//18″	12	1	5-30 +S
31	Ettin	1-2	3	12″	10	2	2-16/3-18
32	Eye of fear and flame	1	2	9″	12	S	S
33-34	Giant, fire	1-2	3	12″	11+2-5	1	5-30 +S
35	Giant, frost	1-2	4	12″	10+1-4	1	4-24 +S
36-38	Giant, hill	1-3	4	12″	8+1-2	1	2-16 +S
39	Giant, mountain	1-2	4	12″	12	1	4-40 +S
40-41	Giant, stone	1-3	0	12″	9+1-3	1	3-18 +S
42	Golem, flesh	1	9	8″	40 hp	2	2-16/2-16 +S
43-44	Gorgon	1	2	12″	8	1	2-12 +S
45	Groaning spirit	1	0	15″	7	1	1-8 +S
46	Guardian daemon	1	1	9″(S)	8	3	1-6/1-12/1-12 +S
47	Guardian familiar	1	8	12″	1(9)	3	1-6/1-4/1-4
48-51	Hydra	1	5	9″	10	10	1-10 (x10)
52	Hydra, pyro	1	5	9″	8	8	1-10 (x8) +S
53	Intellect devourer	1	4	15″	6+6	4	1-4 (x4) +S
54	Invisible stalker	1	3	12″	8	1	4-16 +S
55	Lamia	1-2	3	24″	9	1	1-4 +S
56	Lamia noble	1	6	9″	10+1	1	1-6 +S
57	Lizard, fire	1-3	3	9″	10	3	1-8/1-8/2-16 +S
58-61	Lurker above	1	6	1″/9″	10	1	1-6 +S
62	Magnesium spirit	1	0	36″	6+1	1	3-12 +S
63-64	Mimic	1	7	3″	7-10	1	3-12 +S
65-66	Mind flayer	1-2	5	12″	8+4	4	S
67-68	Mummy	1-2	3	6″	6+3	1	1-12 +S
69-70	Naga, spirit	1-2	4	12″	9-10	1	1-3 +S
71-72	Neo-otyugh	1	0	6″	9-12	3	2-12/2-12/1-3 +S
73	Night hag	1-2	9	9″	8	1	2-12 +S
74	Nonafel	1	5(6)	9″ (12″)	9	1	2-20 or 1-8
75	Revenant	1	10	9″	8	1	2-16 +S
76-77	Roper	1-2	0	3″	10-12	1	5-20 +S
78-79	Shambling mound	1-2	0	6″	8-11	2	2-16/2-16 +S
80-81	Shedu	1-2	4	12″/24″	9+9	2	1-6/1-6 +S
82	Slaad, blue	1	5	7″	8+4	5	2-16/2-12 (x4) +S
83-86	Slug, giant	1	8	6″	12	1	1-12 +S
87-88	Spectre	1	2	15″/30″	7+3	1	1-8 +S
89-90	Sphinx — see *Sphinx Subtable* below						
91-92	Trapper	1	3	3″	12	4+	S
93	Troll, giant two headed	1	4	12″	10	4	1-6/1-6/1-10/1-10
94-95	Umber hulk	1	2	6″ (1″-6″)	8+8	3	3-12/3-12/2-10 +S
96-99	Will-o-wisp	1-3	−8	18″	9	1	2-16 +S
00	Xorn	1-3	−2	9″	7+7	4	1-3 (x3), 6-24 +S

choose, or use equal probabilities as applicable.

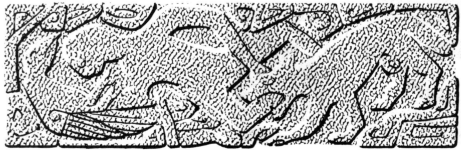

Dragon Subtable

Dice Score	Dragon Type	Age Category	(Hit Points/Die)
01-09	Black	very old	(7)
10-20	Blue	old	(6)
21-30	Brass	very old	(7)
31-36	Bronze	old	(6)
37-49	Copper	old	(6)
50-53	Gold	old	(6)
54-69	Green	old	(6)
70-74	Li lung	old	(6)
75-81	Red	old	(6)
82-87	Silver	old	(6)
88-89	T'ien lung	adult	(5)
90-00	White	very old	(7)

Determine number of hit dice for dragon as normal.

Sphinx Subtable

Dice Score	Sphinx Type	Numbers
01-15	Androsphinx	1
16-43	Criosphinx	1-2
44-72	Gynosphinx	1
73-00	Hieracosphinx	1-3

MONSTER LEVEL VIII

Dice Score	Creature Encountered	Numbers	AC	MV	HD	#AT	D
01	Aerial servant	1	3	24"	16	1	8-32
02-06	Cerebral parasite	2-8	n/a	n/a	n/a	0	S
07-14	Character — see *Character Subtable*						
15	Death knight	1	0	var.	9	1	BW +S
16	Demon, type IV	1	−1	9"/12"	11	3	1-4/1-4/2-8 +S
17	Demon, type V	1	−7/−5	12"	7+7	7	2-8/&6 BW +S
18	Demon, type VI	1	−2	6"/15"	8+8	1	2-13 +S
19	Devil, ice	1	−4	6"	11	4	1-4/1-4/2-8/3-12 +S
20-21	Dragon — see *Dragon Subtable* below						
22-24	Ghost	1	0(8)	9"	10	1	S
25-28	Giant, cloud	1-2	2	15"	12+2-7	1	6-36 +S
29-30	Giant, fog	1-2	1	15"	14	1	4-24 +S
31-32	Golem, clay	1	7	7"	50 hp	1	3-30 +S
33-37	Hydra	1	5	9"	11	11	1-10 (x11) +S
38	Hydra, pyro	1	5	9"	9	9	1-10 (x9) +S
39-40	Intellect devourer	1-2	4	15"	6+6	4	1-4 (x4) +S
41-44	Lurker above	1	6	1"/9"	10	1	1-6 +S
45-52	Mold, brown	---	9	0"	0	0	S
53-56	Mind flayer	1-4	5	12"	8+4	4	S
57-59	Naga, guardian	1-2	3	15"	11-12	2	1-6/2-8 +S
60-61	Neo-otyugh	1-2	0	6"	9-12	3	2-12/2-12/1-3 +S
62-70	Purple worm	1	6	9"	15	1&1	2-24/2-8 +S
71-72	Retriever	1	−2	18"	10	4	3-18 (x4)
73-75	Rust monster	1	2	18"	5	2	S
76	Skeleton warrior	1	2	6"	9+2 to 9+12	1	BW
77	Slaad, green	1	3	9"	9+3	3	2-16/3-8/3-8 +S
78-80	Slug, giant	1	8	6"	12	1	1-12 +S
81-87	Trapper	1	3	3"	12	4+	S
88-94	Vampire	1	1	12"/18"	8+3	1	5-10 +S
95-98	Will-o-wisp	2-5	−8	18"	9	1	2-16 +S
99-00	Xorn	2-5	−2	9"	7+7	4	1-3 (x3)/6-24 +S

Dragon Subtable

Dice Score	Dragon Type	Age Category	(Hit Points/D
01-09	Black	ancient	(8)
10-20	Blue	very old	(7)
21-30	Brass	ancient	(8)
31-36	Bronze	very old	(7)
37-49	Copper	very old	(7)
50-53	Gold	very old	(7)
54-67	Green	very old	(7)
68-72	Li lung	very old	(7)
73-81	Red	very old	(7)
82-87	Silver	very old	(7)
88-89	T'ien lung	old	(6)
90-00	White	ancient	(8)

Determine number of hit dice for a dragon as normal.

Dice Score	Creature Encountered	Numbers	AC	MV	HD	#AT	D
01-03	Achaierai	1-2	8/−1	18″	40 hp/15 hp	3	1-8/1-8/1-10
04-06	Bulette	1-3	−2/4/6	14″ (3″)	9	3	4-48/3-18/3-18 +S
07-16	Character — see *Character Subtable*						
17-19	Devil, pit fiend	1	−3	6″/15″	13	2	5-8/7-12 +S
20-22	Dragon — see *Dragon Subtable* below						
23-28	Giant, storm	1-2	1	15″	15+2-7	1	7-42 +S
29-30	Golem, stone	1	5	6″	60 hp	1	3-24 +S
31-33	Gorgon	1-2	2	12″	8	1	2-12 +S
34-40	Hydra	1	5	9″	12	12	1-10 (x12) +S
41-43	Hydra, pyro-	1	5	9″	10	10	1-10 (x10) +S
44-45	Ki-rin	1	−5	24″/48″	12	3	2-8/2-8/3-18 +S
46-47	Naga, guardian	1-3	−3	15″	11-12	2	1-6/2-8 +S
48-49	Nycadaemon	1	−4	12″/36″	12+36	2 or 1	9-16/9-16 or BW +8
50-61	Purple worm	1	6	9″	15	1&1	2-24/2-8 +S
62-64	Retriever	1	−2	18″	10	4	3-18 (x4) +S
65-67	Rust monster	1	2	18″	5	2	S
68-69	Slaad, grey	1	1	12″	10+6	3 or 2	2-16/4-10/4-10 or 2 BW + 1-8 +S
70-72	Titan, lesser	1	2	21″	17	1	7-42 +S
73-75	Titan, major	1	0	15″	19	1	7-42 +S
76-82	Umber hulk	1-4	2	6″ (1″-6″)	8+8	3	3-12/3-12/2-10 +S
83-85	Vampire*	1	1	12″/18″	8+3	1	5-10 +S
86-94	Will-o-wisp	2-5	−8	18″	9	1	2-16 +S
95-00	Xorn	2-9	−2	9″	7+7	4	1-3 (x3)/6-24 +S

Former evil cleric, with full powers of 7th-10th level.

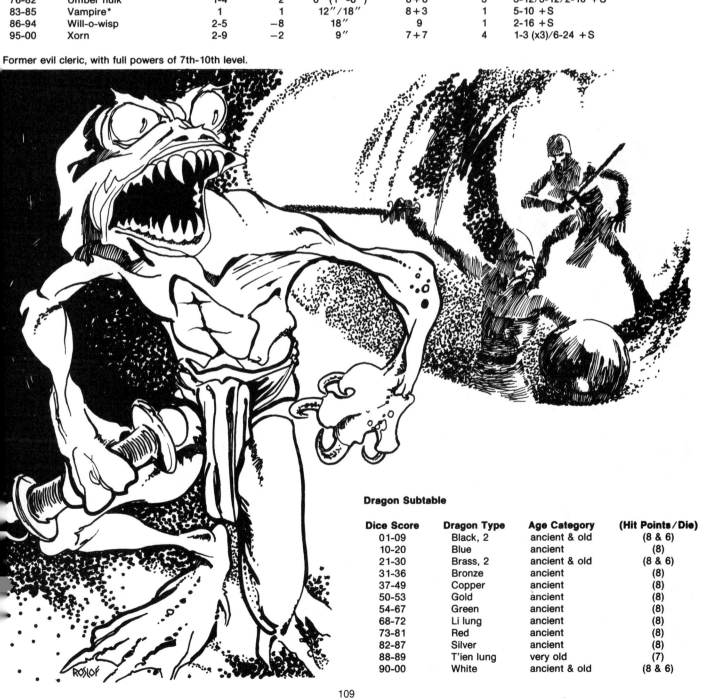

Dragon Subtable

Dice Score	Dragon Type	Age Category	(Hit Points/Die)
01-09	Black, 2	ancient & old	(8 & 6)
10-20	Blue	ancient	(8)
21-30	Brass, 2	ancient & old	(8 & 6)
31-36	Bronze	ancient	(8)
37-49	Copper	ancient	(8)
50-53	Gold	ancient	(8)
54-67	Green	ancient	(8)
68-72	Li lung	ancient	(8)
73-81	Red	ancient	(8)
82-87	Silver	ancient	(8)
88-89	T'ien lung	very old	(7)
90-00	White	ancient & old	(8 & 6)

MONSTER LEVEL X

Dice Score	Creature Encountered	Numbers	AC	MV	HD	#AT	D
01-12	Beholder	1	0/2/7	3"	45-75 hp	1	2-8 +S
13-19	Catoblepas	1	7	6"	6+2	1	1-6 +S
20-26	Character — see *Character Subtable*						
27-29	Demon, prince*	1	Var.	Var.	Var.	Var.	Var.
30	Devil, arch-*	1	Var.	Var.	Var.	Var.	Var.
31-39	Dragon — see *Dragon Subtable* below						
40-41	Elemental prince of evil*	1	Var.	Var.	Var.	Var.	Var.
42-50	Golem, iron	1	3	6"	80 hp	1	4-40 +S
51-53	Lamia Noble	1	6	9"	10+1	1	1-6 +S
54-62	Lich	1	0	6"	11+	1	1-10 +S
63-75	Purple Worm	1	6	9"	15	1+1	2-24/2-8 +S
76-78	Slaad, death	1	−4	12"	15+7	3 or 2	2-20/3-18/3-18 or 2 +1-8 +S
79	Slaad, lord*	1	−6	16"/19"	197 hp	3 or 1	2-16/2-16/2-16 +S
80-89	Titan, elder	1	−3	21"	22	1	8-48 +S
90-00	Vampire**	1	1	12"/18"	8+3	1	5-10 +S

* Select one or find randomly.
** Former magic-user, with full powers, of 9th-12th level.

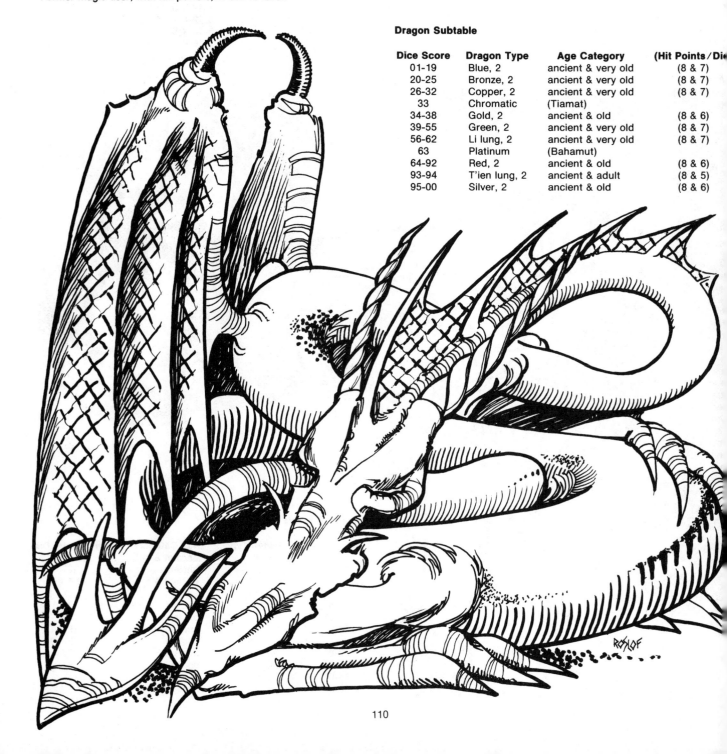

Dragon Subtable

Dice Score	Dragon Type	Age Category	(Hit Points/Die
01-19	Blue, 2	ancient & very old	(8 & 7)
20-25	Bronze, 2	ancient & very old	(8 & 7)
26-32	Copper, 2	ancient & very old	(8 & 7)
33	Chromatic	(Tiamat)	
34-38	Gold, 2	ancient & old	(8 & 6)
39-55	Green, 2	ancient & very old	(8 & 7)
56-62	Li lung, 2	ancient & very old	(8 & 7)
63	Platinum	(Bahamut)	
64-92	Red, 2	ancient & old	(8 & 6)
93-94	T'ien lung, 2	ancient & adult	(8 & 5)
95-00	Silver, 2	ancient & old	(8 & 6)

Arctic Conditions

Creature Type	Predominant Terrain		
	Plain	Rough*	Mountains
Bear, brown[a]	01-05	01-06	01-04
Devil dog	06-07	07-08	05-09
Dragon, white	08-09	09-10	10-15
Frost men	10	11	16-18
Giant, frost	11-13	12-14	19-23
Herd animal	14-53	15-54	24-55
Hoar fox	54-56	55-57	56-58
Ice lizard	57	58	59-60
Men, tribesmen	58-67	59-67	61-66
Owl, giant	68-72	68-75	67-75
Remorhaz	73-74	76-77	76-77
Snake, giant, constrictor[b]	75-80	78-82	78-81
Toad, ice	81-83	83-84	82-83
Wolf	84-92	85-93	84-88
Wolf, winter	93-95	94-95	89-90
Yeti	96-00	96-00	91-00

Includes ruins (cities, temples, fortresses) within up to five miles of the party.

This is treated the same as a brown bear, but is a white-coated polar bear.

This is treated the same as a giant constrictor, but is a white, furred snake.

Monsters in *italic* type are 75% likely to be encountered while they are airborne.

Sub-Arctic Conditions

Creature Type	Predominant Terrain						
	Plain	Scrub	Forest	Rough*	Hills	Mountains	Marsh
Bear, brown	---	01-04	01-08	01-05	01-04	---	---
Bear, cave	---	---	09-12	06-10	05-08	01-10	---
Devil dog	01-02	05-06	13-14	11-12	09-10	---	---
Dragon, white	03-06	07-10	---	13-16	11-14	11-16	01-04
Dragon, silver	---	---	---	---	---	17-18	---
Frost men	---	---	---	---	15	19-20	---
Giant, frost	07-10	11-14	15-18	17-20	16-19	21-24	---
Gnoll**	11-15	15-19	19-22	21-25	20-23	25-28	05-19
Hell hound	---	---	23-24	26-27	24-25	29-32	--
Herd animal	16-40	20-36	25-34	28-39	26-41	33-52	20-49
Hoar fox	41-44	37-40	35-36	40-42	42-43	53-54	50-51
Ice lizard	---	---	---	43	44	55-56	---
Lynx, giant	---	---	37-41	---	---	---	---
Mammoth	45-49	41-49	42-50	---	---	---	---
Mastadon	50-58	50-54	51-55	---	---	---	52-55
Men, tribesmen	59-67	55-64	56-64	44-53	45-62	57-61	56-64
*Owl, giant***	68-72	65-69	65-69	54-58	63-66	62-65	65-72
Quaggoth	73-74	70-73	70-73	59-62	67-70	66-69	73-74
Ram, giant	---	---	---	63-67	71-74	70-74	---
Rat, giant	---	---	74-77	68-72	---	---	75-82
Remorhaz	---	---	---	73-74	---	75-78	---
Rhinoceros, woolly	75-82	74-81	---	---	75-78	---	---
Tiger	83-90	82-89	78-81	75-78	79-82	---	---
Toad, ice	---	---	---	---	---	---	83-86
Troll	---	---	82-86	79-82	83-86	79-86	87-96
Troll, ice	---	---	---	83-84	87-88	87-88	97-00
Wolf	91-00	90-00	87-96	85-92	89-92	89-93	---
Wolf, winter	---	---	---	---	93-94	94-95	---
Wolverine	---	---	97-98	93-96	95-96	---	---
Wolverine, giant	---	---	99-00	97-98	97-98	---	---
Yeti	---	---	---	99-00	99-00	96-00	---

Includes ruins within up to five miles of the party.

20% of these encounters will include *flinds*.

* Night only, except in forest.

Temperate And Sub-Tropical Conditions

Uninhabited/Wilderness Areas

Creature Type	Plain	Scrub	Forest	Predominant Terrain Rough*	Desert	Hills	Mountains	Marsh
Aarakocra	---	---	---	---	---	---	01-02	---
Achaierai	---	---	01	---	---	---	---	---
Adherer	---	01	02	---	---	---	---	---
Algoid	---	---	---	---	---	---	---	01
Al-mi'raj	01	02	03	---	---	---	---	---
Ant, giant	02	03	04	01	---	01	---	---
Assassin bug	03	04	05	02	---	02	---	02
Badger	---	---	06	03-04	---	---	---	---
Badger, giant	---	---	---	05	---	---	---	---
Bear, brown	04	05	07-08	06	---	03-04	03-04	---
Beaver, giant	---	---	---	---	---	---	---	03
Beetle, giant, bombardier	---	---	09	---	---	---	---	---
Beetle, giant, stag	---	---	10	---	---	---	---	---
Beholder	---	---	---	---	---	---	---	04
Berbalang	05	06	---	---	---	---	---	---
Blink dog	06	07	11	07	01	05	05	---
Blood hawk	07-08	08	12	08-09	02	06	06	05
Boar, wild	09	09-10	13	10	---	---	---	---
Bugbear	10	11	14	11	---	07-09	07-08	---
Bulette	11	12	---	---	---	10	---	---
Bull/Cattle, wild	12-13	13-15	15	---	---	11	---	---
Bullywug	---	---	---	---	---	---	---	06-07
Bunyip	---	---	---	---	---	---	---	08
Camel, wild	---	---	---	---	03-05	---	---	---
Carbuncle	---	16	16	---	---	---	---	09
Catoblepas	---	---	---	---	---	---	---	10-11
Cifal	---	---	---	---	---	---	---	12-13
Death dog	---	---	---	---	06	---	---	---
Demi-human[a]	14	17	17-18	12	---	12-21	09-11	---
Disenchanter	15	18	---	---	07	---	---	---
Displacer beast	---	---	19	13	---	---	12	14
Dog, wild	16-17	19	20	14	08-11	22-23	13	---
Dragon[b]	18-19	20	21	15	12-13	24-25	14-15	15
Dragonne	---	---	---	16	14	---	16	---
Dune stalker	---	---	---	---	15	---	---	---
Eagle, giant	20	---	22	17	16	26	17-18	16
Enveloper/Imorph	---	21	23	18	---	27	---	---
Firedrake	---	---	---	19	---	28	19-20	---
Firetoad	---	---	---	20	17-18	29	---	---
Flumph	21	---	---	---	---	---	---	---
Forlarren	---	---	---	21	19	30	---	---
Frog[c]	---	---	---	---	---	---	---	17-22
Galltrit	---	22	24	---	---	---	---	---
Gambado	---	23	---	22	---	---	---	---
Garbug, violet	---	---	---	---	---	---	---	23-24
Gargoyle	---	---	---	---	---	---	21-22	25
Giant[d]	22-23	24-25	25	23-24	---	31-32	23-34	26
Gibberling	---	---	26-27	---	---	---	---	---
Goat, giant	---	---	---	25	---	33-34	35	---
Griffon	24	26	28	26	20-21	35-36	36	---
Herd animal	25-30	27-32	29-30	27-28	22	37-39	---	---
Hippogriff	31-32	33-34	31	29-30	23-24	40-41	---	---
Hornet, giant	---	35-36	32-33	---	---	---	---	---
Horse, wild	33-35	37-38	34-35	31-32	25-28	42-43	---	---
Humanoid[e]	36-38	39-42	36-39	33-37	29-36	44-53	37-46	27-3
Jackal**	39-42	43	---	---	---	---	---	---
Kenku	43-44	44	---	38	37-38	54	---	---
Ki-rin/Lammasu/Shedu	45	45	40	39	39	55	47	38
Leprechaun/Brownie	---	---	41	---	---	56	---	---
Leucrotta	---	---	---	40-41	---	---	48	39
Lion	46-54	46-48	42-43	42-43	40-48	57-58	---	---
Lizard, giant	---	---	44	44-45	49-51	---	---	40-4
Lizard man***	---	---	---	---	---	---	---	44-4
Lycanthrope[f]	55	---	45-46	46-47	52	59-61	49-51	---
Lynx, giant	---	---	47-48	---	---	---	---	---
Mantari	56	---	---	---	53	---	---	48
Meazle	---	---	---	---	---	---	---	49-5
Men[g]	57-73	49-66	49-56	48-56	54-65	62-70	52-68	52-6
Ogre****	74-77	67-71	57-60	57-60	---	71-76	69-73	---
Owl, giant	78	72	61-62	61	66	77	74	64
Owlbear	---	---	63-64	---	---	---	---	65
Pegasus	79-80	73	---	62	67-69	78	75	---

112

Creature Type	Plain	Scrub	Forest	Rough*	Desert	Hills	Mountains	Marsh
				Predominant Terrain				
Pernicon	---	---	---	---	70-71	---	---	---
Porcupine/Skunk/Witherstench	---	74-75	65-66	63	---	79	---	---
Pseudo-dragon	---	76	67	---	---	---	---	---
Shambling mound	---	---	68	---	---	---	---	66-69
Snake[h]	81	77	69-70	64-65	72-76	80	76	70-79
Sphinx[i]	---	---	71-72	66-67	77-85	81	77-80	80-81
Spider[j]	82-83	78-83	73-75	68-69	86-89	82-83	---	---
Stag	84	84-86	76-77	70	---	84-85	---	---
Sussurus	85	---	---	---	90	86	81	---
Thork	---	---	---	---	---	---	---	82
Tick, giant	---	87	78-79	---	---	---	---	---
Tirapheg	---	88	---	71	---	87	---	---
Toad, giant	86	89	80	72	---	88	---	83-85
Treant	---	---	81-82	---	---	---	---	---
Troll	87-88	90	83	73-78	---	89	---	86-88
Umpleby	---	91	84	---	---	---	---	---
Undead[k]	---	---	85-86	79-82	---	90	82-86	89-93
Volt	89	92	---	83	91-92	91	---	---
Vortex	90	---	---	---	93	---	---	---
Wasp, giant	---	---	87	84-86	---	92	87-88	94-95
Weasel, giant	91	93	88	87-88	94-95	93	---	96
Whipweed	---	---	89-90	---	---	---	---	---
Will-o-wisp	---	---	91	89-90	---	---	89-92	97-00
Wind walker	---	---	---	---	---	---	93-94	---
Wolf	92-98	94-98	92-98	91-98	96-00	94-98	95-96	---
Wolf, worg	99-00	99-00	99-00	99-00	---	99-00	97-00	---

Includes ruins within up to five miles of the party.
* 10% of these encounters will be with *Jackalwere*.
** 10% of these encounters will be with *babblers*, and 5% will include a *Lizard king* among the lizard men.
*** 10% of these encounters will be with *ogre magi*, and 5% with *ogrillons*.

Demi-Human Subtable

Demi-Human	Plain	Scrub	Forest	Rough	Hills	Mountains
Dwarf	01-05	01-05	01-05	01-10	01-20	01-70
Elf	06-70	06-60	06-70	11-15	21-30	71-75
Gnome	71-80	61-80	71-95	16-85	31-70	76-95
Halfling	81-00	81-00	96-00	86-00	71-00	96-00

Dragon Subtable (base 50% chance of encounter while creature airborne)

Dragon Type	Plain	Scrub	Forest	Rough	Desert	Hills	Mountains	Marsh
Black	01-02	01-02	01-16	01-30	01-02	01-06	01-04	01-40
Blue	03-04	03-04	17-18	31-32	03-20	07-10	05-15	41-42
Brass	05-06	05-06	19-20	33-40	21-64	11-20	16-17	43-44
Bronze	07-08	07-08	21-22	41-45	65-66	21-25	18-25	45-46
Chimera	09-10	09-10	24-29	46-50	67-68	26-35	26-30	47-48
Copper	11-12	11-14	30-33	51-55	69-77	36-45	31-40	49-50
Gold	13-28	15-16	34-37	56-57	78-79	46-50	41-45	51-52
Green	29-30	17-36	38-77	58-59	80-81	51-52	46-47	53-60
Lan lung	31-32	37-38	78-79	60-61	82-83	53-54	48-49	61-75
Red	33-34	39-40	80-81	62-66	84-87	55-62	50-66	76-77
Shen lung	35-36	41-42	82-83	67-68	---	63-64	67-68	78-81
Silver	---	---	---	---	---	---	69-73	---
Tien lung	37-40	43-45	84-85	69-71	88-89	65-68	74-78	82-83
White	41-42	46-47	86-87	72-73	90-91	69-70	79-95	84-85
Wyvern	43-00	48-00	88-00	74-00	92-00	71-00	96-00	86-00

Frog Subtable

Frog Type	Marsh
Giant	01-70
Killer	71-80
Poisonous	81-00

113

Giant Type	Plain	Scrub	Forest	Rough	Hills	Mountains	Marsh
Cloud	01-02	01-02	01-02	01-02	01-03	01-14	---
Ettin	03-04	03-05	03-09	03-09	04-10	15-19	---
Fire	05-06	06-07	10-11	10-18	11-15	20-29	---
Fog	07-08	08-09	12-20	19-20	16-17	30-31	01-35
Frost	09-10	10-11	21-22	21-24	18-21	32-43	---
Hill	11-80	12-80	23-81	25-74	22-72	44-48	---
Mountain	81-82	81-82	82-83	75-76	73-75	49-59	---
Stone	83-85	83-86	84-88	77-88	76-88	60-88	---
Storm	86	87	89	89	89	89-95	---
Titan	87	88	90	90	90	96-97	---
Troll, giant	88-99	89-98	91-97	91-97	91-97	98-99	36-00
Troll, giant two-headed	00	99-00	98-00	98-00	98-00	00	---

^e **Humanoid Subtable**

Humanoid	Plain	Scrub	Forest	Rough	Hills	Mountains	Marsh
Gnoll*	01-05	01-10	01-09	01-18	01-21	01-14	01-23
Goblin	06-10	11-15	10-18	19-28	22-42	15-46	24-33
Hobgoblin	11-15	16-48	19-27	29-46	43-63	47-60	34-71
Kobold	---	49-77	28-74	47-50	---	---	---
Orc**	16-94	78-97	75-94	51-84	64-84	61-90	72-94
Qullan	95	98	95	85	85	91-95	95
Xvart	96-00	99-00	96-00	86-00	86-00	96-00	96-00

* 10% of all *gnoll* encounters will include *flinds*.
** 5% of all *orc* encounters will include *ogrillons*.

Lycanthrope Subtable

Lycanthrope	Plain	Forest	Rough	Hills	Mountains
Werebear	01-02	01-10	01-02	01-02	01-75
Wereboar	03-25	11-70	03-15	03-15	—
Wererat	26-30	—	16-90	16-20	76-80
Weretiger	31-40	71-90	—	21-30	81-90
Werewolf	41-00	91-00	91-00	31-00	91-00

Men Subtable

Men Type	Plain	Scrub	Forest	Rough	Desert	Hills	Mountains	Marsh
Bandit	01-05	01-10	01-10	01-10	01-05	01-10	01-05	01-05
Berserker	06-07	11-12	—	11-12	—	11-12	06-10	—
Brigand	08-10	13-15	11-15	13-15	06-10	13-20	11-20	06-10
Character	see special note hereafter pertaining to **Characters** — 10% in all cases							
Dervish	21-22	26-27	—	26-27	21-50	31-40	31-35	—
Merchant	23-60	28-60	26-40	28-50	51-75	41-65	36-50	21-35
Nomad	61-90	61-80	—	51-60	76-95	66-80	—	—
Pilgrim	91-95	81-85	41-45	61-80	96-00	81-90	51-65	36-30
Tribsman	96-00	86-00	46-00	81-00	—	91-00	66-00	31-00

Snake Subtable

Snake Type	Plain	Scrub	Forest	Rough	Desert	Hills	Mountains	Marsh
Amphisbaena	01-10	01-05	—	—	01-15	01-05	—	—
Constrictor	—	06-10	01-65	01-05	—	06-10	—	01-70
Poisonous	11-80	11-80	66-95	06-95	16-90	11-90	01-90	71-00
Spitting	81-00	81-00	96-00	96-00	91-00	91-00	91-00	—

Sphinx Subtable

Sphinx Type	Forest	Rough	Desert	Hills	Mountains	Marsh
Andro-	01-05	01-10	01-40	01-10	01-15	01-05
Crio-	06-75	11-30	41-50	11-70	16-35	06-55
Gyno-	76-80	31-50	51-90	71-80	36-55	56-65
Hieraco-	81-00	51-00	91-00	81-00	56-00	66-00

Spider Subtable

Spider Type	Plain	Scrub	Forest	Rough	Desert	Hills
Giant	—	—	01-55	—	—	—
Huge	01-15	01-25	56-75	01-20	—	01-20
Large	16-00	26-00	76-80	21-00	01-00	21-00
Phase	—	—	81-00	—	—	—

Special Note Regarding Characters Encountered In Uninhabited/Wilderness Areas: It is suggested that you use typical parties of dungeon characters for such encounters (90% will be mounted, warhorses where applicable, 10% afoot). Character level will range from 7th through 10th with henchmen of approximately one-half (round up) character level. Mounted fighters will have lances, those afoot will have spears.

k Undead Subtable

Undead Type	Forest	Rough	Hills	Mountains	Marsh
Apparition	01-02	01-02	01-02	01-02	01-02
Coffer corpse	03-07	03-06	03-06	03-06	03-06
Ghast	08-19	07-19	07-16	07-16	07-19
Ghost	20-21	20-22	17-18	17-18	20-21
Ghoul	22-52	23-53	19-38	19-33	22-63
Huecuva	53-54	54-56	39-40	---	64-71
Lich	55	57-59	41-43	34-36	---
Mummy	---	60-67	44-58	37-41	---
Pěnanggalan	56-60	68-72	59-63	42-46	72-76
Shadow	61-73	73-82	64-68	47-56	77-81
Son of Kyuss	74-76	83-84	69-70	57-58	82-84
Spectre	77-84	85-87	71-72	59-68	85-93
Vampire	85-90	88-89	73-80	69-79	94-95
Wight	91-97	90-98	81-97	80-95	---
Wraith	98-00	99-00	98-00	96-00	96-00

Temperate And Sub-Tropical Conditions

Inhabited And/Or Patrolled Areas

Creature Type	Plain	Scrub	Forest	Predominant Terrain Rough*	Desert	Hills	Mountains	Marsh
Anhkheg	01-02	01	01-02	---	---	01	---	---
Ant, giant	03-05	02	03-04	01-02	01	02	---	---
Apparition	---	---	---	03*	---	03	---	---
Assassin bug	06	03	05	04	---	04	---	01
Astral searcher	---	---	---	05*	---	---	---	---
Bear, black	---	04-05	06-08	06-07	---	---	01-02	02-04
Beetle, giant, bombardier	07	06	09-10	---	---	05	---	---
Beetle, giant, stag	08	07	11-12	---	---	---	---	---
Berbalang	---	08	13	08	---	06	---	---
Boar, wild	09-11	09-10	14-16	09-10	---	07-08	---	05-06
Booka	12	11	17	---	---	---	---	---
Bulette	13	12	---	---	---	09	---	---
Bunyip	---	---	---	---	---	---	---	07-08
Carbuncle	---	---	18	---	---	---	---	09
Coffer corpse	---	13	19	11	---	10	---	10
Disenchanter	14	14	---	---	02	---	---	---
Dune stalker	---	---	---	---	03	---	---	---
Dwarf	---	---	---	12-13	---	11-12	03-15	---
Elf	15	15-16	20-23	---	---	13-14	---	---
Flumph	16	---	---	---	---	---	---	---
Ghast	---	---	---	14-15*	---	---	---	---
Ghost	---	---	---	16*	---	---	---	---
Ghoul	---	---	---	17-19*	---	---	---	11-12
Giant, hill	17	17	24	20-21	---	15-18	16-17	---
Gnoll*	18-19	18	25	22-23	04-06	19-20	18-19	13-15
Gnome	20	---	26-27	24-25	---	21-23	20-21	---
Goblin	21-22	---	28	26-27	---	24-25	22-24	---
Groaning spirit	23	19	---	---	---	26	---	---
Halfling	24-25	20	29	---	---	27-29	---	---
Hobgoblin	26	21-22	30	28	---	30	25-26	16
Huecuva	---	---	---	---	---	---	---	17-19
Kenku	27	23	---	29-30	07	31	---	---
Killmoulis	28	---	---	---	---	---	---	---
Leprechaun	29	---	---	---	---	32-33	---	---
Lizard man**	---	---	---	---	---	---	---	20
Lycanthrope, werebear	---	---	31	---	---	---	27	---
Lycanthrope, wereboar	---	24-25	32	---	---	---	---	---
Lycanthrope, wererat	---	26	---	31-32	---	---	---	21
Lycanthrope, weretiger	30	27	33	---	---	---	---	---
Lycanthrope, werewolf	31-32	---	34	33	---	34	28-29	22
Manticore	33	28	---	34	08-09	35	30	23-24
Men, bandit	34-38	29-32	35-37	35-38	10-12	36-39	31-32	25-27
Men, berserker	39-40	33-34	38-39	39-40	13-14	40-41	33-34	28-29
Men, brigand	41-44	35-38	40-44	41-44	15-18	42-47	35-39	30-34
Men, dervish	45-46	39-40	45-46	45-48	19-28	48-49	40-41	---
Men, merchant	47-69	41-58	47-56	49-56	29-49	50-61	50-51	---
Men, nomad	70-71	59-60	---	57-58	50-67	62-63	---	---
Men, pilgrim	72-77	61-67	57-61	59-63	68-71	64-67	52-59	35-37
Ogre	78-80	68-74	62-71	64-68	---	68-75	60-66	39-46
Orc***	81-84	75-84	72-83	69-80	72-81	76-84	67-79	47-64
Osquip	85	---	---	81	82-85	85	---	---
Pĕnanggalan	86	85	84	82-83	86	86	80	65
Pernicon	---	---	---	---	87-89	---	---	---
Rat, giant	87-88	86-88	85-86	84-85	---	87-89	---	66-78
Skulk	---	89	87-88	86	---	90	---	79
Skunk, giant	89-90	90-91	89-92	87-88	---	91-92	---	80-84
Vampire	91	---	93	---	90	---	81-87	80-84
Volt	92-93	92	---	89	91-94	93	---	---
Will-o-wisp	---	---	---	90-91	---	---	88-89	86-00
Wolf	94-00	93-00	94-00	92-00	95-00	94-00	90-00	---

* 10% of all *gnoll* encounters will include *flinds*.
** 10% of these encounters will be with *babblers*, and 5% will include a *lizard king* among the lizard men.
*** 5% of all *orc* encounters will include *ogrillons*.

...erie And Sylvan Settings

...reature Type	Plain	Forest	Hills	Mountains
...-mi'raj	01	01	---	---
...e, carnivorous	---	02-03	---	01-02
...asilisk	---	04	01	03
...ear, brown	---	05-07	02-03	04-08
...ar, wild, giant	02-03	08-09	04-05	---
...ownie	---	10	06-08	---
...ll, wild	04-09	11	09-10	---
...rbuncle	---	12-13	---	---
...ntaur	10-13	14	11-14	---
...himera	14-15	15	15-16	09-14
...ockatrice	---	16	--- :	15
...yad	---	17	---	16
...warf	---	---	17-18	17-23
...	16	18-20	19-22	24
...in	17-19	21	23	25-27
...ome	---	22-23	24-27	28-29
...rbel	---	24-25	28	---
...rgon	20-22	26	29	30
...iffon	23-26	27	30-31	31-32
...arpy	27	---	32	33-34
...ppogriff	28-31	28	33-34	35-37
...culi	---	29-30	---	---
...opard	32-33	31-33	35	38
...prechaun	---	---	36	---
...n, mountain	---	---	37	39-40
...canthrope, werebear	---	34	38	41
...anticore	34-37	35-36	39-40	42
...n, bandit	38-39	37-40	41-42	43
...n, dervish	40-42	41	43-44	44
...n, pilgrim	43-47	42	45-46	45-46
...n, tribesmen	48-52	43-44	47-49	47
...edleman	---	45	---	---
...re	53-60	46-48	50-51	48-52
...gasus	61-66	---	52	53-56
...ryton	67-70	49-50	53-54	57-59
...ie	71-77	51-54	55-56	---
...tyr	78	55-63	57-58	---
...rite	79-80	64-68	59-60	---
...g, giant	81-82	69-73	61-63	60-61
...rge	83-84	74-76	64-68	62-66
...-monster	---	77-83	---	---
...lph	85-87	84	69-73	67-71
...ant	---	85-86	---	---
...ll	88-89	87-88	74-78	72-86
...icorn	90-91	89-95	79-83	---
...ipweed	---	96-97	---	---
...lf	92-00	98-00	84-00	87-00

Tropical And Near-Tropical Conditions

Uninhabited/Wilderness Areas

Creature Type	Plain	Scrub	Forest	Rough*	Desert	Hills	Mountains	Marsh	Shore/Sm. Isle
					Predominant Terrain				
Aarakocra	---	---	---	---	---	---	01-02	---	---
Algoid	---	---	---	---	---	---	---	01-02	01-04
Ant, giant	01-02	01-02	01-02	01-02	---	01-02	---	---	---
Ape	---	---	03-05	---	---	---	---	---	---
Babbler	---	---	---	---	---	---	---	03	---
Baboon	---	03-05	06	03-06	01-03	---	03-05	---	---
Basilisk	03-04	---	---	07-08	04-05	---	---	---	---
Bear, black	---	---	07-10	09-10	---	---	06-08	---	---
Beetle, rhinoceros	---	---	11-13	---	---	---	---	---	---
Boar, warthog	05-06	06-07	---	11-13	---	---	---	---	---
Buffalo	07-10	08-10	---	14-15	---	03-06	---	04-11	---
Bullywug	---	---	14	---	---	---	---	12-14	---
Camel, wild	---	---	---	---	06-10	---	---	---	---
Caterwaul	11	11-12	15-16	16-17	---	07	---	---	---
Centipede, giant	---	---	17-19	---	11-13	---	---	---	---
Cifal	---	---	---	---	---	---	---	15-16	---
Clubnek	12-13	13	---	---	---	---	---	---	---
Couatl	---	---	20-21	---	---	---	---	---	---
Crab, giant	---	---	---	---	---	---	---	---	05-11
Crabman	---	---	---	---	---	---	---	---	12-18
Crocodile	---	---	---	---	---	---	---	17-29	19-31
Crocodile, giant	---	---	---	---	---	---	---	30-31	32-35
Dakon	---	14	22-23	---	---	---	---	---	---
Death dog	---	---	---	---	14-15	---	---	---	---
Disenchanter	14	---	---	---	16	---	---	---	---
Dune stalker	---	---	---	---	17-18	---	---	---	---
Elephant	---	15-17	24-28	---	---	08-10	---	---	---
Elephant, loxodont	---	18-20	29-33	---	---	---	---	---	---
Ettercap	---	21-22	34-35	---	---	---	---	---	---
Firenewt	---	---	---	18-19	19-20	11-12	---	---	---
Firetoad	---	---	---	20-21	21-22	---	---	---	---
Flightless bird	15-19	23-24	---	---	---	---	---	---	---
Flumph	20-21	---	---	---	---	---	---	---	---
Forlarren	22	25	---	22	---	13	---	---	---
Frog, giant	---	---	---	---	---	---	---	32-34	36-48
Garbug, black	---	---	---	---	---	---	---	35-36	---
Giant, fog	---	---	---	---	---	---	---	---	49-52
Giant strider	---	---	---	---	23-24	---	---	---	---
Gorilla bear	---	26-27	36-38	23-24	---	---	---	---	---
Herd animal	23-38	28-37	39-41	25-27	25-26	14-21	09-12	---	---
Hippopotamus	---	---	---	---	---	---	---	37-46	---
Hyena	39-43	38-41	---	28-33	---	22-25	---	---	---
Jackal	44-47	42-44	---	34-36	27-31	26-29	---	---	---
Jackalwere	48	45	---	37	32	30	---	---	---
Jaculi	---	46	42-43	---	---	---	---	---	---
Jaguar	---	---	44-48	---	---	---	---	---	---
Kamadan	---	47	49	38	---	31	---	---	---
Lamia**	---	---	50-51	39-43	33-35	---	---	---	---
Lammasu/Shedu	---	48	---	44-45	36-39	32-33	13-17	---	---
Leech, giant	---	---	---	---	---	---	---	47-55	---
Leopard	---	49-52	52-57	46-47	40-41	---	18-22	---	---
Lion	49-57	53-57	58-60	---	42-44	34-39	---	---	---
Lizard man***	---	---	---	---	---	---	---	56-61	53-59
Lizard, minotaur	---	---	---	48-51	---	---	---	---	---
Lycanthrope, weretiger	---	---	61-62	---	---	40-41	23-24	---	---
Mantari	58	---	---	---	45	---	---	---	60-66
Men, bandit****	59-62	58-61	63-65	52-54	46-49	42-46	25-30	---	---
Men, dervish	63	---	---	55-56	50-57	47-48	31-32	---	---
Men, merchant	64-70	62-66	---	57-59	58-64	49-54	33-37	---	---
Men, nomad	71-72	---	---	60-65	65-77	55-62	---	---	---
Men, pilgrim	---	---	---	66-71	78-79	63-67	38-40	---	---
Men, pirate (or buccaneer)	---	---	---	---	---	---	---	---	67-70
Men, tribesmen	---	67-72	66-68	72-75	---	68-73	41-51	62-73	71-92
Naga, guardian	---	---	---	76-77	---	74	52-54	---	---
Naga, spirit	---	---	---	78-79	---	75-77	55-56	74-75	---
Nonafel	---	---	---	80	---	78	57	---	---
Norker	---	---	---	---	80	---	58	---	---
Pernicon	---	---	---	---	81-82	---	---	---	---
Rakshasa	---	---	---	81-83	---	79-80	59-63	---	---
Rhinoceros	73-80	73-77	---	---	---	---	---	---	---
Roc	81-85	78-83	---	84-86	---	81-85	64-73	---	---
Scorpion, giant	86-89	84-85	69-71	87-88	83-87	---	---	---	---
Snake, giant, amphisbaena	90-91	---	---	---	88-89	---	---	---	---

118

Creature Type	Plain	Scrub	Forest	Rough*	Desert	Hills	Mountains	Marsh	Shore/Sm. Isle
Snake, giant, constrictor	---	---	72-76	---	---	---	---	76-80	---
Snake, giant, poisonous	---	86-90	77-79	89-90	90-91	---	74-77	81-85	---
Snake, giant, spitting	92-94	---	80-81	91-92	92-93	86-87	---	---	---
Spectre	---	---	---	93-94	---	---	---	---	---
Sphinx⁰	---	---	---	95-96	94-98	88-89	78-81	---	---
Spider, giant	---	---	82-84	---	---	---	---	---	---
Spider, huge	---	---	85-88	---	99-00	---	---	---	---
Spider, large	---	91-93	---	---	---	---	---	86-88	---
Tabazi	---	---	89-90	---	---	---	---	---	---
Thork	---	---	---	---	---	---	---	89-90	93-00
Tiger	---	---	91-96	---	---	90-94	82-90	---	---
Tiger fly	95	94-95	---	---	---	---	---	---	---
Toad, giant	---	---	97-98	---	---	---	---	91-96	---
Toad, giant, poisonous	---	---	99-00	---	---	---	---	97-00	---
Wolf/Wild dog	96-00	96-00	---	97-00	---	95-99	91-98	---	---
Xill	---	---	---	---	---	00	99-00	---	---

Includes ruins within up to five miles of the party.

* 10% of these encounters will be with *lamias noble.*

** 5% of these encounters will include a *lizard king* among the lizard men.

*** Slavers.

Sphinx Subtable

1-10	Androsphinx
1-40	Criosphinx
1-70	Gynosphinx
1-00	Hieracosphinx

ASTRAL & ETHEREAL ENCOUNTER TABLES

Astral Encounter Table

Dice

Score	Creature Encountered	Numbers
01-04	Aerial servant	1
05-10	Basilisk* /Astral Searcher	1-2/3-6
11-13	Cockatrice* /Berbalang	1-4/1-3
14-16	Demon, major	1
17-22	Demon, minor	1-3
23	Demon, prince	1
24	Devil, arch-	1
25-28	Devil, greater-	1
29-37	Devil, lesser-	1-3
38	Dragon, chromatic	1
39	Dragon, platinum	1
40-41	Gorgon*/Githyanki	1-2/1-4
42-46	Human traveller — **see Human Subtable****	
47-49	Intellect devourer	1-2
50-55	Invisible stalker	1-3
56-61	Ki-rin	1
62-63	Medusa*	1-2
64-71	Night hag	1-4
72-74	Nightmare	1-4
75-79	Rakshasa	1-3
80-91	Shedu	2-5
92	Titan, elder	1
93-97	Titan, lesser	1
98-00	Titan, major	1

See below next table.

See below next table.

Ethereal Encounter Table

Dice

Score	Creature Encountered	Numbers
01-05	Aerial servant	1
06-10	Basilisk* /Apparition	1-2/1-4
11-13	Cockatrice* /Terithran	1-4/1
14-18	Couatl	1-4
19-26	Djinni	1-6
27	Dragon, chromatic	1
28	Dragon, platinum	1
29-30	Efreeti	1-3

Score	Creature Encountered	Numbers
31-37	Elemental, air	1
38-39	Elemental, earth	1
40-41	Elemental, fire	1
42	Elemental, water	1
43-48	Ghost	1
49-50	Gorgon*	1-2
51-52	Groaning spirit	1-2
53-57	Human traveller — **see Human Subtable**	
58-59	Intellect devourer	1-2
60-62	Invisible stalker	1-3
63-68	Ki-rin	1
69-76	Lammasu	2-8
77-78	Medusa* /Xill	1-2/1-4
79-80	Nightmare	1-4
81-82	Salamander	2-5
83-87	Spider, phase	1-6
88-94	Thought eaters	1-3
95-97	Wind walkers	2-5
98-00	Xorn	3-6

The slash (/) indicates that there is a 50% chance for each.

* These creatures' perceptions extend into the astral and ethereal planes (as do their magical attack forms), but they do not actually travel therein. Their possible appearance applies only to situations in which the encounter allows effect to extend from the Prime Material Plane; otherwise, ignore the encounter result and roll again.

** The **Human Subtable** used for **DUNGEON RANDOM MONSTER ENCOUNTERS** is used, with the following modifications: Party size will be only 1-6. No limits to the number of characters of one class apply. There will always be 1 cleric; if 2 or more in the party, there will also be a minimum of 1 magic-user. Character level will be:

CLERIC	9th - 18th
Druid	7th - 14th
FIGHTER	8th - 15th
Paladin	7th - 16th
Ranger	7th - 16th
MAGIC-USER	11th - 20th
Illusionist	10th - 17th
THIEF	9th - 16th
Assassin	10th - 15th
MONK	8th - 17th
BARD†	11th - 18th

† 7th or 8th level fighter ability, 6th or 9th level (d4 for determination) thief ability.

INDEX OF MAJOR LISTINGS

The **FIEND FOLIO** monsters are here listed alphabetically by general type and by individual name. Against each monster is given the name of the contributor who created the original.

U

V

W

X

Y

Z

Epilogue

I look back with some chagrin on the gestation period of this volume which has been much longer than anyone could ha
anticipated. Publication date is likely to be nearly two years after I wrote the introduction, and during that time many things ha
happened. For one thing, I am now responsible for TSR Hobbies (UK) Limited and have been so for nearly a year — yet at the time
writing the introduction even my wildest dreams could not have predicted that this would have been so. But delay and serendip
are often bedfellows, and I am now able to greet this publication with even more pride because of my new association with t
Company.

It may be appropriate here to say that, though this is the first British contribution to the advancement of DUNGEONS & DRAGONS
and ADVANCED DUNGEONS & DRAGONS™ games, it will certainly be far from the last. TSR Hobbies (UK) Limited has plans! V
do intend to play our part and do at least our fair share in adding to the D&D® and AD&D™ repertoire — there is no reason why t
hobby in the UK should be led to assume that our American brethren, though admittedly the first creators and the ones wl
established the very high quality we have come to accept, are the only ones who can produce original work of exceptional mer

So a statement of policy might be in order here — we at TSR (UK) will do everything we can to promote the cause of these fine gam
because our belief — and my personal experience — is that the gaming hobby gives immense pleasure and satisfaction.

You will be hearing from us again.

The D&D® Players' Association

The Players' Association is an organization which exists to bring together players of the DUNGEONS & DRAGONS® and ADVANCED DUNGEONS & DRAGONS™ Adventure Games of all ages. The services offered are many — club listings, player listings, promotional activities, a regular newsletter, and many others. For full details, write to:

Players' Association
TSR Hobbies (UK) Limited
The Mill, Rathmore Road
Cambridge CB1 4AD

The D&D® Players' Association is affiliated to the ROLE PLAYING GAME ASSOCIATION™ organization in the United States and reciprocal benefits apply.

DUNGEONS & DRAGONS, D&D, ADVANCED DUNGEONS & DRAGONS, AD&D, and ROLE PLAYING GAME ASSOCIATION are trademarks owned by TSR Hobbies, Inc.

INTERESTED IN ROLE PLAYING GAMES?

LOOKING FOR OTHERS WHO ARE, TOO?

THE TSR™ FAMILY PROUDLY PRESENTS

The ROLE PLAYING GAME ASSOCIATION™

Membership

An international organization for TSR™ role playing game fans everywhere!

For less than the cost of buying one new game, YOU can become a member of this exciting new organization! When joining, you will receive:

> A full-color plastic embossed high-quality **membership card**.
> A metal **members' pin**, for lapel or tie.
> A color **certificate** of official membership, suitable for framing.

PLUS . . .

A quarterly newsletter, with articles by your favorite role playing game designers, news of local and national game conventions, questions and answers, and much, much more; a yearly directory of role playing gamers in your area; and the RPGA™ Gift Catalog, where you can get posters, playing aids, limited edition collectors' items, and many other items **not available anywhere else!**

But that's not all! When attending any regional or national GenCon® gaming convention, you can take advantage of many special members-only events, such as role playing game tournaments, lectures, and discussions where members can meet special convention guests — possibly **Jim Ward** (author of GAMMA WORLD™ science fiction game, and many other works), **Brian Blume** (co-author of BOOT HILL™ wild west game), or maybe even the Grand Master Adventurer himself, **GARY GYGAX!!**

So join **now** — prices will go up in the near future. Memberships are available at yearly or (for a limited time only) Lifetime rates. For more information, write to:

RPGA™ Membership
POB 509
Lake Geneva, WI 53147

Please circle appropriate letter.

1) Name of the game

_____

2) Where was this game purchased?
a. Hobby shop
b. Book store
c. Toy store
d. Department store
e. Discount store
f. Mail order catalog
g. Gift
h. Other (please specify)

_____

3) As a player, how would you rate this game overall?
a. Excellent
b. Good
c. Fair
d. Poor

4) How do you feel about the quality of the components that make up this game?
a. Excellent
b. Good
c. Fair
d. Poor

5) How would you rate the attractiveness and sales appeal of the game box (top and bottom)?
a. Excellent
b. Good
c. Fair
d. Poor

6) Who will you play this game with? (check one)
a. Family
b. Friends
c. Schoolmates

7) In terms of completeness, how would you rate the game rules?
a. Overwritten
b. Complete
c. Adequate
d. Lacking
e. Incomplete

8) In terms of clarity, how would you rate the game rules?
a. Clear
b. Adequate
c. Unclear

9) How did you hear about the game?
a. Newspaper
b. Magazine
c. TV
d. Radio
e. From a friend
f. Just saw it in a store

10) What would most influence your decision to buy another TSR™ game? (check one)
a. If I heard it was available (sight unseen)
b. If a friend recommended it
c. If I saw the box and read the description of it
d. If I examined it and liked the contents
e. If I played it first
f. Unlikely to ever buy another TSR™ game

11) Note your highest grade completed:
a. 6th-8th
b. 9th-11th
c. 12th
d. HS + 1
e. HS + 2
f. HS + 3
g. HS + 4
h. Post graduate degree

12) List your sex:
a. Male
b. Female

13) List your marital status:
a. Single
b. Married
c. Divorced, separated, other

14) Name your three favorite games:

_____

_____

_____

15) Which magazines do you read regularly?

_____

_____

_____

16) List your three favorite TV or radio programs:

_____

_____

_____

17) Do you read or subscribe to The Dragon™ Magazine?
a. Yes, I subscribe
b. Yes, I buy over the counter
c. Yes, I read a friend's copy
d. No
e. Would like more information

18) Do you belong to a DUNGEONS & DRAGONS® or gaming club?
a. Yes
b. No

19) How many members are in your club?
a. 1-5
b. 6-10
c. 11-20
d. 21-30
e. Over 30

20) List your age:
a. 10 and Under
b. 11-14
c. 15-18
d. 19-22
e. 23-30
f. 41-65
g. Over 65

21) Are you an RPGA™ Member?
a. Yes
b. No

22) If not, would you like more information?
a. Yes
b. No

23) Please send full name and address:

Name _____

Street _____

City _____

State _____

Zip Code _____

Date _____

TSR
The Game Wizards

© 1980 TSR Hobbies Inc.   All Rights Reserved

BUSINESS REPLY MAIL

FIRST CLASS   PERMIT NO. 159   LAKE GENEVA, WI

POSTAGE WILL BE PAID BY ADDRESSEE

TSR Hobbies, Inc.
POB 756
Lake Geneva, WI 53147

(FOLD HERE, TAPE OR STAPLE TO SEAL)

- -

(FOLD HERE, TAPE OR STAPLE TO SEAL)

NAME _____

ADDRESS_____

_____

_____